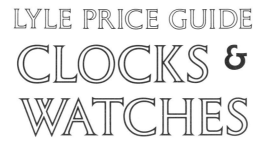

LYLE PRICE GUIDE
CLOCKS &
WATCHES

The publishers wish to express their sincere thanks to the following for their involvement and assistance in the production of this volume:

Editor	TONY CURTIS
Text By	EELIN McIVOR
Editorial	ANNETTE CURTIS
	DONNA RUTHERFORD
	MARY ANDERSON
Art Production	CATRIONA DAY
	DONNA CRUICKSHANK
	NICKY FAIRBURN
Graphics	JAMES BROWN
	MALCOLM GLASS
	DOROTHY GLASS

A CIP catalogue record for this book is available from the British Library

ISBN 86248 - 149 - X

Copyright © Lyle Publications MCMXCIII
Glenmayne, Galashiels, Scotland

Typeset by Word Power, Berwickshire
Printed and bound in Great Britain by
Butler & Tanner Ltd, Frome and London

LYLE PRICE GUIDE

CLOCKS &
WATCHES

TONY CURTIS

CONTENTS

ACKNOWLEDGEMENTS

Allen & Harris, St Johns Place, Whiteladies Road, Clifton, Bristol BS8 2ST
Auction Team Köln, Postfach 50 11 68, D-5000 Köln 50 Germany
Bearnes, Rainbow, Avenue Road, Torquay TQ2 5TG
Bonhams, Montpelier Street, Knightsbridge, London SW7 1HH
Bonhams Chelsea, 65–69 Lots Road, London SW10 0RN
Bonhams West Country, Dowell Street, Honiton, Devon
British Antique Exporters, School Close, Queen Elizabeth Avenue, Burgess Hill, Sussex
Butterfield & Butterfield, 220 San Bruno Avenue, San Francisco CA 94103, USA
Butterfield & Butterfield, 7601 Sunset Boulevard, Los Angeles CA 90046, USA
Canterbury Auction Galleries, 40 Station Road West, Canterbury CT2 8AN
Christie's (International) SA, 8 place de la Taconnerie, 1204 Genève, Switzerland
Christie's Monaco, S.A.M, Park Palace 98000 Monte Carlo, Monaco
Christie's Scotland, 164–166 Bath Street Glasgow G2 4TG
Christie's South Kensington Ltd., 85 Old Brompton Road, London SW7 3LD
Christie's, 8 King Street, London SW1Y 6QT
Christie's East, 219 East 67th Street, New York, NY 10021, USA
Christie's, 502 Park Avenue, New York, NY 10022, USA
Christie's, Cornelis Schuytstraat 57, 1071 JG Amsterdam, Netherlands
Christie's SA Roma, 114 Piazza Navona, 00186 Rome, Italy
Christie's Swire, 1202 Alexandra House, 16–20 Chater Road, Hong Kong
Christie's Australia Pty Ltd., 1 Darling Street, South Yarra, Melbourne, Victoria 3141, Australia
Dreweatt Neate, Donnington Priory, Donnington, Newbury, Berks
Du Mouchelles Art Galleries Co., 409 E. Jefferson Avenue, Detroit, Michigan 48226, USA
Sala de Artes y Subastas Durán, Serrano 12, 28001 Madrid, Spain
Eldred's, Box 796, E. Dennis, MA 02641, USA
Finarte, 20121 Milano, Piazzetta Bossi 4, Italy
Galerie Koller, Rämistr. 8, CH 8024 Zürich, Switzerland
Greenslade Hunt, 13 Hammet Street, Taunton, Somerset, TA1 1RN
Muir Hewitt, Halifax Antiques Centre, Queens Road/Gibbet Street, Halifax HX1 4LR
Hobbs & Chambers, 'At the Sign of the Bell', Market Place, Cirencester, Glos
P Herholdt Jensens Auktioner, Rundforbivej 188, 2850 Nerum, Denmark
G A Key, Aylsham Saleroom, Palmers Lane, Aylsham, Norfolk, NR11 6EH
Kunsthaus am Museum, Drususgasse 1–5, 5000 Köln 1, Germany
Lawrence Fine Art, South Street, Crewkerne, Somerset TA18 8AB
Lawrence's Fine Art Auctioneers, Norfolk House, 80 High Street, Bletchingley, Surrey
David Lay, The Penzance Auction House, Alverton, Penzance, Cornwall TA18 4KE
Brian Loomes, Calf Haugh Farm, Pateley Bridge, North Yorks
Onslow's, Metrostore, Townmead Road, London SW6 2RZ
Phillips Manchester, Trinity House, 114 Northenden Road, Sale, Manchester M33 3HD
Phillips Son & Neale SA, 10 rue des Chaudronniers, 1204 Genève, Switzerland
Phillips West Two, 10 Salem Road, London W2 4BL
Phillips, 11 Bayle Parade, Folkestone, Kent CT20 1SQ
Phillips, 49 London Road, Sevenoaks, Kent TN13 1UU
Phillips, 65 George Street, Edinburgh EH2 2JL
Phillips, Blenstock House, 7 Blenheim Street, New Bond Street, London W1Y 0AS
Phillips Marylebone, Hayes Place, Lisson Grove, London NW1 6UA
Phillips, New House, 150 Christleton Road, Chester CH3 5TD
Russell, Baldwin & Bright, The Fine Art Saleroom, Ryelands Road, Leominster HR6 8JG
Selkirk's, 4166 Olive Street, St Louis, Missouri 63108, USA
Skinner Inc., Bolton Gallery, Route 117, Bolton MA, USA
Sotheby's, 34–35 New Bond Street, London W1A 2AF
Sotheby's, 1334 York Avenue, New York NY 10021
Sotheby's, 112 George Street, Edinburgh EH2 4LH
Sotheby's, Sommers Place, Billingshurst, West Sussex RH14 9AD
Sotheby's Monaco, BP 45, 98001 Monte Carlo
Henry Spencer, 40 The Square, Retford, Notts. DN22 6DJ
G E Sworder & Son, Northgate End Salerooms, 15 Northgate End, Bishop Stortford, Herts
Tennants, 27 Market Place, Leyburn, Yorkshire
Woolley & Wallis, The Castle Auction Mart, Salisbury, Wilts SP1 3SU

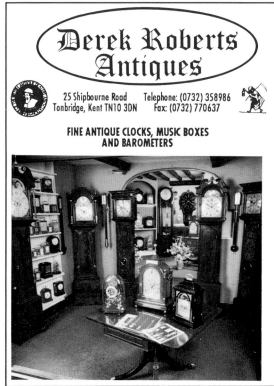

It is small wonder that, from earliest times, man should have felt the need for some way to tell the time with accuracy. Though it is a cliché to say that our lives are all governed by time, perhaps in a busy modern world of schedules, appointments and commitments, we tend to forget that even the natural world is inexorably governed by such rules. Nature has its own inbuilt clock, of course, seen in the migrations of birds and animals, the blossom and fall of the leaves, seedtime and harvest. It is, therefore, a concept of which our first ancestors would have been, of necessity, aware, and one to which they applied their earliest intelligence.

Measurement started, of course, with that most obvious and immediate sign of ongoing time, the sun, and found its form in sundials and shadow clocks, known since the Old Testament period at least. Then there was the clepsydra, or water clock, again dating from Egyptian times and possibly earlier, whereby time was recorded

A Regency satinwood four glass mantel chronometer, the four pillar single chain fusee movement with maintaining power, the wheels with five crossings, the plain backplate signed *French Royal Exchange, London*, 10in. high. (Christie's)   £3,300

by the constant inflow or outflow of a regulated stream of water. The clepsydra can, perhaps, be called the ancestor of the modern clock, as some were fitted with a dial or indicator which was controlled by a pulley or weight. Candle lamps were also used by ancient peoples as time measurers, and have remained in use in some parts of Europe until comparatively recently. Basically, these consist of a glass reservoir on a stem or foot like a candleholder, usually of pewter. A small wick holder is fixed just below the reservoir held in place by two vertical pewter strips one of which is marked with the hours in Roman numerals. The time is indicated by the level of the oil which falls as it is consumed by the burning wick.

Our own word for clock comes from the Latin clocca, which means a bell (cf French cloche or German Glocke). In early times the hour shown on a sundial was indicated by sounding a bell and, in monasteries of the Dark and Middle Ages, perhaps the most time-controlled of all contemporary social communities, (and also, of course, the centres of culture and learning of the day) the monks'

An unusual mahogany dial clock, the painted dial signed *Wm. Carter Hampstead*, with automaton scene, the associated single chain fusee movement with platform lever escapement, the dial circa 1770, the movement and case late 19th century, 15in. diameter. (Christie's)   £1,955

lives would be governed by the bells summoning them to Nones, Compline etc, at set hours of the day and night.

Clocks, as we know them, have been in existence since at least the 13th century, with plenty of references in Dante and other 14th century literature to bear this out. In this country, there is documentary evidence of three turret clocks being made for Edward III between 1365–70, and the oldest surviving mechanical clock in the world is in Salisbury Cathedral. From this period on, the development of timepieces for all went, well, like clockwork.

In the history of modern horology there were, of course, many notable, even pivotal dates. Around 1460–70, for example, some anonymous genius invented the fusee, which equalised the pull of the mainspring on the train, and thus greatly improved accuracy. In 1657

A 19th century French marble mantel clock.
(Ewbank Auctioneers) £396

An 18th century French bracket clock.
(Greenslade Hunt) £1,700

Christiaan Huygens discovered the pendulum. (Galileo is known earlier to have perceived the principle but seems to have failed to apply it.) Then in 1675 Huygens went on to introduce the spiral balance spring for watches, which did for them what the pendulum had done for clocks in the matter of improved timekeeping. Circa 1670, William Clement developed the anchor escapement, which again revolutionised timekeeping by largely eliminating circular error and enabling the use of longer pendulums swinging more slowly, thus affording less opportunity for cumulative error.

Geniuses of every age applied themselves to the clock, whether in terms of the mechanics or the casings, which became as varied as clock tower giants, through domestic clocks of every type to tiny, elegant wristwatches. They are all to be found, together with pictures, descriptions and prices, in this book, which will appeal not only to the expert, dealer and the serious collector alike, but to absolutely everyone. For just about everyone owns a timepiece of some sort, and it is amazing just how much some of them can be worth.

GLOSSARY OF TERMS

ACORN CLOCK

An early 19th century shelf clock produced in New England and Connecticut, in a shape suggesting an acorn.

ALARM MECHANISM

A mechanical attachment which at a preset time will ring a bell or activate some other type of alarm. Found on many types of portable clocks but rarely on tall clocks. The time for activation is usually set by a brass disc numbered 1–12 and a pointer or third hand.

ALLATT or ALLETT, GEORGE (b. circa 1669)

Clockmaker apprenticed to Tompion, who became Free Brother of the Clockmakers' Company in 1691.

ANCHOR ESCAPEMENT

Invented circa 1760. The escape wheel teeth are like those of a saw; the pallets at the ends of an anchor shaped bar intercept the teeth before the pendulum reaches the end of its swing, thus making wheel turn back slightly or recoil; when pendulum begins to swing back, one tooth escapes, passing on impulse to pallet.

ANIMAL CLOCK

Automaton table clock, produced in Augsburg and elsewhere in Germany in the 16-17th centuries, having an animal figure, often a lion or griffon, which moved as the clock ticks or strikes.

ANSONIA CLOCK CO.

American clock factory founded 1851 in Ansonia CT. which produced Connecticut style wall and shelf clocks. Moved to New York in 1879, where remained in business until circa 1930.

ANTIMAGNETIC WATCH

Watch with balance, balance spring, and escapement of non-magnetic material, initially of gold, then palladium and palladium alloys and nickel steel.

ARBOR (1)

Any spindle on a clockwork mechanism, especially the one to which the mainspring is attached.

ARBOR (2)

The shaft or axle to which pinions and wheel are attached on a clock movement.

ARCADED MINUTE RING

Arrangement of numerals on a watch dial to show minutes in a series of twelve arches outside the hour circle, much used in 18th century Holland and also in Geneva.

ARCH

Found above the dial on longcase clocks.

ARCH TOP, PLAIN

A case, usually in bracket clocks, where the arch rises directly from the sides of the case.

ARNOLD, JOHN (1736–99)

English clock and watch maker noted for his chronometers. Developed chronometer escapement for marine chronometers and precision watches. Made ring watch for George III and also supplied regulators for the Royal Observatory.

ASTROLOGICAL/ASTRONOMICAL DIALS

Found on many early clocks, showing the relation of the planets to each other at any one time, and related to the moon phases, which are seen through an aperture in the dial.

ATMOS CLOCK

Self winding clock with torsion pendulum patented in 1913 by the Swiss J E Reutter, manufactured from 1926 by Jaeger Le Coultre.

AUGSBURG CLOCKS

Refers to many types of clocks made in Augsburg in the 16th-early 17th centuries, including tabernacle, nef, automaton, monstrance and crucifix. Revolving dials were frequently used on all types.

AUTOMATIC WINDING

A pocket watch which is wound up by means of a weight actuated by the motion of the body. Originally patented in London by Louis Recordon in 1780, though Abraham Perrelet of Le Locle made a prior claim. The automatic wristwatch was invented by J. W. Harwood of London in 1914.

BACHELDER, EZRA

Denver clockmaker, active 1793–1840.

BACKPLATE

The hindmost of the plates supporting a clock mechanism, usually engraved with the maker's name.

BAIN, ALEXANDER (c 1811-77)

Scottish scientist and clockmaker, who invented a type of electric clock in 1843, the current obtained from metal plates buried in the ground.

BALANCE

An oscillating wheel device in clock mechanisms used to counter the force of the mainspring.

BALANCE SPRING

A spring acting on the balance wheel in a watch mechanism to control the oscillation of the mainspring. Devised circa 1675 by Christiaan Huygens and Robert Hooke, who both claimed priority. Formed the equivalent of the clock pendulum, and made for increased accuracy in watches.

BALLOON CLOCK

A style of mantel clock popular in the late 18th and early 19th centuries, having a balloon shaped case which curved inwards below the dial.

BANJO CLOCKS

This American wall clock derived from the French lyre clock, and was made, as the name suggests, in the form of a banjo, having a pendulum, round face, painted glass panels, and a rectangular base. It was produced between circa 1802–1860 and was introduced by the Willard family of clockmakers in Massachusetts.

An Empire maplewood, ebony and bronze regulateur de table, the ebony line inlaid plinth-form case flanked by bronze female Egyptian caryatids, the eccentric silvered Roman dial with blued moon hands, 20³/₄in. high.
(Christie's)   £23,100

BARBER'S CLOCK

Late 19th century American clock with reversed dial and hand rotation, so that it reads normally when seen in a mirror eg in a barber's shop.

BARLOW or **BOOTH, EDWARD** (1636–1716)

English cleric and horologist who invented rack striking mechanism for clocks 1676, and also a form of cylinder escapement circa 1695.

BARR, G.

A late 18th century maker of Yorkshire style clocks.

BARRAUD & LUND

A London company specialising in electric clocks, founded mid 19th century.

BARREL

A cylindrical box containing the mainspring in both clocks and watches.

BASKET TOP

A pierced metallic and roughly dome shaped case top, popular in the late 17th/early 18th century.

BAYLEY & UPJOHN

London makers of regulator clocks circa 1800.

A Second Empire porcelain and brass elephant clock, for the Turkish market, the elephant with turquoise glaze and with royal blue and gilt decoration. 11½in. high (Christie's) £1,100

BEAT

The tick-tock sound made by the action of the escapement. When the beats are regular, the piece is said to be 'in beat'.

BEEHIVE CLOCK

A Connecticut shelf clock, also known as 'flatiron clock' made circa 1850 and named from its resemblance to a contemporary beehive.

BERTHOUD, FERDINAND (1727–1807)

Swiss born maker of watches and chronometers, active in Paris, where worked with J & P Leroy. Published many works on timekeeping.

BEZEL

The metal rim on the glass covering a clock or watch face.

BIM BANG

Onomatopoeic name imitating the two-tone strike of a popular early 20th century German made mantel clock.

BINNACLE CLOCK

Ship's clock with dial marked with the nautical watches, striking one to eight.

BIRDCAGE CLOCK

A highly decorative 18th century novelty clock of birdcage shape, with a singing bird instead of the strike.

BLIND MAN'S WATCH

Watch which indicates time through touch, having raised studs on dial, or separate pointer moved by finger till it coincides with hour hand.

BLINKING EYE CLOCK

A 17th and 18th century South German clock in the shape of a face with eyes linked to the escapement which blink alternately in time with the tick. Some also made in the US in the 19th century.

BOB

The weight at the base of a pendulum rod, the earliest pear shaped or nearly spherical. Later, the general form was lenticular, though some regulators or special clocks have cylindrical forms.

BORRELL, HENRY

Early 19th century London clockmaker and exporter, producing clocks and watches often with Turkish numerals.

BOUQUET, DAVID (d. 1665)

French watchmaker working in London, and founding member of Clockmakers' Company. Maker of Puritan watch, 1640.

A burr walnut longcase clock, the 11¹/₂in. square dial inscribed *Dan. Quare London*, the five ringed pillar movement with anchor escapement and inside count wheel strike, 8ft. 7in. high. (Christie's) £3,220

BREGUET

Abraham-Louis Breguet (1747–1823) was a Swiss born watch maker, who worked most of his life in Paris. Exiled during the Revolution in 1791, he spent some time in Switzerland and England, returning to Paris in 1795. During his first period in the capital he had worked for Ferdinand Berthoud, but began signing his work from 1782, with the motif *Breguet à Paris*. He produced self winding watches, montres à tact, subscription watches, and tourbillons. His cases were characterised by their thinness, and often had gold or silver dials. As his work became more sought after, it attracted many forgers and he therefore developed a secret signature, consisting of a signature in cursive script combined with the number of the watch, which was only visible if the watch was turned slantwise to the light. This occurs below the figure XII on enamel dials and at either side of the figure on metal dials. It is thought that this was done with a diamond stylus on the pantograph after glazing.

Breguet used cylinder, lever, and spring detent escapements, and from 1793 introduced a parachute device to protect the balance if the watch was dropped or jolted. The bearings of the balance staff are supported on springs and yield to excessive pressure.

Around 1807 he went into partnership with his son, Louis-Antoine and his work was subsequently signed *Breguet et Fils*. He was appointed Horloger de la Marine in 1815.

BROCOT, ACHILLE (1817–78)

French clockmaker who invented the pin-pallet form of deadbeat escapement for pendulum clocks. Also invented adjustable Brocot suspension, whereby a key inserted in the dial regualtes time-keeping by altering the length of the pendulum swing.

BROKEN ARCH

A pediment on a clock, the centre part of which is missing, or 'broken'.

BROWN, JONATHAN CLARK (1807–72)

Clock maker in Bristol, Connecticut, where produced acorn clocks.

BULLE CLOCK

French battery clock with uncased movement under glass dome. Invented by Professor Favre-Bulle and Marcel Moulin, 1920.

BULLOCK, EDMUND

Mid 18th century Shropshire clockmaker, his work usually signed and numbered.

BUNYAN, ROBERT

Late 18th century Lincoln clockmaker.

CALENDAR CLOCK

A clock which shows, through separate openings in the dial, the day, month, and sometimes also the year.

CARTIER

Louis Cartier (1875–1942) began designing his jewellery in the years of peace and prosperity which the First World War brought to an end, and his name soon became synonymous with elegance and luxury. Unlike many exponents of Art Nouveau, who worked in materials chosen for their aesthetic appeal rather than their intrinsic value, Cartier predicted that the rich would never abandon precious stones, and continued to work with them.

At this time too the firm gained its reputation for fine clocks and watches. Table clock cases were enamelled in Fabergé style in pinks, violets and blues, fired over patterned engine-turned grounds. The famous series of wristwatches for men, the Tank and Tonneau and the Santos Dumont, were developed, and have never lost their appeal.

Most watches were however designed for the pocket or to hang from a chain across the waistcoat. They are flat and well proportioned, the dials with a two tone moiré finish, the hands are spear-shaped and the winding crowns are set with sapphires. Ladies' designs were even more graceful, with the round, square or oval dials discreetly framed in diamonds and mounted on moiré silk bracelet bands.

During the 1920s these classical designs gave way to the severe angles and sharp contrasts of Art Deco, with its juxtapositions of rock crystal, mother of pearl, turquoise and onyx. Even the mystery clock, invented by Maurice Coüet in 1913, was subjected to this stern functionalism. Men still tended to prefer the pocket watch, which remained neat, square or oval, while the short sleeves of woman's dresses lent themselves to the wristwatch, which became narrower, mounted in rat tail silk cords, platinum chains or bands of grey and white pearls. The most expensive were worn as centrepieces to flexible diamond bracelets.

CATTELL, WILLIAM (d. 1697)
Apprenticed to Edward Stanton in 1665/5 and became a Freeman of the Clockmakers' Company in 1672.

CENTRE SECONDS
A clock or watch where the seconds hand is placed on the same arbor as the hour and minutes hands.

CHAIN FUSEE
An early 19th century innovation, prior to which the fusee was connected to the mainspring barrel in clock mechanisms by gut, which, as it could expand and contract, influenced the clock's accuracy.

CHALET STYLE CLOCK
A novelty clock from the Black Forest in the form of a chalet, often with a cuckoo, dating from circa 1850.

CHAMBER CLOCK
Smaller iron version of the turret clock, made in the 15th and 16th centuries.

CHAPTER RING
The applied circle on a clock face on which the hours are inscribed.

CHIME
Where the hours and quarters are sounded on more than one bell, as distinct from a strike.

CHINESE MARKET CLOCKS
Clocks made in the late 18th century in England specially for export to China, often very ornate, with special effects, such as revolving glass bars to create impression of falling water. Dials often include centre-seconds hand.

CHINESE OR FLEURIER WATCH
Made in Switzerland from late 18th century for the Chinese market. Of circular shape, 2–6 in. in diameter, in silver, gilt or gold case, richly ornamented, some with musical mechanism.

CIRCULAR MOVEMENT
A clock movement within circular as distinct from rectangular plates, common in French clocks from the mid 19th century.

CLEMENT, WILLIAM
17th century clockmaker who pioneered the use of anchor escapement, and made longcase and lantern clocks, also some turret clocks.

COACHING CLOCK
A large watch with swing handle for suspending in a carriage, in the same way as a sedan or carriage clock.

COCK (CLOCK)
The bracket supporting the pendulum.

COCK (WATCH)
The bracket attached to the plate which supports the upper end of the balance spring.

COFFIN CLOCK
American wall clock in form of coffin, enclosing banjo-shaped movement, made in late 18th century.

COLE, JAMES FERGUSON (1799–1880)
English watchmaker noted for his precision timepieces. Made many watches with lever escapement.

COLUMN CLOCK
French mantel clock, produced circa 1780, the marble case consisting of two side columns with portico top, the clock hanging between the columns.

COMPENSATION BALANCE
A usually bimetallic balance which compensates for the influence of heat or cold on the pendulum.

COMTOISE CLOCK
Provincial French clock made in Franche-Comté from late 17th century, mostly weight driven longcase or wall bracket types.

CONICAL PENDULUM
Introduced in clocks by J Bodeker in 1587, top attached to last wheel of clock train, bob at bottom revolves in circular path, the frequency of rotation increasing as the bob moves outward and upward.

CONSULAR WATCH
Superseded the pair-cased watch from the early 19th century, with wide glazed bezels meeting at the centre so that the body of the watch cannot be seen.

COSTER, SALOMON (d. 1659)
Dutch clock maker who made first pendulum clock for Huygens in 1657.

COTTAGE CLOCK
Name given to small Connecticut spring clocks in wood cases made in the second half of the 19th century.

COTTEY, ABEL (1655–1711)
English born clock maker who emigrated to America in 1682 where he set up business in Philadelphia. Possibly the first American clock maker, producing pine tall case clocks, with 8 day brass movements.

COUNTWHEEL STRIKE

The mechanism controlling the number of strikes at each hour; consists of a wheel with notches at increasing intervals around the rim, the lever, or detent, continuing to strike until it catches in one of the notches.

CRUCIFIX CLOCK

Pillar clock in form of Christ on the Cross, made in Augsburg from early 17th century, with automaton figures on base, revolving globe at top, with hour hand indicating time. Much copied in the 19th century.

CRUTCH

The arm which connects the pendulum to the pallet arbor.

CUCKOO CLOCK

A clock in which the hours are announced by an automaton in the form of a cuckoo. Originated circa 1730.

CURTIS, LEMUEL (1790–1857)

Massachusetts clockmaker apprenticed to the Willard family. Designed the girandole clock and also made various forms of wall clocks.

DATE APERTURE

An opening in a clock face where the day of the month is displayed.

DEADBEAT ESCAPEMENT

Invented by Graham circa 1715, this eliminates the recoil of a clock's escape wheel as the pallets catch on the teeth, thus improving accuracy.

DEBAUFRE, PETER & JACOB (fl circa 1700)

French watchmakers working in London who first applied jewelling to watches circa 1704. Peter also developed type of verge escapement with two escape wheels.

DELANDER, DANIEL

Late 17th/early 18th century London clockmaker.

DENNISON, AARON (1812–95)

Pioneer of American machine-made watches, working with Edward Howard in Roxbury and then Waltham, trading as Boston Watch Co. Emigrated to England in 1870 and established the Dennison Watch Co in London, which ceased trading in 1967.

DENT, EDWARD (1790–1853)

English clock and watchmaker established in London in 1840, awarded commission for Big Ben, eventually carried out by his stepson Frederick.

DEPTHED

Where clock mechanisms are mounted with the help of a depthing tool, so the wheels and pinions are correctly meshed and run true, thus helping accuracy and to limit wear and tear.

DETENT

A catch for regulating the strike, the pawl or click that takes into the ratchet wheel.

DIAL

The face of a clock or watch on which are marked the hours, minutes and seconds.

DROCOURT, PIERRE & ALFRED

Paris clockmakers, active circa 1860–89.

DRUM

The spool on which the cord to the weight is wound.

DRUM CLOCK

Common form of early table clock dating from early 16th century, the precursor of the square and hexagonal table clock, having iron movement usually of skeleton form, rarely with striking mechanism.

DUCHESNE, CLAUDE (d. circa 1730)

Freeman of the Clockmakers' Company in 1693, who specialised in complicated astronomical and musical clocks.

DUCHESNE CLOCK

Musical clocks made in England in the early 18th century by the French clockmaker Claude Duchesne.

DUTCH STRIKE

A striking mechanism whereby the hours are struck normally, but at the half hour the next hour is struck first on a smaller bell.

DUTTON, MATTHEW

Apprenticed in 1771 in London and became Master of the Clockmakers' Company in 1800 and 1825.

EARNSHAW, THOMAS (1749–1829)

London clockmaker who perfected spring detent escapement for marine chronometers and made first effective compensation balance.

EAST, EDWARD (c 1610–c 1693)

English clock and watchmaker, among first makers of night clocks. Clockmaker to Charles I & II.

EIGHT DAY MOVEMENT

A clock movement which runs for eight days without rewinding.

CLOCKS & WATCHES

ELEPHANT CLOCK
A novelty clock made in the 18th and 19th centuries with the case in the form of an elephant.

ELLICOTT, JOHN
(1706–82) English inventor and clockmaker to George III, who worked on pendulum and cylinder escapement. Son of John Ellicott the Elder.

EMERY, JOSIAH (c 1725–1797)
Swiss-born watchmaker working in London, who developed lever escapement for watches.

ENGLISH DIAL
A 19th century wall clock, often hung in public places, with large painted sheet iron dial, anchor escapement and pendulum.

ESCAPEMENT
That part of a clock mechanism which controls the driving force of the spring or weight and transmits its energy to the controller pendulum or balance. Various types include verge, anchor, cylinder, deadbeat, duplex, lever and pin-pallet.

ESCAPE WHEEL
The final wheel of the time train of a clock or watch which gives impulse to the pendulum or balance.

FALLING BALL CLOCK
A spherical clock hung from a chain linked to the mechanism so that the clock's own weight provides the driving force, the hours being marked on a circular band round the circumference.

FARRIS, WILLIAM
Late 18th century Philadelphia clockmaker.

FINIAL
The turned, cast or moulded ornaments, usually of brass or wood, at the top of various clock cases.

FLY
The final component of the striking train, a rapidly revolving vane which acts as governor for the rate of striking.

FOLIOT
An early and simple form of balance always found with verge escapement. Consists of a horizontal rod fixed to a pivoted bar carrying the verge pallets, with suspended weights at each end, the regulation achieved by moving these weights.

FORM WATCH
A watch made in usually novelty form, such as a skull, crucifix, dog etc. Dates from 17th century, while in the 18th, mandolines, baskets of flowers etc. were more popular shapes.

FOUCHER, BLAISE (d. 1662)
French watch maker and enamel painter from Blois. Decorated cases with mythological scenes.

FOUNTAIN CLOCK
Ornate French automaton clock produced from circa 1845 made to resemble a fountain, with rotating glass spirals giving the impression of water emptying into a receptacle. Cheaper versions produced circa 1900 in Germany.

FOUR GLASS CLOCK
English wooden cased clock with glass sides, up to 12in. high, made from circa 1820. Also French four glass regulator, a larger version of the carriage clock with pendulum movement made circa 1850 by firms like Leroy, and Marti. Copied in America by the Ansonia Clock Co.

FRANKLIN CLOCK
An early American weight driven clock, said to be based on a design by Benjamin Franklin; also a type of wooden movement shelf clock made 1825–30 by Silas Hoadley of Connecticut.

FRETS
Metallic plates of pierced decoration used to hide the balance in lantern clocks and later used in clock cases to facilitate clear chiming.

FRIESLAND CLOCK
An 18th century Dutch bracket clock with ornate brass or gilt openwork case.

FRISARD, JACOB (1753–1812)
Swiss watchmaker who made movements of 'singing-bird' boxes in Geneva, also for a time in London.

FRODSHAM, CHARLES (1810–71)
English clockmaker and businessman who, in association with the finishers Nicole and Nielsen, produced slim watches in Breguet style, also fine clocks and chronometers. Acquired Arnold & Son in 1843 and took over Vulliamy in 1854. In 1868 designed make and break device for electrically recording time shown by chronometer.

FROMANTEEL FAMILY
A family of clockmakers of Dutch origin working mainly in England. Asahuerus (d. 1685) introduced pendulum longcase clocks in London

from 1658 and also made bracket clocks. His son John made longcase and bracket clocks and worked with Coster in Holland.

FUSEE

A cone shaped and spirally grooved drum linked to the spring barrel by a length of gut or chain, equalizing, on the lever principle, the pull of the mainspring on the train. Invented circa 1470 and still in use.

GARNIER

A family of Paris clockmakers active in the 19th century. Paul Jean is perhaps the most prominent.

GIMBAL

A mounting for a ship's compass clock or chronometer which keeps the instrument horizontal despite the listing of the vessel.

GIRANDOLE CLOCK

An early 19th century banjo shaped clock with circular base, designed by Lemuel Curtis circa 1818.

GLOBAL CLOCK

A spherical clock with moving band marked with the hours around the circumference.

GOLIATH CLOCK

Large Swiss pocket watch, often with eight-day movement used from circa 1880 as a travelling clock. Usually in outer case of leather, tortoiseshell etc. as travelling case fitting.

GONG

A piece of hardened, tempered wire wound on a volute on which the hours are struck, instead of a bell. First used late 18th century.

GOTHIC CLOCK

Iron clocks made mainly in Germany in the 15th and 16th centuries in the shape of a tower with four pillars, arched canopy and steeple. Also used of pointed topped Connecticut shelf clocks introduced circa 1845.

GOULD, CHRISTOPHER

Famous late 17th century maker of longcase clocks, working in London.

GRAHAM, GEORGE

(c.1673–1751) Celebrated English clockmaker who worked with Tompion and modified Tompion's early form of cylinder escapement, perfecting the deadbeat escapement in 1715. Introduced mercury compensated pendulum in 1726. Produced over 3000 watches and some 170 various clocks.

GRANDE SONNERIE

Clocks striking the quarter followed by a repetition of the hour usually on different bells. Introduced late 17th century.

GRANDFATHER CLOCK

Popular name for the longcase clock, introduced after invention of anchor escapement in 1670.

GRANDMOTHER CLOCK

A smaller longcase clock not exceeding 6ft. 6in. in height.

GRAVITY CLOCK

A type of clock which, suspended from a chain or ratchet, is powered by its own weight.

GRIDIRON PENDULUM

A pendulum made from several rods of steel or iron linked to rods of brass, the differences in rates of expansion and contraction of the metals thus being cancelled out, keeping the length constant and thus also the duration of the swing.

GROLLIER DE SERVIERE, NICOLAS (1593–1686)

French clockmaker from Lyon who designed unusual clocks, such as the ball clock.

HABRECHT, ISAAC (late 16th century)

Swiss German clockmaker who designed astronomical clock for Strasbourg Cathedral.

HAIRSPRING

The fine spring which regulates the movement of the balance wheel.

HALF HUNTER

A watch with a protective hinged front cover with a central glass panel so the dial can be seen even with the cover closed. Traditionally invented by Napoleon.

HARLAND, THOMAS (1735–1807)

English-born clockmaker who emigrated to America in 1773, settling in Norwich CT. Made many tallcase clocks, characteristically with 'whale's-tail' hood.

HARRISON, JOHN (1693–1773)

English horologist who invented gridiron compensation in 1725. Devoted most of his life to accurate marine timekeeping for determining longitude at sea.

HARWOOD, JOHN (1893–1964)

Lancashire watchmaker and jeweller who invented the first self-winding wrist watch wound by a small weight, pivoted at the centre and oscillated by normal activity of wearer.

HENLEIN OR HELE, PETER (c 1479–1542)
Nuremberg watchmaker, first reported maker of pocket watches c 1510– c 1520.

HILL, MATTHEW
Late 18th century English clockmaker, specialising in Act of Parliament and wall clocks.

HIPP, MATTHAEUS (1813–93)
Swiss clockmaker who pioneered electric clock. Invented Hipp toggle attached to pendulum rod, giving impulse to pendulum as arc shortens by brushing to and fro over notch on two open electric contacts.

HOADLEY, SILAS (1786–1820)
Connecticut clock maker who worked with Eli Terry. Made 30 hour longcase clocks with wooden movements, also shelf and pillar and scroll clocks.

HOLLOW COLUMN CLOCK
Weight driven shelf clock with weights concealed in hollow columns which appear to be part of the case. Popular early 19th century.

HOOD
The upper removable portion of a longcase clock, containing the movement and dial. Hinged front doors introduced only in the 19th century.

HOOKE, ROBERT (1635–1703)
English scientist, mathematician and inventor, who possibly invented anchor escapement, and worked with Tompion to produce first English balance spring watches.

HOURGLASS CLOCK
An early 19th century Connecticut mantel clock in the shape of an hourglass.

HOWARD CLOCK
A banjo clock manufactured in the mid 19th century by Edward Howard (1813–1904) and later the American Waltham Watch Co.

HUNTER
A watch with a solid hinged cover over the dial which must be opened, usually by pressing a push-piece, to read the time.

HUYGENS, CHRISTIAAN (1629–95)
Dutch scientist, astronomer and clockmaker who studied in Leyden and Breda. Worked in Paris 1665–81. Invented pendulum clock in 1657 and developed balance spring for watch in 1675.

INGERSOLL, ROBERT HAWLEY (1859–1928)
American mail order pioneer who sold the first dollar watch. Early examples were robust, non-jewelled and simple, manufactured by the Waterbury Clock Co. which Ingersoll subsequently bought out. Sold 70 million watches before Company failed in 1922 because of Swiss competition.

INGOLD, PIERRE FRÉDÉRIC (b. 1787)
Swiss born clockmaker who worked for Breguet in Paris and pioneered the making of duplicate watch parts by machinery. Invented the Ingold fraise, for rounding up wheels and cutting teeth.

IRON CLOCK
Early German 15th century domestic clock, often in the form of a church tower.

IVES, JOSEPH (1782–1862)
Connecticut clockmaker who also worked in New York 1825–30. Inventor of wagon spring clock and made longcase clocks with wooden, then brass movements. Also designed wall mirror clock circa 1818–9.

JACK OR JACQUEMART
Automaton figure which strikes bell on clock sounding hours or quarters. Used on medieval turret and domestic clocks. Also used for 19th century French and Swiss jacquemart watches, where puppet figures appear to strike bells.

JACQUET DROZ, PIERRE (1721–90)
Swiss maker of musical clocks, watches and automata.

JENKINS, HENRY
Late 18th century maker of fine astronomical clocks.

JEWELS
Used as the bearings or pivots to reduce wear and friction and first introduced by Facio de Duillier in 1704. Sapphires and rubies are most usual.

JONES, HENRY (d. 1695)
English clock and watchmaker, apprenticed to East in 1654. Made oval watches, bracket and longcase clocks.

JUMPING DIAL
Digital recording dial for clocks and watches, with hour and minute numeral 'jumping' into view through apertures on the dial.

JUMP, JOSEPH (d. 1899)
Clockmaker apprenticed to Vulliamy in 1827 who continued working on his own account in London, in Bond Street and Pall Mall.

JUNGHANS, ERHARD (d. 1870)
German clockmaker who with his brother Xavier transformed the family straw-hat business into the Junghanssche Uhrenfabrik in Schramberg in 1861, using American mass production techniques to make domestic clocks.

JURGENSEN
Urban Brunn Jurgensen (1776–1830) was a Danish watch and chronometer maker who studied under Berthoud and Breguet in Paris around the turn of the century. He then spent some time with Arnold in London. He became the principal supplier of chronometers to the Danish navy.

KARRUSEL WATCH
A precision movement designed in Coventry in 1894 by the Swede Bahne Bonniksen, accurate to one second per day.

KIDNEY DIAL
Form of dial aperture found on Massachusetts shelf clock which extends below the dial itself. The space beneath the dial is decorated or signed with maker's name.

KNIBB, JOSEPH
(d. circa 1711) From Oxford but worked mostly in London. Member of Clockmakers' Company 1670. Maker of lantern, longcase, bracket and wall clocks. Devised system of Roman striking mechanism for bracket clocks and pioneered anchor escapement and long pendulum.

KULLBERG, VICTOR (1824–1890)
Swedish watch and chronometer maker apprenticed to Jurgensen in Copenhagen, then worked in London making fine chronometers and watches. Won awards for timekeeping at Greenwich trials in 1862.

LAMP CLOCK
(1) A timepiece in which the hours are marked on a glass reservoir and the time indicated as the level of oil falls as it is consumed by a lighted wick.
(2) A lamp with a clockwork mechanism which pumps the oil from a reservoir to the wick.

LANCET CLOCKS
This was a type of bracket clock, with the case tapering to a pointed arch, which was introduced in England circa 1800.

LANDSCAPE DIAL
Watches with painted landscape decoration on dial, made in France, Holland and England in the late 18th/early 19th century, often in gold or enamelled cases. Many produced for the Turkish market.

LENTICLE
The glass let into the door of a longcase clock allowing the movement of the pendulum bob to be seen.

LEPINE, JEAN-ANTOINE (1720–1814)
French-Swiss watchmaker, who became maker to Louis XV. Introduced Lépine calibre watch movement circa 1770, which was widely adopted by French and Swiss makers.

LEROY, JULIEN (1686–1759)
Paris clock and watchmaker appointed maker to Louis XV in 1739. Made tower clocks, equation and astronomical timepieces, and devised improved mechanism for verge watches.

LEROY PIERRE (1717–85)
Son of the above who worked on marine chronometers. Devised duplex escapement and detent escapement for chronometers circa 1765.

LEVER ESCAPEMENT
A modification of anchor escapement introduced in the mid 18th century, whereby the pallets restraining the escape wheel are positioned on either end of a seesawing lever on a central pivot when rocked by a pin attached to the balance wheel.

LOCKING PLATE
A plate with notches set at increasing intervals round its circumference allowing the striking train to sound the correct number of blows before the locking arm falls and stops the train.

MAINSPRING
Invented circa 1450, a coiled strip of steel that provides the motive power for portable clocks, used in conjunction with a fusee.

MAINTAINING POWER
A device used in weight clocks, and clocks and watches with a fusee, consisting of a subsidiary spring which keeps the movement going while the mainspring is being wound.

MAIN WHEEL
The first and largest wheel of the train.

MALTESE CLOCK
Wooden case clock with carved or gilt decoration and painted dial. Produced in 19th century Malta as a cottage industry. Early examples may only have hour hand.

MANTEL CLOCKS
The mantel clock is essentially a French version of the bracket clock, designed to stand on a mantelpiece or shelf, though some do include wall brackets of the same material as the clock face. They often have feet, however, which indicates their more usual position.

MARGETTS, GEORGE
Made a Free Brother of the Clockmakers Company in 1779 and worked in Cheapside. Interested in the chronometer escapement and astronomical work.

MASSACHUSETTS SHELF CLOCK
An American shelf clock made in the early 19th century by the Willard family and others, circa 30in. high, with tablet, mirror or door in the base, and surmounted by pillars and finials.

MASSY
A prominent family of London clockmakers, active mid 17th/early 18th century.

MASTER CLOCK
A controlled central clock which regulates one or more slave clocks or dials by transmitting constant electrical impulse. Invented by Alexander Bain in 1840.

MATTING
A system of dulling the surface of the brass plate dial, usually confined to the centre of the chapter ring.

MINUTE WHEEL
The wheel driven by the cannon pinion.

MONSTRANCE CLOCK
Ornate clock made in Augsburg in early 17th century, in the shape of a monstrance, the case often gilt brass or rock crystal, supported on a pillar. Has yearly calendar dial indicating saints' days.

MONTH CLOCK
A clock that will go for 32 days without rewinding.

MONTRE A TACT
A watch devised by A-L Breguet with front and back cover, for telling time by touch in the dark, often also with ordinary dial at front. cf. blind man's watch.

MORRILL, BENJAMIN (b 1794)
American clockmaker producing New Hampshire mirror clocks and shelf clocks.

MUDGE, THOMAS
(1715–94) English clock and watchmaker, apprenticed to Graham, who invented lever escapement for pocket watches circa 1759. Watchmaker to George III from 1776 and also regularly supplied Ferdinand of Spain with watches.

NAPOLEON CLOCK
Mainly poor quality German hour and half-hour striking clocks made in first half of this century, so-called because outer case resembled Napoleon's cocked hat.

NAWE, FRANCIS (d. 1593)
A Huguenot watchmaker born in Brabant, who came to work in London circa 1580.

NEF CLOCK
Ornamental clock, usually German, in the form of a ship and dating from late 16th century.

NEUCHÂTEL CLOCK
Refers to bracket clock with waisted case made from mid 18th century onwards. Neuchâtel in Switzerland is a major centre for watch and clock production.

NEVE, HENRY
A Huguenot clockmaker who worked in London in the early years of the 18th century.

NEW HAMPSHIRE MIRROR CLOCK
Shelf clock made circa 1830 in New Hampshire, or rectangular shape with case door extending the full length of the clock and having dial on upper section with long mirror below.

NICOLE, ADOLPHE (fl mid 19th century)
Swiss watchmaker who moved his firm to Soho circa 1840. Patented his employee, Henri-Féréol Piguet's, chronograph mechanism. In partnership with Emil Nielsen (d. 1899) produced fine watch movements for eg. Charles Frodsham and J F Cole from circa 1865.

NIGHT CLOCK
A clock that shows the time in the dark, usually by means of a light shining through a pierced dial.

NUREMBERG EGG
An early German watch, often drum shaped, misnamed through the confusion of Uhrlein (little clock) with Eierlein (little egg).

OFF CENTRE PENDULUM

A pendulum which is not hung in the centre; specifically used to refer to early 19th century American shelf clocks by Eli Terry and Seth Thomas.

OGEE CLOCK

A 19th century New England shelf clock with ogee (or S shaped) mouldings on the door and sides. Produced from the early 19th/early 20th century. Also known as OG clock.

OIGNON WATCH

French watch common in late 17th and 18th centuries, having thick movement, many examples only with single hand, in engraved gilt brass or silver case. So called because of its shape.

ORGAN CLOCK

A clock on which the hours are sounded by bellows operating on organ pipes instead of bells.

ORMSKIRK WATCH

A watch made in 19th century Ormskirk, Lancs. often with verge escapement, the movement often with going barrel and some with open mainsprings.

ORRERY CLOCK

Named after the 4th Earl of Orrery, by whom first commissioned, a clock showing the relative positions of the earth, moon, sun and sometimes also the planets.

PAIRCASED WATCH

Watch with a double case, standard from circa 1650–1800, the movement itself being encased and this fitted into another, often very ornate, outer case.

PALLET

The arms on either side of a clock linkage which alternately engage and release the escapement wheel and regulate its movement.

PAPERWEIGHT CLOCK

A small (4–6in. high) late 19th century clock with case of moulded glass and solid brass base.

PENDULE D'OFFICIER

This may well be the forerunner of the carriage clock, being small, square and encased in brass or gilt. It was introduced around 1770, and was much used by officers in Napoleon's army. The term also specifically refers to a travelling clock model devised by Abraham Louis Breguet.

PENDULETTE

French clock in the form of a large watch, often with folding case.

PENDULUM

A rod with weight or bob attached, the earliest form invented by Christiaan Huygens in 1657.

PERPETUAL CLOCK

A calendar clock which corrects itself for the short months, and leap year, usually consisting of a slotted wheel revolving once a year (or four years) with slots of varying length which control the movement of a lever, allowing it to pass one or more teeth of the calendar wheel at a time.

PICTURE FRAME CLOCKS

This type of clock was French in origin and was made from the late 18th century onwards. It consisted of a gilt framed picture, with the clock face set in an appropriate place, say on the tower of a lighthouse, against a ground of coloured velvet. Many had striking mechanisms, as well as musical boxes. They were also produced from circa 1830–1870 in the Black Forest and in Malta.

PIERRET, VICTOR-ATHANASE (1806–93)

French horologist who invented night clock in 1863.

PILLAR CLOCKS

This was a style popular in mid 16th century Europe and again in the 19th century. The movement is usually in the base and there is a revolving hour band, globe or similar device mounted on the top of a pillar. The time is indicated by a pointer, or the hand of a figure or the like.

From circa 1830 the Japanese also produced weight driven pillar clocks for ordinary household use. These were about 1–4ft. high, designed to be hung on the central pillar of the house, with a glazed case around the movement at the top, and having a single foliot, balance wheel, or more rarely, a pendulum.

PILLAR PLATE

The plate of a watch movement immediately behind the dial, to which one end of each pillar is riveted, the other end being fixed to the back or top plate by pins or screws.

PINION

A small-toothed wheel in which the ratio of the axial length to diameter is greater than in a wheel. In clock movements wheels and pinions alternate in the train.

PLATE CLOCK (TELLERUHR)

A 17th century European clock made until c 1750. Later examples may have brass or silvered chapter ring with decorated centre and hands elaborately pierced. Originally designed to hang or stand on a small pedestal.

PLATE FRAME

Framework of flat parallel plates forming the base of a clock or watch movement.

PLATES

Back, front, side, top and bottom. These form the case of a clock or watch. Degree of decoration, particularly on back plates, can be a useful guide to dating a clock.

POPE, JOSEPH

A Boston clockmaker, active 1790–1810.

PROJECTION CLOCK

Night clock with lamp behind pierced dial which casts a shadow of the hour numerals and hands on the wall, produced in England and Europe in the early 19th century.

PRUNK UHR

A Baroque German clock type so ornate that the decoration often almost obscures the dial; may also have moving figures and a complex chime.

PULSE WATCH

A medical watch made in the late 17th century with a lever for starting and stopping the second hand.

PURITAN WATCH

An early 17th century oval watch, named for its plainness of design.

QUARE, DANIEL

(1648–1724) English clock and watchmaker who invented the repeating watch circa 1680. As a Quaker he was precluded from appointment as Royal Clockmaker but became master of Clockmakers' Company in 1708. Made longcase, bracket clocks and some unusual watches.

QUARTER CLOCK

A clock which strikes the quarters and half hours as well as the hours.

RACK AND SNAIL STRIKING

System invented by Edward Barlow in 1676 whereby the movement of the hour hand regulates the strike mechanism. In England has now mainly superseded the locking plate.

RACK CLOCK

Dating from circa 1600, a type of clock deriving power from its own weight as it slides down a toothed vertical rack, which engages with pin in the movement. Also exists as a spring driven trick form dating from the 18th century.

RADELOFF, NICOLAS (fl circa 1650)

Danish clockmaker famous for his weight driven clock in Renaissance style, with wooden base on animal shaped supports and floridly decorated architectural case.

REGULATORS

The regulator is a precision timepiece dating from the early 18th century, intended for performance rather than decoration. A typical example is of undecorated longcase type with compensation pendulum, deadbeat escapement and other refinements such as roller bearings and jewelling. The dial is plain, of brass, silvered brass or white enamel, often with a centrally mounted minute hand and minute ring on the circumference enclosing subsidiary hour and seconds dials.

RELIGIEUSES

The pendule religieuse is an early French pendulum mantel or wall clock produced between 1660–90. The case was rectangular, architectural in style with corner pillars, and in many ways similar to the English bracket clock, but less deep. The top is usually arched, with central and side finials, though some examples have a dome shaped top. The dial has gilt hands and chapter ring set against a velvet backing, with decorative motifs in ormolu occurring below the dial. The case is generally of oak, veneered in ebony and tortoiseshell, and later examples can have elaborate gilt and ormolu ornamentation. It gets its name from the fact that its outline bears some resemblance to a nun's habit.

REMONTOIRE

A device for converting the power from the mainspring to a constant force, equalizing variations, usually in the form of a small ancillary spring continually rewound to maximum tension by the mainspring and which acts as the power source rather than the mainspring itself.

REPEATER

A clock or watch which, by pulling a lever or pressing a button, will strike the preceding hour, often the quarter and sometimes the five or single minute most recently past.

RIEFLER, SIGMUND (1847–1912)

Hamburg maker of observatory clocks, who invented the highly accurate Riefler escapement, the impulse given to the pendulum through a spring suspended from rocking member resting on knife edges. Also patented mercury filled pendulum in 1899.

RITTENHOUSE, DAVID

A distinguished Philadelphia maker of clocks and scientific instruments, active 1750–90.

ROD

The metal shaft of a pendulum, made usually of brass and steel to cancel out variations caused by temperature changes.

ROMAN STRIKE

System devised by Joseph Knibb in late 17th century to reduce the power needed, especially in spring driven clocks, to drive the striking train, the hours being struck on two different toned bells, one striking for single I, and the other once for V and twice for X. Thus the maximum number of strikes ever heard was four (IIII, VIII VVII).

ROSKOPF WATCH

Originally a cheap, roughly-made watch produced at La Chaux de Fonds in Switzerland by George Roskopf in the mid 19th century, having a form of pin pallet escapement. Name now applied to any watch of this type.

SADDLE or SEATBOARD

Wooden platform to which the movement of a tall clock is fastened.

SAMBO CLOCK

19th century American clock made in Connecticut, in the form of a banjo-playing Negro.

SAVONETTE

A watch with a dial protected by a domed metal cover, the equivalent of a hunter watch.

SCAFE, WILLIAM

Notable London clockmaker who was Master of the Clockmakers' Company in 1749 and 1764. Made clocks with distinctive dials, and, rarely, Act of Parliament clocks.

SCHOTTENUHREN

Miniature editions of Black Forest clocks, standing around 3–4 in. high, made in Germany and Austria from around the mid 18th century.

SEIKO WATCH

Japanese firm founded in 1873 by K Hattori & Co making lever watches, using American and Swiss assembly methods. Now world's largest manufacturer of precision jewelled lever watches.

SELF-WINDING WATCH

Watch in which the mainspring is wound either through vibrations of a weighted lever with the movements of the wearer's body or by the action of opening and closing the case via a series of levers and ratchet wheel.

SELIG, CONRAD

Notable clockmaker working in Reading, Pennsylvania in the first quarter of the 19th century.

SHEEPSHEAD CLOCK

A lantern clock in which the chapter ring extends considerably beyond the rectangular casing.

SILENT STRIKING CLOCK

Clock with a device to shut off the strike as required, e.g. at night.

SIX HOUR DIAL

Dial with six instead of twelve divisions, often with hours 1–6 in Roman numerals with 7–12 superimposed in Arabic numerals.

SKULL WATCH

A type of form watch, made in Germany, Switzerland or France in the 17th century, the lower jaw of the skull shaped ivory or silver case opening to remove dial.

SPANDREL

Decorative corner pieces found on clock dials, often gilded. Earliest form on English clocks c. 1670 consisted of cherub's head and wings, c. 1720 of scrollwork crowns and masques, later 18th century, of debased rococo patterns.

SPHERICAL WATCH

The oldest watch shape, earliest dating from circa 1550. Typically ormolu-cased with dial opposite pendant, the movement of brass plates and iron wheels, going and striking trains with springs and fusees.

SPOON

A device for raising the hood in early longcase clocks, consisting of a trigger in the trunk of the case, so that the hood cannot be removed without unlocking the door of the clock.

CLOCKS & WATCHES

SPRING DRIVEN

Clockwork movements powered by the tension in the mainspring rather than by weights and a pendulum.

STAARTKLOK

A mid 18th century Frisian Dutch clock with anchor escapement, mounted in hood like a longcase clock, the pendulum swinging in a flat, wall mounted case widened at the base, with window showing the bob.

STACKFREED

A 16th century German watch device consisting of a curved spring pressing against a snail shaped cam attached to the mainspring, the resultant varying friction roughly equalizing the decrease in power of the spring as it unwinds. Later superseded by the more efficient fusee.

STANDARD TIME COMPANY

Founded 1876 and specialising in highly accurate clocks, supplied mainly to business firms.

STAUNTON, EDWARD

Distinguished late 17th century London maker of longcase and bracket clocks.

STEEPLE CLOCK

Early Gothic clock case with pinnacles resembling a church steeple, widely copied in the 19th century.

STENCILLED CLOCKS

Name applied to many American shelf clocks with painted and stencilled columns and splats, usually with wooden movements, produced circa 1825–40.

STOCKUHR or STUTZUHR

An Austrian type of mantel clock standing on a base about 10 in. square, with supporting columns, often with a mirror behind. The skeleton dial sometimes revealed automaton figures, and was flanked by decorations on each side, frequently dolphins, surmounted by the imperial eagle; popular in the early 19th century.

STOP WATCH

Watch in which the seconds hand can be started and stopped at will without stopping the whole movement. In earliest forms, circa 1680–90 the whole movement would stop.

STREET SIGN CLOCKS

Having a clock in an advertising sign was an ingenious idea, designed to catch the eye of the passer by, in the hope that not only would he read the time, but also all about the product. Most date from around the turn of the century, and value varies according to condition, and also according to what product is being advertised.

SUBSCRIPTION WATCH

A large circular watch made to order from subscribers by Breguet, the case, circa 2in. in diameter, usually silver with gold bezel and pendant ring, a single hour hand indicating hours and minutes.

SUBSIDIARY DIAL

Smaller dial in a clock or watch face which shows the seconds, moon-phases etc.

SULLY, HENRY (1680–1728)

An English clockmaker who finally settled in Paris, where collaborated with Julien LeRoy. Worked on marine timekeeping in the 1720s.

SUN AND MOON DIAL

A feature of some watches circa 1700, where the minutes were shown normally, but the hours indicated by the sun for day and the moon for night on a revolving plate visible through a semicircular aperture on the upper part of the dial. Twelve hours starting and ending at VI marked at circumference.

SUNRAY CLOCK

17th century clock developed at the time of Louis XIV, Le Roi Soleil, with central circular dial and carved gilded sunrays emanating from it.

SUSPENSION

Refers to the method of supporting the pendulum of a clock, e.g. spring, silk, knife-edge.

SWINGING DOLL

These were novelty clocks, produced in the US in the late 19th century, the frame in such a form, or having such an attachment, that a small doll could be suspended in a swing.

TABERNACLE CLOCK

A type of 16th century clock case usually of fretwork or openwork often in the shape of a tower, the going train in front of the striking train, the verge escapement similar to that of a lantern clock but usually with mainsprings and gut-driven fusees. Some more elaborate examples may have dials on all four sides.

TALLCASE CLOCK

Another name for a longcase clock, used particularly in America.

TAMBOUR WATCH

An early mid 16th century German watch of drum shape, pierced and decorated, the iron movement, usually with striking or alarm mechanism, is latched to the case. Also refers to a later type of French watch with movement secured to case by screws.

TANNER, JOHN

Distinguished Newport clockmaker, active 1740–60.

TAVERN CLOCK

Alternative name for Act of Parliament clock.

TELL-TALE CLOCK

Clock used to check that the nightwatchman was doing his rounds, the forerunner of the modern clocking in machine, devised late 18th century by John Whitehurst (1713–88). Rotating 24 hour dial carried projecting pins at half hour intervals depressed by pushpiece outside case to leave record of visits by nightwatchmen.

TEMPLE CLOCK

A French clock of architectural style, featuring a Roman or Greek temple (with small gilt cupids, known as temple d'amour). Produced circa 1790–1810, usually with horizontal dial band.

TERRY CLOCK

Strictly, clock made by Eli Terry (1772–1852) of Connecticut but used loosely of all pillar and scroll clocks.

TERRY, ELI (1772–1852)

Connecticut clockmaker and inventor, who patented the equation clock in 1797. Made mainly shelf clocks with wooden movements. Patented box case clock in 1816 and was also the probable designer of the pillar and scroll clock.

TERRY, SILAS BURNHAM (1807–76)

Son of Eli Terry, produced shelf, steeple and wall clocks.

THOMAS, SETH (1785–1859)

Connecticut clockmaker who was also a skilled carpenter. From circa 1808 collaborated with Eli Terry. Produced tall case and pillar and scroll clocks. Set up in business from 1813, his firm established as the Seth Thomas Clock Company in 1853.

THURET or TURET, ISAAC (d. 1700)

French clockmaker to Louis XIV from 1686. Produced oignon watch, mantel clocks and pendules religieuses. Succeeded by his son Jacques (d. circa 1738).

TIDAL DIAL

A dial that indicates daily the time of high tide at any given port, the earliest dating from 16th century.

TING TANG

Onomatopoetic name for the quarter chime on 19th century Black Forest clocks.

TOMPION, THOMAS

Thomas Tompion (1638–1713) is perhaps the best known English clock and watch maker, who is famed for his mechanical skill and craftsmanship. He was born in Northhill, Beds., and moved to London in 1671, where he became a brother of the Clockmakers' Company by redemption.

In 1674 he met Dr Robert Hooke, who brought him to the attention of Charles II, after which he received many royal commissions.

In that year he set up in business, producing large numbers of accurate timepieces. He made watches with balance springs and applied the first version of cylinder escapement for watches in 1695. He also produced many fine longcase, bracket, lantern and travelling clocks, some of which had elaborate astronomical or calendar work.

In 1703 he was master of the Clockmakers, and such was the measure of his greatness even amongst his contemporaries, that when he died he was buried in Westminster Abbey.

TORSION PENDULUM

Pendulum in which the bob rotates by the twisting and untwisting of a long suspension spring, most often found on year clocks.

TORTOISE or TURTLE CLOCK

French brass table clock invented by Nicolas Grollier de Servière in the 17th century, much reproduced, consisting of a shallow bowl, surrounded by horizontal chapter ring surmounting a decorative stand containing the movement. When bowl filled with water, a metal tortoise or turtle, controlled through magnet driven by the movement, appears to swim round circumference, indicating hours.

TOURBILLION

Device invented by Breguet, a carriage-holding escapement of a watch or chronometer which revolves in the course of a minute to avoid positional error.

TRAIN

Set of cogs and pinions in a clock mechanism, devoted to various purposes, such as striking, going, astronomical, etc.

TREGENT, JAMES (1759–1808)

Clockmaker renowned for his well proportioned cases, with dials reputedly made by his brother Anthony, an enameller in Battersea.

TRUMPETER CLOCK

Clock having a military bugler sounding the hours, on the same principle as the cuckoo clock.

TURNIP WATCH

Similar to French Oignon watch, an English term for watches with thick movement, popular particularly in the provinces between 17th-19th centuries.

TURRET CLOCK

Clock with large, usually iron, movement, mounted in church tower or public building. Some have only striking mechanism and no dial, others have elaborate automaton figures. First examples have verge escapement and foliot, later anchor and gravity escapement.

TWO PILLAR CLOCKS

These are mantel clocks, popular particularly in France in the Empire period, architectural in style, the dial generally being flanked by two pillars, the pendulum suspended beneath.

TWO TRAIN MOVEMENT

One with two separate mechanisms, one for the going, the other for the strike.

UP AND DOWN DIAL

A subsidiary indicator on high quality watches and chronometers to show the state of winding of the mainspring.

URN or VASE CLOCK

A French mantel clock in the form of an urn or vase, mounted on a base, introduced during the Louis XVI period. The horizontal hour and minute band revolves at the top of the urn with a decorative arrow or snake's head indicating the time.

VERGE ESCAPEMENT

Oldest form of escapement, found as early as 1300, consisting of a bar (verge) with two flag shaped pallets that rock in and out of the teeth of the crown or escape wheel to regulate the movement.

VIENNA REGULATORS

This is an Austrian wall clock with a long pendulum and a glass fronted door in the trunk. The pendulum is usually fast beating, i.e. 2/3 second. From the 1840s similar examples were made in the Black Forest area.

VULLIAMY

The Vulliamys were a notable family of Swiss clockmakers, who flourished from the 18th to the mid 19th century. Justin (1712–97) emigrated to London in around 1730, where his son, Benjamin (1747–1811) became mechanical adviser to George III. He also made the regulator for the Kew Observatory and produced longcase clocks with grasshopper escapement, and French influenced bracket and ornamental types. In turn his son, Benjamin Lewis (1780–1854) became the foremost clockmaker of his day. He carried on his father's business and also produced carriage clocks and other French types such as the elephant clock.

WAG ON THE WALL

American term applied to any wall clock where the pendulum is not cased.

WALL CLOCKS

Wall clocks are really self explanatory, and the term covers a whole range of different forms designed to be wall mounted. In its narrower sense, however, the term is perhaps most often applied to the variant of the English 30 hour lantern clock with a square dial plate and case similar to the top of a longcase clock and made between circa 1660–1800.

WALTHAM CLOCKS

Made by the company of that name in Boston and noted for their simple elegance and fine quality.

WALTHAM WATCH CO

Founded 1850 in Boston, this was the first company to mass produce watches.

WANDERING HOUR CLOCK/WATCH

Timepiece which shows the time through a dial with semicircular aperture through which hour numeral moves. The minute scale is on the circumference of the semicircle. Introduced circa 1700.

WARNING
The partial unlocking of the striking train which precedes the full release at the moment of striking.

WATCHCOCK
Metal plate which protects the balance wheel of a watch, often highly ornate, of gilt brass. Also known as watchbridge.

WATCH KEYS
Used for winding watches and now themselves also highly collectable.

WATCH STAND
A table stand on which a pocket watch could be hung, thus converting it temporarily to a miniature clock.

WATERBURY WATCH CO
Early US watch company, producing inexpensive timepieces in New York in the 1880s and 90s.

WEBSTER, ROBERT and WILLIAM
Distinguished London clockmakers, Robert active 1680–99, William 1730–50.

WEIGHTS
The masses used to provide the motive power in fixed clocks, usually of lead in early clocks, later of cast iron. From late 17th century the weights on some fine clocks were applied with brass sheeting. Weights of many American longcase clocks are cylinders of thin sheet iron filled with scrap iron or other heavy material.

WHEEL CENTRE
Wheel to which the cannon pinion is attached.

WHEEL, GREAT
The wheel attached to the going barrel, fusee or, in weight driven clocks, the gut barrel.

WHITEHURST, JOHN (1713–88)
English clockmaker in Derby then in London, who made turret clocks and invented the tell-tale clock.

WILLARD, AARON (1757–1844)
Massachusetts clockmaker who worked in Roxbury from 1780 before setting up factory in Boston circa 1792. Made tallcase and wall clocks, also banjo clock with eagle finials and curved scrolls on either side of the trunk. Succeeded by his son Aaron Jr. in 1823.

WILLARD CLOCKS
Made by the Willard family, clockmakers in Massachusetts. Aaron (1757–1844) is credited with inventing the banjo clock; his brother

Simon (1753–1848) patented the Massachusetts clock in 1802. Both, with their sons, also made longcase and wall clocks.

WILLARD, SIMON (1753–1848)
Brother of Aaron Willard, working in Grafton and then Roxbury, Massachusetts. Made tall and wall clocks and patented Massachusetts clocks in 1792. Also made lighthouse clocks.

WILLIAMSON, JOSEPH
Late 17th/early 18th century English clockmaker, credited with inventing the equation clock.

WINDMILLS, JOSEPH
Late 17th/early 18th century London maker of clocks and watches.

WINDMILL WATCH
A watch form fashionable circa 1800, having a painted landscape scene on the dial with a windmill, the sails of which turned with the action of the watch movement.

WING-LANTERN CLOCK
An English lantern clock with a wide swinging pendulum between the going and striking train, the case extended on either side by 'wings' with a glass front through which the pendulum can be seen.

WOOD, DAVID
Newburyport RI. clockmaker of note, active 1765–90.

WOOD, JOHN
Philadelphia clockmaker, active 1770–93.

WOODEN CLOCK
Clock with a wooden movement, usually pendulum driven.

YEAR CLOCK
Clock designed to go for a year without rewinding.

YORKSHIRE CLOCK
Broad and ill-proportioned longcase clock type made in the late 18th/early 19th century, not necessarily from Yorkshire.

ZAPPLER CLOCK
Miniature clock made in Austria from 1800, notable for the rapid movement of the pendulum or double pendulum in front of dial. Cases often of embossed brass or mother of pearl, circa 2$\frac{1}{2}$ in. high.

Also known as a tavern or coaching clock, these large English wall clocks date from the early 18th century and were incorrectly named after an Act of 1797–8 whereby a tax was levied on clocks and timepieces. The dial is usually either round or shaped, and very prominent, often about 30in. diameter and both dial and case are often lacquered or painted. Alternatively the dial can be painted white within a mahogany case. They are weight driven, and usually non-striking.

An Act of Parliament timepiece, signed beneath the dial Thomas Fenton, London. £1,250

A mahogany Act of Parliament clock, the 22in. dial signed Thos. De La Salle, London. £3,500

A mid-Georgian black japanned Act of Parliament clock signed *Willm. Calvert, Bury* on the shaped 28in. dial with Roman and Arabic gold painted chapters, 6in. high. (Christie's) £1,540

A George III 'Act of Parliament' clock signed *Justin Vulliamy, London*, the timepiece movement with tapered rectangular plates, spring suspended pendulum to anchor escapement, last quarter 18th century, 58in. high. (Christie's) £5,423

A George III scarlet japanned Act of Parliament clock signed *Owen Jackson Cranbrook*, on the shaped 26in. green repainted dial with Roman and Arabic chapters, 58in. high. (Christie's) £1,100

A late 19th century black japanned Act of Parliament clock, the circular dial with gilt Roman numerals and Arabic minutes, 60in. high. (Spencer's) £3,000

A George III black lacquered and chinoiserie decorated tavern wall timepiece, signed Frans. Perigal, London, 1.44m. high. £1,500

A Georgian black lacquered tavern wall timepiece, the shield-shaped dial with gilt chapter, the weight driven movement with anchor escapement, 5ft.2½in. high. (Phillips) £3,400

George III black-painted Act of Parliament wall timepiece, dial signed Henry Riddle, London, 5ft. 2in. high. £2,250

A mahogany tavern time-piece with five pillar movement, 43½in. £1,000

Black japanned and gilt decorated 'Act of Parliament' tavern clock by John Wilson, Peterborough. £3,250

A mid Georgian black japanned tavern or Act of Parliament clock signed Robert Allam, London, on the shaped 30in. dial, 59in. high. £6,000

A mid Georgian black japanned longcase Act of Parliament clock, 31in. dial signed Will. Threlkeld, London, 6ft. 10in. high. £2,000

A George II black lacquered striking Act of Parliament clock, the dial of typical cartouche outline with ogee-moulded frame surmounted by two gilt-wood flambeau finials, 61in. high. (Christie's) £8,625

A Georgian tavern clock signed Willm Murrell Horsham, 4ft. 8½in. high. (Phillips) £2,400

A lacquered tavern time-piece, with 25in. cream painted wooden dial, the case inscribed J. Bartho-lomew, 57in. high. £4,250

An 18th century striking Act of Parliament clock, signed Ino. Wilson, Peterborough, 56½in. high. £1,500

Shavallo battery advertising clock 'Saves Time'. £20

A walnut double dial calendar shelf clock, by Seth Thomas Clock Co., 32in. high. £1,600

An advertising clock for Busch Light Beer, 110v electric, unused and in original packing with operating instructions, 35cm. diameter. (Auction Team Köln) £74

'Ingersoll Watches' enamel sign, circa 1900. £150

Chemico Specialities embossed tin clock, made for The County Chemical Co. Ltd., Birmingham. £130

Hudson's Soap sign, 18in. high, circa 1900. £100

A fine early Victorian mahogany railway drop-dial clock, by Vulliamy, the 12in. painted mahogany dial with *G.W.R.* logo, 23½in. high. (Bonhams) £3,200

Advertising clock for Palethorpes Sausages, 1940's, 12in. square. £75

Late 19th century 'Coca-Cola' walnut regulator timepiece, by Gilbert Clock Co., 30in. long. £400

Carved and painted
watchmaker's sign, New
England, late 19th century, 29in.
high.
(Skinner)   £1,000

An Art Deco theatre clock, cast
iron, with the current time on
the left and the end of the
programme on the right, circa
1920.
(Auction Team Köln)   £108

The Spalding Co. iron advertising trade sign, the cast-iron
pocket watch frame with zinc
painted face, 22¼in. high,
circa 1890.   £450

An early Victorian mahogany
drop-dial railway clock, the
restored 12in. white dial with
Roman numerals and initialled
G.W.R., 23in. high.
(Bonhams)   £550

A Coca Cola neon advertising
clock with second hand and
surrounding neon tube with
typical Coca Cola Stop Sign
symbol, in green hammered
casing, 40 x 39cm, 1942.
(Auction Team Köln)   £294

A Telechrom electric advertising
clock, with drum under the dial
for six advertising signs which
change automatically every 5
minutes, painted silvered dial,
54cm. high, 1910.
(Auction Team Köln)   £140

A desk clock from Watts
Tyre & Rubber Co. of
Gloucestershire, in work-
ing order.   £20

Jolly Tar wall timepiece,
manufactured by Baird
Clock Co., New York,
30½in. high.   £1,500

Boston Beer Co. wall timepiece, manufactured by the
New Haven Clock Co., circa
1900, 14in. diam.   £650

Late 19th century moulded iron and zinc jeweller's trade sign, America. £600

Hudson's Soap sign, 18in. high, circa 1900. £100

Nestle's Milk For All Time Richest In Cream, circular printed tin simulated wood wall clock, 48cm. diameter. (Onslow's) £300

A Pan American Exposition 1901, Buffalo, USA advertising clock in the form of a frying pan, signed on reverse, *Mfd by C F Chouffet Jeweler – Buffalo NY*, 29cm. high. (Auction Team Köln) £75

Chemico Specialities 'Light Your Lamps' embossed clock produced for The County Chemical Co. Ltd., Birmingham. £130

An Ever Ready Safety Razor advertising clock, made of wood with American 8 day movement, the price of 12 blades on the pendulum. (Auction Team Köln) £1,367

A mahogany railway drop-dial clock, 12in. white dial with Roman numerals and initialled *G.W.R.*, 27in. high. (Bonhams) £380

Late 19th century Clock Shop trade sign, iron and zinc painted, 23in. wide. £225

Late 19th century pressed wood advertising timepiece. by Baird Adv. Clock Co., 31in. long. £1,500

AUTOMATON CLOCKS

These are clocks and watches with animated figures or objects, which are set in motion by the going or striking train. The earliest examples date from the 17th century, and were usually to be found on public buildings, with the figures emerging and perhaps enacting a small drama when the clock struck. It was a type particularly beloved of German and French clockmakers, who adapted the principle to smaller timepieces. Negroes and animals were popular subjects, as was the Crucifixion, which was favoured by German and French clockmakers of the 17th century.

'Monkey Cobbler', automaton with papier-mâché head, glass eyes, and articulated jaw, seated on a box.
(Phillips) £650

A mid 17th century South German negro automaton clock, 11½in. high. £6,000

Napoléon III bronze and ormolu mantel clock with automaton rocking ship, the case of naturalistic form with the ormolu figure of Neptune, 21in. high.
(Christie's) £1,100

A Black Forest clock automaton, the brightly painted limewood figure of a clockmaker moves his head and whistles a tune, while carrying under his arm a small Black Forest clock with pendulum and key, circa 1950.
(Auction Team Köln) £609

A Napoléon III bronze and ormolu singing bird mantel clock, the glazed case applied with trailing foliage and with acanthus leaf mouldings, 16½in. high.
(Christie's) £2,640

Mid 19th century Swiss musical automaton of singing birds, on oval base, 60cm. high. (Christie's) £1,400

A three-dimensional wood model picture clock showing a French Chateau, under glass dome, 21½in. high.
£1,800

A singing bird automaton with clock, Swiss, probably by Jacquet Droz, circa 1785, 20in. high. (Christie's)
£30,703

Late 18th century gilt
metal musical automaton
clock for the Oriental
market, 19¾in. high.
£22,500

A cast iron blinking eye
timepiece, 'Sambo',
America, circa 1860, 16in.
high.   £1,400

Mid 19th century Swiss
musical automaton of
singing birds, 38in. high.
£1,000

A 19th century French ormolu
mantel clock with automaton,
the circular case raised above a
glazed base housing a singing
bird, 1ft. 4½in.
(Phillips)   £2,300

A Louis XVI ormolu-mounted
Paris porcelain musical
automaton clock, playing a
selection of six tunes through ten
organ pipes, cam-and-rod drive
through a composition tree to an
automaton bird atop flapping its
wings, rotating and opening and
shutting its beak, 26¼in. high.
(Christie's)   £11,550

A late 19th century South
German automaton quarter
striking bracket clock, the
stained wooden case in the style
of a church with onion spire
finial and belfry, 30in. high.
(Christie's S. Ken)   £1,210

A 19th century mechanical
organ automaton with clock,
26in. high.   £12,500

A Swiss automaton mantel
clock, 9in. high.   £2,500

An automaton clock in the
form of a ship's bridge,
12½in. high.   £3,000

A Federal mahogany gilt-
wood and eglomise banjo
clock, Mass., 1815-25,
40in. high.   £1,500

A Federal mahogany and
eglomise banjo clock, by
Warren, Mass., 1815/30,
30in. high.   £3,000

A Federal mahogany and
giltwood presentation banjo
timepiece, Mass., circa 1820,
40in. high.   £1,800

Federal mahogany and giltwood banjo timepiece, probably
Boston, circa 1820, with
original painted eglomise tables,
32in. high. (Skinner Inc.)
          £1,302

Federal gilt gesso and
mahogany banjo timepiece,
Aaron Willard Jr., Boston,
circa 1820, the circular brass
moulded bezel enclosing a
painted iron dial, 40in. high.
(Skinner Inc.)   £4,601

Antique American banjo clock
in mahogany, by A. Willard,
Boston, gilt acorn finial, painted
dial, reverse painted throat and
tablet, 33½in. high.
(Eldred's)   £1,535

Fine custom-made banjo clock
by Foster S. Campos of
Pembroke, Mass., inlaid
mahogany case with
presentation bracket, 41½in.
high.
(Eldred's)   £806

Rare Federal gilt gesso painted
banjo timepiece, the eight-day
weight driven movement
stamped A Willard Boston 1808,
45in. high.   £120,000

A Federal presentation
mahogany banjo time-
piece, by A. Willard,
circa 1820, 40½in. high.
          £2,400

Federal giltwood mahogany banjo timepiece, by Lemuel Curtis, Mass., circa 1820, 32in. high. £6,000

Mid 19th century banjo timepiece with alarm, signed A. Willard, Jnr., Boston, 33½in. high. £10,000

Early 19th century Federal mahogany giltwood and eglomise banjo clock, 33½in. long. £1,500

Federal gilt and mahogany banjo timepiece, attributed to Aaron Willard, Boston, circa 1815, dial inscribed *A. A. Cheney Brookline, Mass,* 42½in. high. (Skinner) £3,877

A fine Federal mahogany and eglomisé panel banjo clock, Lemuel Curtis, Massachusetts, circa 1815, the circular glazed dial door with brass bezel enclosing a white-painted dial with Roman numeral chapter ring, 33½in. high. (Christie's) £12,496

Presentation banjo timepiece, Waltham Clock Co., Waltham, Massachusetts, 20th century, eagle finial, brass bezel, 43in. high. (Skinner Inc.) £1,111

A Federal giltwood banjo timepiece with painted dial and eight-day weight driven movement, circa 1820, 41in. high. £1,250

A Federal mahogany gilt-wood and eglomise banjo clock, by Aaron Willard, 1820/25, 33¾in. high. £3,000

Classical gilt and mahogany lyre-form banjo timepiece, probably Massachusetts, circa 1820, 40in. high. (Skinner Inc.) £1,227

BRACKET CLOCKS

That the first 'bracket' clocks were designed to stand on tables as often as against a wall is indicated by the fact that they often have elaborately engraved backplates and a glazed back door. Also, they had handles on the top, so that they could be carried from room to room. As they became mass produced and hence cheaper, however, these details were often omitted. The earliest bracket clocks, dating from the 17th century also had a 'cock' fixed to the backplate to conceal the suspension of the pendulum.

The bracket clocks with which we are more familiar today, in wooden cases, appeared in the second half of the 17th century before the longcase clock became popular. They were generally rather squat in form, and quite plain, with a flat or portico top and had a verge escapement. They quickly became more elaborate, however, but, although the anchor escapement was introduced in 1675 it was not generally adopted for bracket clocks until midway through Queen Anne's reign. The longer, heavy disc pendulum usually associated with anchor escapement took longer to find favour, due to the obvious disadvantages such a feature would have when the timepiece was being carried about.

From the first, brackets clocks were usually fitted with a striking train sounding the hours, while some also struck the quarters. At the end of the 17th century the basket top was introduced while in the 18th century luxury versions with musical mechanisms became popular with those who could afford them. Decoration also became more elaborate in the early part of the century and clocks acquired ormolu or silver mountings and finials. The arched dial found favour at this time too. Towards the end of the century, however, styles became plainer, and broken arch, arch top, lancet and balloon tops were introduced.

An 18th century Italian quarter-striking bracket clock, 25in. high. £1,850

An olivewood bracket clock, the 8in. dial signed Joseph Knibb, 14½in. high.   £35,000

Late 18th century George III gilt and cut glass mounted floral painted quarter-chiming musical bracket clock for the Turkish market, signed Benj. Barber, London, 37½in. high. £45,000

A substantial Edwardian bracket clock with arched brass dial, fronting a three-train movement with Westminster chime. £1,000

A George III satinwood 'balloon' bracket clock, the enamel dial signed Webster London, 24in. high. £6,000

A George III bracket clock with enamel dial, by Robt. Henderson, 15½in. high. £10,000

An Austrian fruitwood
quarter striking bracket clock,
signed B. Schmidt, 20in. high.
£1,500

An early 19th century
bracket clock by Barwise,
London, 13¼in. high.
£2,150

An early George III padouk-
wood automaton organ clock,
by Wm. Vale, London, 37in.
high.   £12,000

A Queen Anne kingwood
striking bracket clock, the
dial signed Cha. Gretton,
14in. high.   £25,000

A 19th century Chinese
hardwood bracket clock, the
rectangular case decorated with
carved motifs, the twin fusée
movement with verge
escapement, striking on a bell,
1ft. 3in. high.
(Phillips)   £380

A Chinese carved hardwood
bracket clock on stand, the
movement with twin chain
fusees, 22½in. high. £1,500

A Victorian director's bracket
clock with 8-day fusee movement chiming on eight bells,
30in. high.   £2,250

A chiming and repeating
dome top bracket clock,
nine bells and one gong,
19½in. high.   £1,750

An early George III 8-day
bracket clock with verge
striking movement by Wm.
Allam, 15.5in. high.
£12,000

BOULLE

French ormolu mounted boulle bracket clock in Louis XV style, with strike. £1,250

A boulle bracket clock of Louis XIV design, inscribed J. Le Lacheur, Guernsey, with an eight-day bell-striking movement, 15in. high. (Hy. Duke & Son) £550

An ormolu mounted scarlet boulle bracket clock, dial signed V. Courtecuisse & Cie Lille, 45in. high. £3,000

A Regence ormolu mounted boulle bracket clock, dial signed Mynuel a Paris, 32in. high. £2,250

An ormolu mounted boulle mantel clock, the enamel dial signed Grohe Paris, 11½in. high. £750

A 19th century tortoiseshell and cut brass inlaid bracket clock, signed Lepeltier a Paris, 2ft.2½in. high. £1,350

Early 18th century bracket clock in red and green boulle case, the backplate engraved Jerome Martinot, Paris, 37in. high. £1,350

An ebonised wood and gilt bronze bracket clock by Winterhalder & Hoffmeir, 27¼in. high, circa 1880. £650

An ormolu mounted scarlet boulle bracket clock, the glazed dial with Roman enamel numerals, 48in. high. £3,500

BOULLE

A Regency boulle bracket clock, the dial signed Paliand a Besancon, 39½in. high. £2,000

A Louis XV style red boulle bracket clock with two-train movement by Gay Vicarino & Co., Paris, 44cm. high. £650

A Louis XIV French ormolu mounted boulle bracket clock, signed Gribelin a Paris, 49½in. high. £3,250

An ormolu mounted boulle bracket clock, the chapter ring signed J. Gudin a Paris, 41½in. high. £2,500

A Louis XV ormolu mounted boulle bracket clock, the movement signed G. I. Champion A Paris, the shaped case surmounted by a figure of Father Time, 43in. high. (Christie's) £3,300

A Louis XV premiere and contre partie boulle bracket clock with shaped circular face, signed Calon a Paris, 48in. high. (Christie's) £1,870

A contre-partie polychrome boulle bracket clock, the enamel face signed Gille L'Aine a Paris, basically 18th century, 31in. high. £2,500

Early 19th century boulle timepiece, the movement signed Barraud & Lunds, 10½in. high. £1,000

Mid 19th century ormolu mounted bracket clock, France, backplate engraved 'Fiault Paris, Reparee par Bourdin', 45in. high. £2,000

EBONISED

A Queen Anne ebonised bracket clock, the 6¼in. sq. dial signed James Tunn, London, 15in. high.£2,400

A George II ebonised striking bracket clock, plaque signed Willm Morgan London, 21½in. high. £1,500

A George I ebonised striking bracket clock, the dial signed Ed. Bayley London, 19in. high. £1,850

A Charles II ebony striking bracket clock, the plinth case with carrying handle and gilt metal foliate mounts to the cushion-moulded top, the tulip engraved backplate signed John Knibb London Fecit, 11¼in. high. (Christie's) £19,800

Tho: Tompion Londini Fecit, a Charles II ebony striking early miniature bracket clock, unnumbered, circa 1675–80, the well-moulded plinth-form case with later bun feet and side frets, 9³/₄in. high. (Christie's) £37,400

A Charles II ebony Dutch striking small bracket clock by Joseph Knibb, London, within a phase III case with gilt foliate scroll escutcheons to the door and foliate mounts to the caddy top, circa 1680s, 11in. high. (Christie's) £26,796

An ebonised musical bracket clock, the three train fusee movement with anchor escapement, chiming two tunes on eight bells, 21in. (Lawrence Fine Arts) £1,760

An ebonised bracket clock, the five pillar repeating fusée movement with anchor escapement, signed *Geor. Yonge, Strand, London*, 16¹/₄in. high. (Lawrence Fine Art) £1,540

An ebonised bracket clock, the two train fusee movement now with anchor escapement, signed on a silvered arc Wm. Threlkeld, London, 36½in. (Lawrence Fine Arts) £990

EBONISED

Late 18th century ebonised striking bracket clock, signed A. Van Eeden, Haarlem, 20in. high. £1,750

A late Victorian ebonised chiming bracket clock, inscribed Thompson, Ashford, 24in., with later wall bracket. £1.250

A mid-Georgian ebonised striking bracket clock, the dial signed John Fladgate London, 18½in. high. £2,250

An Austrian ebonised grande sonnerie bracket clock, the bell top case with crowned cherub carrying handle and winged paw feet, mid 18th century, 23¹/₂in. high.
(Christie's New York) £1,795

Josephus Pryor, a Charles II ebony striking bracket clock of large size, the plinth shaped case with gilt carrying handle to cushion moulded top, glazed sides, the 10in. square skeletonised dial with silvered chapter ring.
(Christie's) £11,000

Dan: Quare London 62 (Graham No. 550), a George I ebonised striking bracket clock of small size, the case with large giltmetal handle to cushion moulded top, circa 1715, 11⁷/₈in. high.
(Christie's) £66,000

A Regency ebonised striking miniature bracket clock, the border engraved backplate signed Kenth. Maclennan London, behind the bell, 10½in. high. (Christie's) £1,320

A small and very fine veneered ebony quarter repeating bracket clock, the 6in. dial signed Tho. Tompion Londini fecit, 12½in. high. £55,000

A William III ebony striking bracket clock, circa 1700, the 7¹/₄ x 8in. dial signed *Tho: Tompion Londini fecit*, 15¹/₂in. high.
(Christie's) £77,000

BRACKET CLOCKS

EBONISED

A small ebony veneered bracket clock, signed John Drew Londini Fecit, 14½in. high. £3,000

A Charles II ebonised turntable bracket clock, by E. Bird, London, 19in. high. £10,000

Mid 18th century George II ebonised quarter-chiming bracket clock, signed B. Gray, London, 15½in. high. £7,500

A small ebony silver-mounted striking bracket clock, circa 1708, the 4³/₄ x 5¹/₄in. dial signed *Tho: Tompion & Edw: Banger London*, 9in. high. (Christie's) £572,000

A late Stuart ebonised striking bracket clock with gilt metal repousse basket top, carrying handle and pressed door mounts, engraved backplate signed Isaac Papavoine Londini Fecit, 14½in. (Christie's) £4,180

An early 18th century ebony veneered pull quarter repeat alarum bracket clock, the fusée movement with five finely finned pillars, signed *William Post, London Bridge*, 20¹/₂in. high. (Lawrence) £3,850

A Charles II ebonised striking bracket clock with 6¾in. sq. dial, backplate signed Nathaniel Hodges, 13¾in. high. £5,000

An ebony veneered quarter repeating bracket clock, the dials signed Henry Fish, Royal Exchange London, 17½in. high. £4,000

A William III ebonised striking bracket clock with gilt metal repousse basket top, dial signed Cha. Gretton, 14½in. high. £4,000

EBONISED

A Queen Anne ebonised
bracket clock, the dial
signed Dan. Quare, London,
20in. high.   £12,500

A George II ebonised quarter
striking bracket clock, the
dial signed Jams. Snelling,
London, 14¾in. high. £4,500

A Charles II ebonised
striking bracket clock, dial
signed J. Windmills, London,
14¼in. high.   £7,500

Ellicott London, a fine George
III musical striking bracket
clock, the case with foliate urn
finials to bell top, handles and
cast pierced sound frets to side
doors, 32in. high.
(Christie's)   £12,100

A late 19th century bracket
clock in ebonised case with
gilt metal mounts, full chimes
of Westminster and Eight Bells,
34in. high overall, by Canova,
Halesworth and Southwold.
(Prudential)   £2,300

A George III ormolu mounted
ebonised musical bracket clock
for the Turkish market, the case
with pineapple finials to bell top
applied with ormolu floral
mounts, 28¹/₂in. high.
(Christie's)   £2,640

A Queen Anne ebony
striking and quarter repeating bracket clock, signed
Sam. Aldworth, 14in. high.
          £7,500

A James II ebonised Roman
striking bracket clock of
Phase III Type, signed
Joseph Knibb, 12in. high.
          £15,000

An early Georgian ebonised
bracket timepiece with gilt
brass handle, the backplate
signed Dan. Quare, London,
12¾in. high.   £4,500

EBONISED

A small early George III ebonised bracket clock, the dial signed Jno. Dwerri-house, 16in. high.   £2,000

A late 17th century ebony veneered bracket timepiece, by Henry Jones, London, 36cm. high.   £5,250

An ebonised wood bracket clock, by J. Lukavetzki Brunn, No. 174, 16in. high.   £1,100

Thomas Tompion London, an ebony veneered quarter repeating bracket clock, circa 1700, the caddy top case surmounted by a carrying handle, 15½in. high. (Phillips)   £70,000

A Georgian ebonised and brass mounted quarter chiming musical bracket clock, signed De Lasall, the triple fusee movement converted to anchor escapement, 1ft. 7¾in. high. (Phillips)   £2,300

A rare mid 18th century ebony and silver mounted miniature bracket clock, signed on an oval cartouche, Charls Clay, London, the movement with engraved backplate, 7½in. high. (Phillips)   £9,500

An ebony quarter-repeating bracket clock, the 7in. dial signed Henry Callowe, 15½in. high.   £15,000

An ebonised quarter-repeat-ing bracket clock, the back-plate signed Nathaniel Hod-ges, 12½in. high.   £7,500

A George III ebonised bracket clock, the 7in. dial signed Alexdr. Cumming, London, 18½in. high.   £1,500

EBONISED

An 18th century ebonised bracket clock, signed S. de Charmes, London, 39cm. high. £2,000

An ebonised quarter repeating bracket clock, the 7in. dial signed J. Windmills London, 15½in. high. £3,250

A small ebonised bracket clock, the 6in. dial signed Josiah Emery London, 14½in. high. £5,000

A good George II ebonised striking bracket clock with moonphase, the brass-lined case with handle to inverted bell top, signed *John. Hodges St. Clemt. Lane London*, 18½in. high. (Christie's) £4,620

A Georgian ebonised and brass mounted bracket clock, the square silvered dial with mock pendulum and date apertures, signed Edward Clarke, London, 1ft. 5½in. high. (Phillips) £1,600

An ebonised and brass-mounted bracket clock with pierced brass caddy top hood and scrolled carrying handle, inscribed *Jo. Buckingham, London*, 19in. high overall, 17th century. (Christie's) £6,050

An ebony quarter striking bracket clock, the 7in. dial signed Wm. Speakman London, 14in. high. £3,500

An ebonised chiming bracket clock, circa 1880, 25in. high, and a conforming bracket, 10½in. high. £1,300

A William III quarter repeating ebony bracket clock, signed Claudius Du Chesne, Londini Fecit, 16½in. high. £15,000

BRACKET CLOCKS

An ebony veneered quarter-repeating bracket clock, the 7½in. dial signed Windmills London, 18½in. high. £3,000

Henry Massey, London, a late 17th century ebonised basket top bracket clock, the square brass dial with signed silvered chapter ring, 16in. high. (Phillips) £2,400

An early George III ebonised bracket clock, the 7in. dial signed Jno. Harrison Newcastle, 18in. high. £1,500

An early 18th century ebonised bracket clock, the five ringed pillared movement reconverted to verge escapement, signed Saml Pitts, London, 1ft. 4in. high. (Phillips) £2,300

A George III ebonised quarter chiming bracket clock, the case with handle and four flambeau finials to inverted bell top, the dial signed *Graham's Nephew & Successor Puckridge London*, 20½in. high. (Christie's) £3,300

An 18th century ebonised bracket clock, signed *Alex' Cumming, London*, the twin fusée movement with signed and engraved backplate and with verge escapement, 1ft, 9½in. high. (Phillips) £1,750

An 18th century ebony bracket clock, signed James Tregent, Leicester Square, London, 1ft.5½in. high. £3,750

A 19th century ebonised and brass mounted bracket clock, the silvered dial signed Payne, 163 New Bond St., London, 1ft.2½in. high. £1,600

An 18th century ebonised and gilt brass mounted quarter chiming bracket clock, signed Wm. Webster, 52cm. high. £4,500

EBONISED

George III ebonised
bracket clock, dial
signed by Wm.
Hughes, London, 14in.
high.   £5,000

An 18th century ebonised
bracket clock, the 17cm. square
brass dial inscribed *Jonathan
Lowndes, Pall Mall, London,*
16in. high.
(Spencer's)   £2,000

Early George III ebon-
ised bracket clock,
dial signed Willm.
Allam, London, 14in.
high.   £6,500

A Georgian ebonised bracket
timepiece, signed on a cartouche
in the arch Robt Gymer, Norwich, the five pillared movement with verge escapement and
pull quarter repeating on two
bells, 1ft.7¼in. high. (Phillips)
£900

An 18th century ebonised
musical and repeating bracket
clock, made for the Turkish
market, the case of rectangular
form with a bell top, signed
Edward Pister, London, the
three train movement with
verge escapement, 22½in.
(Phillips)   £3,400

A George III ebonised and
brass mounted bracket clock,
the arched brass dial with
silvered chapter ring and
date aperture, signed James
Tregent, London, 1ft 8in.
high, together with a wall
bracket. (Phillips)   £2,600

An 18th century ebonised
quarter chiming bracket clock,
signed *Chas Bosley,* chiming
on six bells, 46cm. high.
(Phillips)   £2,500

A small ebony-veneered
quarter-repeating alarm
bracket timepiece, the 6in.
dial signed Jam: Cuff London, 13½in. high.   £3,500

A small ebony veneered quarter-repeating bracket clock,
the 6¼in. dial signed Joseph
Knibb, London, 12in. high.
£20,000

EBONISED

George III ebonised striking bracket clock by Thos. Grignion, London, 15in. high. £6,000

A Charles II ebonised striking bracket clock, the square dial signed Hen. Jones London, 16in. high. £4.750

A George III ebonised musical bracket clock, dial signed Robt. Ramsey London, 24in. high. £5,250

A Georgian ebonised bracket clock with engraved spandrels and date aperture signed Peter Nichols, Newport, the twin fusee movement converted to anchor escapement, 1ft.8in. high. (Phillips) £750

A highly unusual early ebony bracket clock by Simon Bartram, the corners of the 5½ inch square gilt dial engraved with winged masks, the escapement with pendulum fixed to pivoted verge arbor, circa 1660–1665, 12¼in. high. (Christie's) £8,294

An 18th century ebonised bracket clock, the case with inverted bell top and carrying handle, the arched brass dial with silvered chapter ring signed *Jnº Watts, Canterbury*, 1ft. 7in. high. (Phillips) £1,500

An 18th century Austrian ebonised quarter striking bracket clock with gilt metal handle, 12in. high. £2,250

A George II ebonised grand sonnerie bracket clock, the dial signed Thos. Hughes, London, 9¾in. high. £7,500

An ebonised quarter chiming bracket clock, signed on an inset plaque Danl. Catlin, Lynn, 20in. high. £1,300

EBONISED

A George III ebonised striking bracket clock, the dial signed George Flashman London, 14in. high. £1,500

A Regency ebonised bracket clock, the dial signed W. French, Royal Exchange, London, 40cm. high. £1,350

A Queen Anne ebonised timepiece bracket clock, signed Fromanteel, London, 14¼in. high. £3,000

A Charles II silver-mounted ebony striking bracket clock of Phase II type, the velvet-covered dial signed *Joseph Knibb Londini Fecit* on a pierced foliate silver disc to the centre, 12in. high. (Christie's) £41,800

A late Stuart ebonised time-piece repeat bracket clock by Francis Robinson in Ye Temple, the case with handle and cast foliate mounts of Knibb pattern, restoration, 12in. high. (Christie's) £6,050

An ebony veneered quarter repeating bracket clock, the five pillar chain fusee movement with verge escapement, signed *Sub:i Boverick, London,* 46.5cm. (Lawrence Fine Arts) £6,820

A mid Georgian ebonised striking bracket clock, the dial signed Stepn. Rimbault, London, 19½in. high. £2,300

A George III ebonised striking bracket clock, the break-arch case with bracket feet, backplate signed Lynford Paddington, 14in. high. (Christie's) £1,045

A George I ebony striking bracket clock with alarm, circa 1725, the dial signed *Geo: Graham London*, 14in. high. (Christie's) £82,500

EBONISED

Rare silver mounted ebony bracket clock with velvet dial, by John Knibb, Oxford, 11½in. high. £32,500

An early silver mounted ebony spring clock, back-plate signed Joseph Knibb, 16in. high. £45,000

An ebonised gilt brass mounted quarter chiming bracket clock, signed Lambert & Co., London, 16½in. high. £2,000

Victorian ebonised ormolu mounted chiming bracket clock, the case on foliate paw feet with detached fluted Corinthian columns to the sides, 26in. high. (Christie's) £1,650

An ebony veneered month bracket clock, the 8½in. dial signed Jonathan Puller, Londini Fecit, 14½in. high excluding later feet. £25,000

An unusual 18th century ebonised quarter chiming bracket clock, the arched brass dial with silvered chapter ring signed *Jos Kirk*, 1ft. 7½in. high. (Phillips) £2,200

An early George III ebonised striking bracket clock, the dial signed Robt. & Peter Higgs, London, 17½in. high. £10,000

Late 17th century ebony veneered quarter-repeating bracket clock, signed I. Lowndes, London, 14½in. high. £6,000

Mid 19th century George II ebony quarter-repeating bracket clock, signed Rich'd. Gregg, London, 13in. high. £5,000

EBONISED

Small and early ebony veneered quarter-repeating bracket clock by John Ebsworth, London, 13in. high. £4,500

A 17th century bracket clock by Joseph Windmills, in an ebonised case, London, circa 1695. £20,000

An ebonised bracket clock, dial signed Jonathan Lowndes, circa 1685, 13in. high. £3,250

An ebonised quarter chiming bracket clock, the arched brass dial with silvered chapter ring and subsidiaries for pendulum regulation, the triple fusée movement with anchor escapement, 2ft. 3¼in. high. (Phillips) £950

A late 17th century ebony 'double six hour' grande sonnerie bracket clock, the 6½in. square dial now inscribed Tompion Londini, 35.5cm. high. £13,500

A George II ebony bracket timepiece with alarm and original wall bracket, circa 1750, unnumbered, the dial signed *Geo: Graham London*, 21in. high. (Christie's) £46,200

A Charles II ebonised striking bracket clock, backplate signed R. Pingo Neare The Pallmall, Londini in a lambrequin, 13½in. high. £3,000

A George III ebonised miniature striking bracket clock, signed Williams, 168 Shoreditch on Arabic chapter disc, 14½in. high overall. £4,000

An early George III ebonised striking bracket clock with brass handle, dial signed Sam. Toulmin, Strand, London, 18½in. high. £1,400

FRUITWOOD

A mid 18th century fruitwood case eight-day striking bracket clock, 20½in. high. £2,250

A Georgian fruitwood bracket clock, signed on a cartouche Henry Heve, London, 43cm. high. £2,500

A George II fruitwood striking miniature bracket clock with carrying handle, the backplate signed Wm. Hughes, 10in. high. £7,500

INLAID

A small Regency mahogany bracket clock, the five pillar fusée movement with anchor escapement, signed *Dwerrihouse, Carter & Son, Berkeley Square*, 13in. high.
(Lawrence Fine Art) £2,200

A Regency mahogany brass and ebony inlaid quarter chiming bracket clock, with circular enamel dial signed Grimalde & Johnson, Strand London, 12in. high.(Phillips) £1,800

A mahogany bracket clock, the eight inch dial with Roman numerals, moon hands and signed *Scott, Dublin*, contained in a domed case, 17in. high.
(Lawrence Fine Art) £528

A 19th century mahogany bracket clock, the twin fusee movement with anchor escapement, 43cm.
(Phillips) £620

A 19th century mahogany and brass inlaid bracket clock, anchor escapement signed Thos Glase, Bridgnorth, 1ft 7in. high, together with a wall bracket. (Phillips) £850

An Edwardian inlaid mahogany chiming bracket clock, circa 1900, 26in. high, with a mahogany bracket, 15in. high. £1,500

INLAID

A brass inlaid mahogany bracket timepiece, the single train fusee movement with anchor escapement, 12¾in. (Lawrence Fine Arts) £495

A George IV mahogany lyre-form musical bracket clock, signed Frodsham, London, 37in. high. £6,000

A Regency mahogany and brass bound bracket clock by Handley & Moore, London, 17½in. high. £1,300

A Victorian mahogany striking bracket clock, the glazed circular cream painted dial signed *Jas. McInnes Dunbarton* with concentric calendar ring, blued steel moon hands, 18¼in. high. (Christie's) £550

A brass inlaid mahogany bracket clock, the two train fusee movement with shaped plates, signed Edward Newman, London, 17½in. (Lawrence Fine Art) £924

A Regency mahogany striking bracket clock, the boxwood lined arched case with fish-scale frets and lion-mask-and-ring handles, signed *Perigal & Duterrau*, 17¼in. high. (Christie's) £1,100

A 19th century mahogany and brass inlaid bracket clock, with brass mounted canted angles on ball feet, the circular painted dial signed *E. Handscomb Woburn*, 1ft. 9¾in. high. (Phillips) £500

Georgian style inlaid mahogany mantel or bracket clock with 8-day striking movement, the dial inscribed Finnigans Ltd., Manchester, 12½in. high. £375

A George III inlaid mahogany small bracket clock, the white dial within brass bezel above inlaid panel, turned acorn finials now fitted with 19th century French countwheel striking movement, 14in. high. (Christie's) £1,914

INLAID

An inlaid balloon bracket clock, signed J. Leroux, London, 18¾in. high. £1,000

A 19th century mahogany and brass inlaid bracket timepiece, the circular case surmounted by a flame finial, 2ft. ½in. high. (Phillips) £480

A George III satinwood bracket clock, the movement signed Tregent, Strand, London, 21in. high. £4,000

A Regency brass inlaid mahogany bracket clock, signed *Thos. Halder, Arundel*, the twin fusee movement with anchor escapement, striking the hour on bell, circa 1820, 19¾in. high. (Christie's) £1,021

An Edwardian inlaid mahogany mantel or bracket clock, with silvered dial, 16¾in. high. £350

A 19th century mahogany and brass inlaid bracket clock, signed Wand & Hills, Rochester, the twin fusee movement with anchor escapement, 1ft. 11in. high. (Phillips) £500

Regency mahogany cased bracket clock with brass inlay and mounts, the striking movement inscribed *E Watson, King Street, Cheapside*, 18in. tall. (G. A. Key) £900

A late 19th century mahogany bracket clock, the circular painted dial signed *Camerer Cuss & Co., London*, the twin fusée movement with anchor escapement, 1ft. 6in. high. (Phillips) £650

A George IV brass inlaid mahogany bracket clock with hour striking movement and painted dial, 19¾in. high. (Tennants) £950

BRACKET CLOCKS

LACQUERED

A George II brown japanned bracket clock, dial signed Jn. Cotton London, 16¼in. high. £1,500

A mid Georgian scarlet japanned quarter striking, musical and automaton bracket clock in the style of G. Grendey, 37in. high. £75,000

A scarlet lacquer striking bracket clock, the brass dial signed Jas. Smith, London, 20in. high. £1,750

A George III black lacquer striking bracket clock with alarm, 6³/₄in. dial signed in the silvered aperture *Ralph Goat, London*, on cast bracket feet, 21in. high.
(Bonhams) £2,000

An 18th century C. European red lacquered quarter chiming bracket clock, the backplate signed Iohan Maurer in Prag, 57cm. high. £7,500

A George III scarlet japanned musical bracket clock for the Turkish market by Wm. Kipling London, the bekk-top case decorated overall with gilt chinoiseries, 25in. high
(Christies) £28,600

An early George III dark japanned musical chiming bracket clock for the Turkish market, dial signed Edward Pistor, London, 23½in. high. £4,750

Dutch japanned bracket clock, c. 1750, red laquered case, enamelled dial and calendar dial inscribed Ellicot London, 24in. high.
(Skinner Inc) £1,168

19th century bracket clock with silvered brass dial, the black lacquered case decorated with a polychrome chinoiserie pattern, 14in. high.
(G. A. Key) £320

LACQUERED

An early japanned bracket clock case containing a modern German clock, 15½in. high. £800

A Georgian green lacquered bracket clock, signed Stepn. Rimbault, London, 1ft.8in. high. £2,500

A George II green japanned striking bracket clock, the dial signed Fra Dorrell, London, 18¼in. high. £9,000

MAHOGANY

A Regency mahogany bracket clock in rectangular-shaped case, with stepped chamfered top, ring handles and pierced scalloped side frets, twin-chain fusée movement, 16½in. high. (Christie's S. Ken) £1,100

An early Victorian mahogany quarter chiming bracket clock, signed *Cradock King Street, Covent Garden, London*, the massive five pillar triple chain fusée movement with anchor escapement, 37in. high overall. (Christie's) £902

A Georgian mahogany bracket clock, the bell top case surmounted by a carrying handle, signed Thomas Gardner London, the twin fusée movement with verge escapement, 1ft. 8½in. high. (Phillips) £1,000

A mahogany bracket time-piece, signed Daniel Dickerson, Framlingham, 13in. high. £750

A mahogany chiming musical bracket clock, the 8in. dial signed John Taylor London, 24in. high. £3,250

A mahogany bracket clock, signed Debois & Wheeler, Grays Inn Passage, 17¼in. high. £750

MAHOGANY

A George III mahogany bracket clock with alarm, signed John Taylor, London, 54cm. high. £1,750

George III mahogany bracket clock, inscribed Wright, watchmaker to the King, 17in. high. £1,500

A George III mahogany striking bracket clock, the dial signed Thos, Wagstaffe London, 19in. high. £3,000

A Georgian mahogany bracket clock, signed Joseph Pomroy, London and with strike/silent subsidiary in the arch, the five pillared movement with verge escapement and engraved back-plate, 1ft.8½in. high.
(Phillips) £2,100

A George III faded mahogany striking bracket clock, the seven-inch dial signed on a silvered plaque, *John Rycutt, London*, matted centre with false pendulum aperture and date, 18in.
(Bonhams) £3,000

A George III mahogany musical bracket clock, the arched silvered dial signed *Sam¹ Whatson*, the twin fusée movement now converted to anchor escapement, 1ft. 6in. high.
(Phillips) £2,000

A Victorian mahogany eight-day chiming and striking bracket clock with 7¼in. arched brass dial, 23¼in. high.
(Bearne's) £800

A Georgian mahogany quarter chiming bracket clock, the painted dial signed Geo. Wilkins, Soho, 2ft.2in. high. £2,000

A George III mahogany striking bracket clock, signed Eardley Norton, London, 15¾in. high. £10,000

59

MAHOGANY

Late 19th century mahogany 8-day domed bracket clock with silvered dial, 12in. high.
£325

A Regency Gothic mahogany bracket clock, the painted dial signed Manners & Sons, Stamford, 21½in. high. £1,500

A mahogany veneered bracket clock, signed in the arch Richd. Ward, Winchester, 18½in. high. £2,500

A George III mahogany striking bracket clock, the 8in. white painted dial signed *Willm Fidgett, London*, with anchor escapement, in a moulded break arch case, 1ft. 5in. high.
(Bonhams) £850

A mahogany bracket clock, the two train chain fusée repeating movement with anchor escapement, blued steel moon hands and signed *Cooper*, 15in. high.
(Lawrence Fine Art) £1,760

George III mahogany striking bracket clock, the case with handle to the arched top and on brass bracket feet, the painted dial signed *John Hardy Preston*, 15in. high.
(Christie's) £1,100

A George II mahogany striking bracket clock, the 6in. dial signed *Delander, London*, on a brass plaque to the matted centre, with false pendulum aperture and date, 16in.
(Bonhams) £6,000

A George III mahogany musical bracket timepiece, the arched case surmounted by a spire and finial, signed M. Miller London, the twin fusee movement with verge escapement, 1ft. 7¾in. high. (Phillips) £2,200

A George III mahogany bracket clock, with caryatid and floral mounts to the corners, on bracket feet, the arched silvered dial signed *Thos Oldmeadon Lynn*, 1ft. 10in. high.
(Phillips) £1,600

MAHOGANY

A Regency mahogany bracket clock, Gothic shaped case, by Payne, London, 24in. high. £1,800

A George III mahogany striking bracket clock with brass handle, signed Benj. Ward London, 18½in. high. £4,250

A mahogany bracket clock by Charles Frodsham, 24in. high, circa 1850. £625

A George III mahogany striking bracket clock, the 8in. arch dial signed on a silvered plaque *George Norris, London*, with strike-silent in the arch, 21in. high.
(Bonhams) £1,700

A Georgian mahogany bracket clock, the arched painted dial with pierced gilt hands, signed D.Evans London, now converted to anchor escapement, 1ft 8½in. high. (Phillips) £1,100

A late 18th century mahogany quarter chiming bracket clock, the case with inverted bell top, signed on a recessed cartouche *Higgs Y Diego Evans Bolsa Real Londres*, 2ft. 2½in. high.
(Phillips) £2,900

An 18th century mahogany bracket clock, signed on a recessed cartouche Wm Fothergill, Knaresbro, with verge escapement and engraved backplate, 1ft. 4in. high.
(Phillips) £3,600

A good George III mahogany bracket clock, the arched case surmounted by a spire and urn finial, the circular enamel dial signed *Grant, Fleet Street, London*, 1ft. 7in. high.
(Phillips) £4,000

A George III mahogany bracket clock, the arched case surmounted by a carrying handle, the twin fusée movement with verge escapement, 1ft. 4in. high.
(Phillips) £1,500

MAHOGANY

A George III bracket clock by Benjamin Dunkley, with brass dial, the mahogany case with brass carrying handles, 22in. high overall. £600

A George III mahogany bracket timepiece, signed in the arch Perigal, Coventry Street, London, 26cm. high. £1,500

A George III mahogany striking bracket clock, the dial signed Francis Dorrell London, 19in. high. £3,500

A Georgian mahogany bracket clock, signed Baker London, the twin fusée movement with verge escapement, signed on the backplate, 1ft. 4½in. high. (Phillips) £3,400

An 18th century bracket clock, the rectangular mahogany case formerly ebonised with a bell top, signed *John Miller, London,* 21in. high. (Phillips) £1,400

A Regency mahogany and brass mounted bracket clock, the case with stepped canted top and cone finial, flanked by lion mask ring handles, 1ft. 7in. high. (Phillips) £805

Late 18th century George III mahogany bracket clock for the Canadian market, signed Fras. Dumoulin a Montreal, 16½in. high including handle. £2,600

Early 19th century George III mahogany striking bracket clock, signed Edw. Tomlin, Royal Exchange, London, 15½in. high. £2,250

A Victorian mahogany chiming bracket clock with chime/silent and selection of 8-bell or Westminster chime, 26in. high. £2,500

MAHOGANY

A 19th century mahogany cased 8-day bracket clock, the silvered dial signed James Doig of Edinburgh, 16in. high. £400

A George III mahogany bracket clock, dial signed Tomlin Royal Exchange London, 13in. high. £2,250

A Regency period mahogany and brass bracket clock, dial signed Thomas Pace, London, 19in. high. £1,400

A George III mahogany bracket clock, the arched silvered dial signed Kemp, Yoxford and with strike/silent subsidiary in the arch, 1ft. 9¹/₄in. high. (Phillips) £2,000

A mahogany bracket clock in cushion-topped case surmounted by pineapple finials, signed Dwerrihouse, Berkley Square, 19in. high. (Christie's) £1,485

A Georgian mahogany bracket clock, signed Daniel Prentice, London, the twin fusee movement with engraved backplate, 1ft 5in. high. (Phillips) £1,250

A Georgian style mahogany bracket clock, the arched case, surmounted by a carrying handle, decorated with two raised panels, 1ft.1in. high. (Phillips) £2,000

George III mahogany calendar bracket clock, dial signed Juan y Melchor Brockbank, London, 20in. high. £3,500

A Regency gothic mahogany bracket clock, the lancet case with brass and ebony line inlay signed Bentley & Beck Royal Exchange London, 23in. high. (Christie's) £935

MAHOGANY

A late George II mahogany quarter-repeating bracket clock, the 6½in. dial signed Dan. Torin, Lon., 17in. high. £2,750

A George III mahogany striking bracket clock, by Ellicott, London, 16in. high. £3,500

A George III Irish mahogany quarter-repeating alarm bracket timepiece, dial signed Chris. Clarke Dublin, 14½in. high. £2,500

A George III mahogany bracket clock, silvered arch dial, signed *Willm. Dorrel, London*, Roman numeral dial, strike/silent in the arch, 17½in. (Bonhams) £1,300

A Regency mahogany bracket clock, the arched silvered dial with alarm set disc, signed John Walker, London, 1ft. 5¼in. high. (Phillips) £2,200

An Edwardian mahogany bracket clock, the 19cm arched gilt brass dial with black Roman numerals and Arabic seconds, stylised paw feet, 73cm high. (Henry Spencer) £1,000

A George III mahogany bracket clock, the arched brass dial signed Benjn. Ward, London, 52cm. high. £4,250

A 19th century Masonic bracket clock, marked Swinden & Sons, Birmingham, in castellated mahogany case, 14½in. high. £400

A Regency 8-day striking twin fusee bracket clock in figured mahogany case, signed on dial Loof of Tunbridge Wells. £750

A George I ebonised striking bracket clock, the dial signed *Quare & Horseman London 280*, the six ringed baluster pillar movement with twin chain fusee, verge escapement, 17³/₄in. high. (Christie's) £18,400

A George III ebonised striking small bracket clock, the dial signed *Tregent London*, the five pillar twin fusee (wire lines) movement with verge escapement, 11³/₄in. high. (Christie's) £20,700

A William and Mary ebony miniature striking bracket clock; circa 1690/95, the plinth-form case with foliate cast giltmetal handle to domed top, foliate lock-plates to the door and pierced wood sound frets to the three sides, the dial signed *Tho: Tompion Londini Fecit*, 9¹/₂in. high. (Christie's) £85,800

A George III mahogany striking bracket clock, the white painted Roman chapter disc signed *Rivers & Son, Cornhill London successors to Dan. de. St. Leu watch maker to Her Majesty*, the four-pillar twin chain fusee movement with anchor escapement, 16¹/₂in. high. (Christie's) £1,980

MAHOGANY

A late Georgian mahogany musical bracket clock, chime/not chime lever signed Rivers & Son, Cornhill, London, 24in. high. £4,500

A George III mahogany bracket clock with calendar and striking automaton, signed A. Butler, 13¼in. high. £3,250

A mahogany bracket clock of pagoda form, the movement inscribed Robert Roskell & Son, Liverpool, 21in. high. £650

A George III mahogany and ormolu musical bracket clock, the silvered dial signed John Taylor London, triple fusee movement chiming on eight bells, 28in. high. (Christie's) £6,600

A 19th century mahogany bracket clock, the case with chamfer top, surmounted by a finial, raised on four brass ball feet, the circular painted dial signed *Frodsham*, 18½in. high. (Phillips) £750

A late George III mahogany miniature bracket timepiece alarm, the engraved silvered dial signed Perigal, Coventry Street, London, chain fusee movement with verge escapement, 9½in. high. (Christie's) £3,080

A Regency mahogany and gilt brass mounted bracket clock, the brass dial signed Robt. Wood, London, 43cm. high. £1,750

A Regency mahogany striking bracket clock, the painted dial signed Collett, Chelsea, 15½in. high. £1,600

An early George III faded mahogany striking bracket clock, the dial signed Henry Sanderson, 18in. high. £4,750

MAHOGANY

A George III style mahogany chiming bracket clock, signed Thwaites & Reed, London, 20in. high.
£2,250

A George III mahogany striking bracket clock, the silvered dial signed James Wild London, 16in. high.　£2,750

George III mahogany bracket clock, dial signed Frampton, Bury, 17in. high, sold with mahogany wall bracket.　£1,500

A fine George III bracket clock, in a mahogany case, the lunette inscribed *John Scott, London,* the centre with bob aperture and calendar, 15¹/₂in. high. (Woolley & Wallis)　£4,000

A good 19th century mahogany and gilt brass mounted bracket clock of small size, the circular enamel dial signed Vulliamy, London, with anchor escapement, 9in. high. (Phillips) £5,800

A George II bracket clock, by Thomas Satcher, London, with 7in. arched brass dial, 15¾in. high (with pendulum and keys). (Bearne's) £1,150

A George III mahogany striking bracket clock, dial signed Devereux Bowly, London, 20in. high.
£4,750

A George III mahogany striking bracket clock with brass handle, dial signed John Taylor London, 19½in. high.
£2,000

A George II striking mahogany bracket clock, date aperture and plaque signed Tho. Hall, Rumsey, 19½in. high.　£3,000

A George III mahogany quarter chiming bracket clock, the dial signed *Bryant & Son London*, the five pillar triple fusee movement chiming on eight bells with strike on further bell, now with anchor escapement, 24in. high.
(Christie's) £4,600

A Victorian ebonised and well proportioned small bracket timepiece, the dial signed *Jump, London*, the four pillar single chain fusee movement with maintaining power and cut bi-metallic compensated balance, 9¹/₂in. high.
(Christie's) £2,300

An early Victorian rosewood quarter chiming Gothic bracket clock, the dial signed *J.M. French Royal Exchange London*, the five pillar triple chain fusee movement with anchor escapement, chiming on eight bells with hour strike on further bell, 28in. high.
(Christie's) £2,300

A William and Mary silver-mounted ebonised striking bracket clock, the later dial inscribed *Francis Robinson London*, the five ringed pillar twin fusee (wire lines) movement with verge escapement and strike on bell above, 15¹/₂in. high.
(Christie's) £6,325

A George III mahogany striking bracket clock, the dial signed *John Conell Royal Exchange London*, the triple fusee movement now reduced to two trains; the going now with anchor escapement, 25¹/₂in. high.
(Christie's)   £2,300

A George III mahogany automaton striking bracket clock, the dial signed *Charles Storey London*, the arch painted with three automaton stone masons at work, the five pillar twin fusee movement with verge escapement, 22in. high.
(Christie's)   £3,680

A George III ormolu musical miniature bracket clock for the Chinese market, the case of tabernacle form with punched foliate decoration overall with canted foliate angles and beaded borders, the fusee movement signed *John Mottram, London*, 12³/₄in. high.
(Christie's)   £4,400

A Charles II walnut bracket timepiece, the plinth-shaped case on solid moulded foot having glazed sides with pierced wood sound frets, the 5³/₄in. square dial signed *Joseph Knibb London* beneath the silvered chapter ring with finely matted centre, 11¹/₂in. high.
(Christie's)   £35,200

MAHOGANY

A Regency mahogany chiming bracket clock, dial signed Yonge & Son Strand London, 20in. high. £2,000

George III mahogany bracket clock, dial signed Vulliamy, London, 15in. high. £3,000

A George III mahogany striking bracket clock, the dial signed George Jefferys Chatham, 21¼in. high. £3,000

A rare Chippendale brass-mounted mahogany bracket clock, signed *Leslie & Price, Philadelphia*, 1793-1799, 17¼in. high. (Sotheby's) £4,301

An unusual Scottish Regency mahogany striking bracket clock, the case with cushioned moulded top and gilt wire lattice sound frets to sides, signed *David Whitelaw Edinburgh*, 33¾in. high. (Christie's) £2,200

A Victorian mahogany bracket clock, the movement by Streeter & Co., 18 New Bond Street, London, 15in. wide, 29in. high. £1,500

A Regency mahogany bracket clock, the arched brass dial signed Aynsth. & Jono. Thwaites, London, 1ft.6½in. high. £4,250

A George III mahogany bracket clock, the circular enamel dial signed Biddell, London, 53cm. high. £2,000

An 18th century mahogany bracket clock, the arched brass dial signed Sidney Smith, Sedgley, 48cm. high. £2,000

MARQUETRY

A George III Vernis Martin bracket timepiece, signed Isaac Rogers, London, 25in. high. £6,000

A marquetry bracket clock, probably English provincial, circa 1700, 14in. high. £3,750

A rosewood and marquetry bracket clock, dial signed Evershed & Son, Brighton, circa 1890, 19¾in. high. £1,750

METAL

19th century French brass and champleve enamel bracket clock. £1,000

Small George III gilt metal bracket clock, signed Henry Favre, London, 7½in. high. £7,000

A gilt metal automaton quarter-striking and musical bracket clock for the Chinese market, circa 1800, 9in. high. £4,500

OAK

A 19th century ornately carved neo-Renaissance bracket clock, the silvered dial with applied gilt mouldings, playing two melodies on 8 bells, English, 70cm. high. (Duran) £1,056

An oak bracket clock, dial signed James McCabe, 8½in. high. £2,000

A Victorian carved oak quarter chiming bracket clock, the case with carved wood dolphin finials to domed scale-carved top, signed T. Bassnett Liverpool, 29¾in. high. (Christie's) £1,760

A Victorian ormolu mounted walnut striking
bracket clock, the architectural case on twin
foliate scroll feet supporting the outset angles,
the dial signed *Geo. Prior London* on a silvered
disc in the arch, 19¹/₂in. high.
(Christie's)   £3,850

A Regency mahogany striking bracket clock, the
silvered engraved dial signed *A. Purvis North
Audley St. Grosvenor Sqe*, the five pillar twin-
fusee movement with anchor escapement and
strike on bell above, 16in. high.
(Christie's)   £2,760

An interesting Charles II ebonised miniature
striking bracket clock, the restored dome top
with foliate gilt metal carrying handle, the
10 x 11.5cm. dial signed *Henry Massy London*,
9¹/₂in. high.
(Christie's)   £3,740

A Louis XV ormolu mounted tortoiseshell
bracket clock, the white enamel chapter disc
signed *Francis Perigal, Royal Exchange London*,
with Turkish chapters, the four pillar chain fusee
movement with anchor escapement, 33¹/₂in. high.
(Christie's)   £2,750

A George III mahogany striking bracket clock, the white painted dial signed *W. Bullock Bradford*, the five-pillar twin fusee movement now with anchor escapement and strike/trip repeat on bell, 17¹/₂in. high.
(Christie's) £1,650

A George III ebonised and ormolu mounted quarter striking small bracket clock, the five pillar rear wound twin chain fusee movement with shaped plates, foliate engraved backplate signed *Marriott, London*, 15in. high.
(Christie's) £6,600

A William & Mary ebonised striking bracket clock, the six ringed pillar twin fusee movement with verge escapement, pendulum holdfast on backplate signed *Joseph Windmills London* within a foliate cartouche, 13¹/₄in. high.
(Christie's) £10,450

A George III mahogany quarter chiming bracket clock, the case on gilt brass ball feet, glazed sides and gilt metal handle to arched top, the dial signed *Jas. Bennett Norwich* on a silvered sector within the matted centre, 17¹/₂in. high.
(Christie's) £1,760

BRACKET CLOCKS

OAK

A bracket clock with eight-day striking movement, by Thompson, Ashford, 24in. high, in an oak case. £450

An oak gothic quarter chiming bracket clock, the three train chain fusee movement with anchor escapement, signed *Craighead Webb, Royal Exchange, London,* 82.5cm. (Lawrence Fine Arts) £1,265

A good Victorian blonde oak and ebony bracket clock by Charles Frodsham of London, the arched silvered dial with black Roman numerals to the chapter ring. (Henry Spencer) £1,500

RED WALNUT

A red walnut quarter repeating bracket clock, signed on the chapter ring Asselin, London, 19in. high. £1,400

A mid Georgian mahogany or red walnut striking bracket clock with brass handle, 19in. high. £1,800

A George III mahogany or red walnut striking bracket clock, the plaque signed Yeldrae Notron London 1053, 18in. high. £1,850

RELIGIEUSE

A Louis XIV ebony and boulle religieuse with ormolu dial, 16½in. wide. £2,500

A documentary Louis XIV bronze mounted tortoiseshell religieuse, signed Gaudron a Paris, the case inscribed L.B., circa 1710, 18in. high. £5,000

An ebonised pendule religieuse, signed Nicolas Brodon, Paris, circa 1680, 18in. high. £4,500

ROSEWOOD

Victorian rosewood cased bracket clock, inlaid with brass floral decoration. £1,700

A rosewood bracket clock with movement by Yonge & Son of the Strand, 11in. high. £3,750

A rosewood bracket time-piece, signed Wm. Speakman, London, 20½in. high. £475

A 19th century rosewood and inlaid bracket timepiece, 32cm. high. £800

A French 18th century gilt brass mounted and inlaid rosewood bracket clock, signed Jean Tolly a Paris, 36in. high. £1,500

A Regency period bracket clock, the brass inlaid lancet case of Egyptian styling, circa 1810, 20in. high. £2,000

A Regency rosewood and brass inlaid mantel timepiece, the silvered dial signed Carpenter, London, 9½in. high. £3,000

A rosewood bracket clock, the twin fusee movement with domed plates, anchor escape-ment and bell striking, signed *Wilson, Stamford*, 32.5cm. (Lawrence Fine Arts) £935

A Regency rosewood bracket clock, the case with gadrooned top, the shaped silvered dial signed G.Searle, London, the twin fusee movement with anchor escapement. 1ft. 4in. high. (Phillips) £1,300

A George III faded mahogany striking bracket clock, the dial signed *James Wild London* on a shaped silvered plaque in the matted centre, the four-pillar chain fusee movement with original verge escapement, 16in. high.
(Christie's) £4,950

A George III mahogany striking bracket clock, the arched silvered engraved dial signed *William Henlett Bristol*, the five pillar twin fusee movement now with anchor escapement, 20½in. high.
(Christie's) £1,955

A Charles II ebonised striking bracket clock, with verge escapement, rosette-engraved and numbered outside countwheel strike on backplate signed *William Cattell in Fleet Street Londini Fecit*, 12in. high.
(Christie's) £6,280

A George III mahogany striking bracket clock, the case with foliate brass handle to triple-pad top, foliate pierced brass frets to glazed sides and on wood block feet, the dial signed *Daniel Vauguion London*, 15½in. high.
(Christie's) £6,600

An important silver-mounted ebony miniature striking bracket clock, circa 1695, the 8 x 8.5cm. dial signed *Tho: Tompion London Fecit*, with twin chain fusees, verge escapement with pendulum steel-suspended, 6³/₄in. high.
(Christie's)   £441,500

A George III mahogany striking bracket clock, the well figured case with handle to bell top, glazed sides and on block feet, the dial signed *Alex. Wilson, London* on a shaped silvered reserve in the matted centre, 16¹/₂in. high.
(Christie's)   £4,180

A Regency boxwood inlaid mahogany striking bracket clock, glazed brass bezel to the painted Roman dial signed *J. Price Chatham*, the five-pillar twin fusee movement with anchor escapement, 15³/₄in. high.
(Christie's)   £1,760

A Charles II ebony quarter repeating bracket timepiece, the 15.5cm. square dial signed *Tho. Tompion Londini Fecit*, single fusee (wire lines) movement, verge escapement with calibrated bob pendulum, 12³/₄in. high.
(Christie's)   £58,700

BRACKET CLOCKS

ROSEWOOD

An eight-day movement bracket clock, by Wm. Alexander, 22in. high, 1828-44. £1,250

A good Regency rosewood striking bracket clock, the Indo-gothic lancet case on brass pad feet with turned mouldings, signed *Brockbank and Atkins London 1902*, 20½in. high. (Christie's) £1,760

An early 19th century rose-wood bracket clock by B. Lautier of Bath, 43cm. high. £2,750

TORTOISESHELL

A George III tortoiseshell striking bracket clock, the dial signed Geo. Clarke London, 17in. high. £3,750

Benj. Barber London, a fine George III tortoiseshell and ormolu mounted musical bracket clock, the case with ogee top surmounted by urn-and-flambeau finials and applied with foliate ormolu mounts. (Christie's) £19,800

An ormolu mounted George III Turkish market musical small bracket clock by Markwick Markham Perigal, London, the scroll engraved backplate enclosing signature, mid 18th century, 17in. high. (Christie's New York) £14,025

A late Stuart tortoiseshell veneered case for a minia-ture bracket clock, 10in. high. £1,500

A tortoiseshell bracket clock, dial signed G. Yonge & Son, 13½in. high. £2,250

A Continental tortoiseshell bracket timepiece, basically circa 1700, 16in. high. £2,250

WALNUT

A gilt brass mounted walnut quarter chiming bracket clock, 32¾in. high. £1,000

An 18th century bracket clock in burr walnut case, with eight-day movement by Jos. Kirk, 16in. high. £2,750

A walnut quarter repeating bracket clock with 7½in. brass dial, backplate signed Jacob Massy, London, 17in. high. £3,000

A substantial late 19th century walnut quarter chiming bracket clock, signed *John Carter,* the triple fusee movement chiming on eight bells, 75cm. high. (Phillips) £1,050

A walnut chiming bracket clock, by Viner London, No. 2208, 22in. high, and a walnut bracket, 8in. high. £1,000

A walnut bracket clock with verge escapement and pull quarter repeating on two bells, the florally engraved backplate signed in a cartouche Johannes Fromanteel Londini Fecit, 12½in. high. (Phillips) £3,200

A Regency walnut cased bracket clock with silvered dial, maker Raw Bros., London. £625

A walnut chiming bracket clock, the three train fusee movement striking quarter hours on 8 bells or four.gongs, 15in. high. £2,000

A Victorian English walnut veneer chiming bracket clock, white painted dial signed *F. Dent, 61 Strand, London,* triple fusée, signed anchor movement chiming on eight bells, 31in. (Bonhams) £850

A Regency ebonised striking small bracket clock, the repainted dial signed *J. Bowen London*, the five-pillar twin fusee movement with anchor escapement, 9¹/₂in. high.
(Christie's)   £3,520

A mahogany gilt-metal mounted quarter chiming bracket clock, the dial signed *R. Sutton Stafford*, the massive five pillar triple chain fusee movement with anchor escapement, 27in. high.
(Christie's)   £1,495

A George III fruitwood striking bracket clock, the dial signed *Mattw: Hill London*, the five pillar twin fusee (wire lines) movement with verge escapement and strike on bell, 16in. high.
(Christie's)   £1,265

A Regency ebonised striking bracket clock, the 6in. square engraved silvered dial signed *Ellis Exeter*, the five pillar twin fusee (wire lines) movement with anchor escapement, 16in. high.
(Christie's)   £1,100

A George III mahogany striking bracket clock, the dial signed *Brockbank Cornhill*, the five pillar twin fusee (wire lines) movement now with anchor escapement, 18in. high.
(Christie's) £4,025

A George III mahogany striking bracket clock, the dial signed *Thos. Read London*, now with anchor escapement, strike on bell, 16in. high.
(Christie's) £2,760

A Charles II ebonised striking early bracket clock, the 6½in. square gilt dial signed *Thomas Tompion Londini fecit*, twin fusee (wire lines) movement now with anchor escapement, the right hand side of the backplate finely engraved with tulips amongst scrolling foliage, 12¾in. high.
(Christie's) £65,300

A George I ebonised small bracket timepiece, circa 1715, the dial signed *GEO: GRaHaM London* beneath the silvered chapter ring, five pillar single gut fusee movement with verge escapement and spring suspended pendulum with unusual rise-and-fall rack regulation, 27.4cm.
(Christie's) £15,400

CARRIAGE CLOCKS

BAMBOO

The carriage clock, as its name suggests, was originally designed, with its spring driven movement, for use whilst travelling. It was a French innovation, probably derived from the pendule d'officier pioneered by Abraham Louis Breguet of Paris in the 18th century. Essentially, it has a rectangular case, 3–12in. high, with a carrying handle and often incorporated such complex refinements as repeat and date mechanisms and sometimes even a dial showing the phases of the moon. Early examples usually had silvered dials, and were housed in ormolu cases, often embellished with Corinthian columns. The type became particularly popular in the course of the 19th century when examples typically had fine cast brass cases with thick bevelled glass windows resting on grooves in the frame. Later the glass at the top became smaller and was let into a metal plate. Carrying handles were usually round, tapering towards the ends, and because there was often a repeat button on the top front edge, the handles folded backwards only. French clockmakers began to produce the clocks en masse, with production also beginning from circa 1820 in England, America and Austria.

BAROMETER

A 19th century French brass and enamel mounted carriage clock, bearing the Drocourt trademark, in a bamboo case, 7½in. high. (Phillips) £1,300

A French porcelain panelled 'bamboo' carriage clock, 7in. high. £2,400

A late 19th century French carriage clock in gilt 'bamboo' chinoiserie case, inscribed John Bennett, Paris, 8in. high. £1,850

A brass miniature carriage timepiece, with gilt chapter ring signed Wm. Drummond & Sons Melbourne, bamboo case, 3½in. high. (Christie's) £1,650

A 19th century French gilt brass and champleve enamel carriage timepiece and barometer, centred by a thermometer, 15cm. high. (Phillips) £750

A grande sonnerie calendar carriage clock cum barometer, the barometer inscribed R. W. Inglis 1897, 6½in. high. £3,000

A clock/barometer desk set, with white enamel dials, in bevelled-glazed brass-framed oval case, surmounted by a folding scroll loop handle, 5in. high. (Christie's) £462

DECORATED FACE

A lacquered brass grande sonnerie giant carriage clock, 8¼in. high. £2,150

Gilt metal travelling or mantel timepiece with arched silver dial, 5¼in. high. £1,000

A small carriage timepiece, the 1in. dial signed Payne London, 3in. high. £1,500

A miniature French brass carriage timepiece, with enamel dial within a gilt mask with pierced decoration, in an anglaise case, 3in. high. (Phillips) £520

A gilt brass striking carriage clock with later lever platform, strike/repeat on gong, the porcelain dial signed Walsh Brothers Melbourne, 7½in. high. (Christie's) £1,870

A 19th century French brass carriage clock, the lever movement striking on a gong with alarm and push repeat, 8in. high. (Phillips) £540

A 19th century French gilt brass carriage clock, the lever movement striking on a gong with push repeat, 19cm. high. £800

A gilt metal striking carriage clock, the dial with concave ivory Arabic chapter, the case with stamp of Drocourt, 6¾in. high. £1,000

Late 19th century French brass repeating alarm carriage clock, the dial signed E. Caldwell & Co., Philadelphia, 7½in. high. £1,250

A silver gilt miniature striking carriage clock
with bi-metallic balance to silvered lever
platform and striking on gong, the backplate
engraved *Made in Paris expressly for Albert
Barker*, London 1901, 3¹/₂in. high.
(Christie's)   **£500**

A Viennese gilt metal and porcelain mounted
carriage timepiece with alarm, the backplate
stamped *Repassirt L. Doering Leipsig*, the Arabic
dial painted with a forest scene, corniche case,
5in. high.
(Christie's)   **£715**

A gilt brass porcelain mounted striking carriage
clock with later lever platform, strike/repeat on
gong, white enamel Roman chapter disc with
blued spade hands and retail signature *Mamoah
Rhodes & Sons., Paris*, 6³/₄in. high.
(Christie's)   **£1,210**

A Victorian gilt brass giant carriage
chronometer, the massive movement with four
large double-screwed pillars, the spotted
backplate signed *E. White 20 Cockspur Street
London*, 9¹/₄in. high.
(Christie's)   **£5,720**

A silver-cased perpetual calendar astronomical carriage timepiece, London 1897, casemaker: Anthony Charles Jones, the hump-back case on sconce feet with chain handle to top, the plain backplate signed *Jump*, 6¹/₄in. high.
(Christie's)   £52,800

A gilt metal and enamel miniature carriage timepiece, the going barrel movement with Chinese stamp to backplate, the columnar case with multi-coloured champlevé enamel columns, 3¹/₂in. high.
(Christie's)   £550

An English gilt brass striking giant carriage clock, the twin chain fusee movement with unusual baluster pillars, the backplate stamped *Payne & Co., 163 New Bond St., London*, 8¹/₄in. high.
(Christie's)   £3,960

A gilt brass striking calendar carriage clock with cut bi-metallic balance to silvered lever platform, strike/repeat/alarm on gong on backplate with stamp for *Drocourt*, 6in. high.
(Christie's)   £825

DECORATED FACE

A gilt brass grande sonnerie carriage clock, 7¾in. high. £2,250

English carriage clock by Smith & Sons, London, 9in. high. £2,250

A lacquered brass miniature carriage clock with silvered lever platform, 3in. high. £900

A French brass carriage timepiece, the movement with replacement lever platform escapement, contained in a pillared rectangular case, 6in. (Lawrence Fine Arts) £352

A gilt brass grande sonnerie striking carriage clock, the massive going barrel movement having duplex escapement with cut bimetallic balance on large gilt platform, with blued Breguet hands and silvered alarm hand, 7¹/₂in. high. (Christie's) £14,300

A gilt brass and enamel striking carriage clock with cut bimetallic balance to lever platform, signed Edward & Sons Glasgow, Paris made, 6¼in. high. (Christie's) £2,530

A French gilt brass carriage clock, the lever movement striking on a gong with push repeat numbered 7936, 18.5cm. high. (Phillips) £580

A fine 19th century gilt brass repeating carriage clock, inscribed Ch. Oudin, the movement striking the hours and half hours, 15cm. (Phillips) £2,400

A petite-sonnerie repeating and alarm carriage clock, with Arabic numerals and signed A H Rodanet, Paris, 6in. high. £1,200

DECORATED FACE

French glass and brass carriage timepiece, dial signed Mappin & Webb Ltd., Paris, circa 1900, 6½in. high. £275

An English carriage clock, enamel dial signed Dent London, 8¾in. high. £6,000

Late 19th century American brass and glass carriage timepiece with eight-day movement, 9.1/8in. high. £300

A miniature French 19th century brass and enamel carriage timepiece, bearing the mark of Auguste Margaine, in an anglaise case, 10cm. high. (Phillips) £840

A late 19th century French carriage clock, 2in. silvered annular chapter ring, set within a pierced bird and foliate and polished gilt background, signed *EGLG Paris*, 6¹/₄in. (Bonhams) £380

A 19th century French gilt brass carriage clock, the lever movement striking on a bell and signed on the backplate Ch. Frodsham Paris, 6in. high. (Phillips) £750

A gilt metal striking carriage clock with silvered lever platform, the gilt chapter ring signed Leroy Paris, 6¼in. high. £750

An English chronometer carriage timepiece, by Dent, London, with mahogany carrying case, 8½in. high. £10,000

A 19th century French gilt brass carriage clock, the backplate bearing the Drocourt trademark, 6½in high. £1,500

A gilt-brass and enamel quarter repeating miniature carriage timepiece, the going barrel movement with quarter repeat on two gongs, 3¼in. high.
(Christie's)   £977

A gilt brass striking carriage clock with plain balance to silvered lever platform, strike/repeat on bell on backplate stamped *Dent A Paris*, 5in. high.
(Christie's)   £825

A gilt brass grande sonnerie striking carriage clock, with strike/repeat/alarm on two gongs with three position selection lever in base, stamp for *Henri Jacot* on backplate, 5¾in.
(Christie's)   £1,540

Gilt brass striking and musical carriage clock for the Chinese market with foliate engraved gilt lever platform with steel bat's-wing balance, with stamp for *Japy Frères*, 7¼in. high.
(Christie's)   £1,650

A gilt brass and enamel miniature carriage timepiece, with plain balance to cylinder platform, backplate stamped *France*, 3¼in. (Christie's) £440

A gilt brass grande sonnerie giant striking calendar carriage clock with large diameter bi-metallic balance to silvered lever platform, the backplate with stamp for *Drocourt*, 8½in. high. (Christie's) £10,450

A gilt brass engraved striking carriage clock, strike/repeat/alarm on gong on backplate with stamp for *Drocourt*, cannelée case engraved with scrolling foliage, 5¾in. (Christie's) £1,540

A gilt metal striking carriage clock, with cut bimetallic to silvered lever platform, strike on gong to backplate with stamp for *Margaine*, 16in. high. (Christie's) £440

A Richard & Co. petite
sonnerie repeating car-
riage clock with fluted
handle, 7½in. high
£1,000

An inlaid horn miniature
carriage timepiece with
9ct. gold handle, feet and
scrolls, London, 1908, by
Wm. Comyns, 2½in. high.
£450

A carriage clock with a
dished silvered chapter ring,
the movement stamped
Maurice et Cie, 5¼in. high,
with a leather travelling
case. £1,000

A quarter-repeating and
cloisonne enamel carriage
clock, 3in. high. £4,750

A 19th century French gilt
brass carriage clock, signed
on the back plate E. Dent,
Paris, 944, 5½in. high.
£2,750

English carriage timepiece,
dial signed Adams, Lon-
don, 9in. high, in leather
case. £2,500

English gilt metal car-
riage clock, signed
Bloomsbury, London,
4¾in. high. £1,250

A brass carriage timepiece,
the movement with cylin-
der escapement, 6¼in.
high. £325

Gilt and silvered brass
timepiece carriage clock
by Payne, London, 5½in.
high. £1,000

ENAMEL CASE

A French champleve enamelled repeating carriage clock with 2in. enamelled dial, 6¼in. high. (Bearne's)   £1,150

French carriage clock in brass and champleve enamel case.   £3,500

French brass and champleve enamel carriage clock in Corniche type case, 7in. high.   £1,200

Good quality French gilt brass and enamel carriage clock, silvered dial, MacKay & Chisholm, Edinburgh Retailer's mark, 6¾in. high.
(G. A. Key)   £680

A gilt brass and enamel carriage timepiece with later platform lever escapement, backplate stamped *France*, silvered chapter ring with Arabic chapters, 5¼in. high.
(Christie's)   £682

A French brass and champlevé enamel carriage clock, the lever movement, with alarm and push repeat striking on a bell, signed for *L Urard & Co., Tientsin*, 8in. high.
(Phillips)   £1,350

A gilt brass and enamel striking carriage clock with uncut bimetallic balance to silvered lever platform, 5½in. high.   £2,000

A champleve enamelled brass carriage clock with cut compensated balance to lever platform, 7in. high.
                £3,750

A gilt metal and enamel striking carriage clock, ivorine dials within multicoloured champleve enamel mask, 7in. high.   £3,500

A gilt brass striking carriage clock with later platform lever escapement, strike/repeat on gong on backplate stamped *E.M. & Co.*, Corinthian case, 7in. high.
(Christie's) £660

A French gilt brass and champlevé enamel combination carriage timepiece with Arabic dial signed *H Dumont Paris*, the backplate with stamp for *Duverdry & Bloquel*, the aneroid barometer flanked by a thermometer and with compass above, 6in. high.
(Christie's) £1,870

A silver-gilt and enamel quarter striking carriage clock with bi-metallic balance to silvered lever platform, strike/repeat/alarm on two gongs, the case hallmarked *London, 1894*, original red leather travelling case and key, 4³/₄in. high.
(Christie's) £825

An early gilt brass Continental grande sonnerie carriage clock with calendar and alarm, the white enamel dial signed *Michaele Minas* within the Roman chapter ring with pierced hands, 5¹/₄in. high.
(Christie's) £990

A gilt and silver brass striking carriage clock with bi-metallic balance to silvered lever platform, strike/repeat on gong, the porcelain dial painted with a lakeside scene, 6³/₄in. high. (Christie's) £572

An engraved gilt brass and enamel musical striking carriage clock for the Chinese market, strike/repeat/alarm on bell on back-plate with stamp for *Japy Freres*, 6³/₄in. high. (Christie's) £1,540

A gilt-brass singing bird striking carriage clock, strike/repeat/alarm on bell on backplate with stamp for *Japy Freres*, white enamel dial signed *Brevet D'Invention S.G.D.G.*, 10¹/₄in. high. (Christie's) £4,370

Arnold's Charles Frodsham No. 986, a fine Victorian gilt-brass striking carriage clock with twin up-and-down indications, the white enamel Roman dial signed *Charles Frodsham Clockmaker to the Queen 84 Strand London 986*, the twin fusee movement with lever escapement, the backplate signed *Arnold's Charles Frodsham Clock maker to the Queen 84, Strand London. 986*, 8¹/₄in. high. (Christie's) £32,200

ENAMEL FACE

An enamel-mounted carriage clock, 6½in. high, with a travelling case.
£1,650

French late 19th century enamelled brass and glass repeating carriage clock, by Tiffany & Co., 6¾in. high. £2,000

A repeating gilt brass carriage clock, circa 1890, 6½in. high.
£2,000

A 19th century French gilt brass and enamel carriage clock, bearing the Drocourt trademark, in an engraved gorge case, 6¾in. high.
(Phillips) £1,400

A gilt brass striking carriage clock, the enamel dial signed Goldsmiths Company 112 Regent St. London and Paris, Corinthian case, stamp of Margaine, 6½in. high. (Christie's) £880

A French brass carriage clock, the enamel dial with a painted scene of a watermill and signed for Henry Atkinson & Wells Paris, 7¹/₂in. high.
(Phillips) £650

A 19th century French brass and enamel carriage clock, the lever movement striking on a gong with push repeat, 18cm. high.
(Phillips) £1,300

Gilt metal and enamel quarter-striking carriage clock with foliate handle, 6in. high.
£2,250

A French brass carriage timepiece, the movement with cylinder escapement and stamped R & Co. (Richard), 16cm. (Lawrence Fine Arts)
£242

ENAMEL FACE

An enamel-mounted carriage clock with black enamel dial, 4½in. high. £1,500

Small enamel mounted carriage timepiece, stamped Margaine, 3¼in. high. £3,000

Lacquered brass and enamel striking carriage clock, 6½in. high. £1,500

A French miniature brass carriage timepiece, the circular enamel dial within a florally decorated silvered mask, in a caryatid case, 4¼in. high, together with a travelling case. (Phillips) £640

A French gilt brass and enamel panelled strike/repeat carriage clock, the eight-day movement with platform lever escapement striking on a gong, signed in the base *L. Contreau, 36 Bld des Italiens, Paris*, 4in. high. (Christie's S. Ken) £2,530

A gilt metal grande sonnerie carriage clock with enamel dial, case with stamp of Henri Jacot, 7in. high. £2,500

A grande sonnerie carriage clock, the base with the stamp of Henri Jacot, 7in. high. £1,500

A miniature French gilt brass and enamel panelled carriage timepiece, bearing the *Drocourt* trade mark, and signed for *Klaftenberger, Paris*, 3¾in. high. (Phillips) £1,200

A French brass carriage clock, the circular enamel dial within a floral champlevé mask in a pillared case, 20cm. high. (Phillips) £700

A gilt brass porcelain mounted striking carriage clock with bi-metallic balance to silvered lever platform, strike/repeat on gong, backplate with stamp for *Margaine*, 5¹/₂in. high.
(Christie's) £990

A gilt metal porcelain mounted striking carriage clock, strike/repeat on gong on plain backplate, the gilt Roman chapter disc with blued spade hands within a gilt mask, 6¹/₂in. high.
(Christie's) £825

A fine silver grande sonnerie striking duplex carriage clock, the twin-going barrel movement with grande sonnerie strike on two gongs, the backplate signed *Ingold A Paris*, 8¹/₂in. high.
(Christie's) £11,500

An engraved gilt brass and enamel striking carriage clock, strike on gong on backplate stamped *G. L. 474*, foliate engraved cannelée case, 6¹/₄in.
(Christie's) £1,760

OVAL CASE

A gilt metal striking oval carriage clock for the Oriental market, stamp of Japy Freres, 6in. high.   £2,000

A miniature oval carriage timepiece with white enamel dial, 3in. high.   £650

A silvered brass oval miniature carriage clock, the case with stamp of A. Margaine, 8cm. high.   £450

An oval Drocourt grande sonnerie calendar and alarm carriage clock, the engine turned and silvered mask with white enamel dials, 5½in. high.
(Christie's)   £1,760

A gilt engraved brass striking oval carriage clock with alarm on gong, white enamel Roman chapter disc with blued moon hands, alarm disc below VI 6¼in. high.
(Christie's)   £1,320

A gilt metal striking oval carriage clock with uncut bimetallic balance to silvered lever platform, plain oval case, 5½in. high.   £900

A 19th century French oval miniature brass carriage timepiece, with replaced lever platform bearing the *Henri Jacot* trademark, 10cm. high.
(Phillips)   £800

A gilt metal striking oval carriage clock with scroll handle and on rosso antico marble stand, 5½in. high, excluding stand.   £2,200

An attractive French gilt brass grande sonnerie alarm carriage clock, together with key, 8in. high over handle.
(Spencer's)   £1,300

OVAL CASE

An oval engraved gilt brass
grande sonnerie carriage clock,
7½in. high.   £2,500

A gilt metal grande sonnerie
oval carriage clock with
enamel dial, 6.1/8in. high.
                          £2,400

Aneroid barometer of
carriage clock form,
signed R. & J. Beck,
London, 3¼in. high.
                      £450

A French 19th century gilt
brass carriage clock, the movement with replaced lever platform, the case with curved
side panels, 7½in. high.
(Phillips)   £520

A fine and rare brass grande
sonnerie and minute repeating/
alarm carriage clock in oval
Corinthian case, signed by the
retailer *Bailey, Banks & Biddle
Co., Philadelphia*, 4³/₄in. high.
(Christie's S. Ken)   £4,180

A miniature French oval gilt
brass and porcelain panelled
carriage timepiece, with lever
platform escapement, the
porcelain dial decorated with a
young girl and boy, 4in. high.
(Phillips)   £1,700

A 19th century French oval gilt
brass carriage clock, the enamel
dial signed for *Mercier & Fils,
Genève*, in an oval case, 17cm.
high.
(Phillips)   £800

Gilt metal grande son-
nerie oval carriage clock
in engraved case with
scrolling handle, 6in.
high.   £1,500

A gilt brass oval striking carriage
clock with strike/repeat on gong,
enamel dial with Breguet style
hands, 4½in. high. (Christie's)
                        £660

PORCELAIN MOUNTED

Porcelain mounted carriage clock, dial signed J. W. Benson, London, 8½in. high, backplate stamped Drocourt.
£10,000

A 19th century French gilt brass and porcelain mounted carriage clock, 18cm. high.
£3,000

A gilt brass porcelain mounted striking carriage clock, the dial and side panels pai.ted in the Sevres style, 5½in. high.
£4,500

Gilt brass porcelain mounted miniature carriage timepiece with bi-metallic balance to lever platform, the blue porcelain dial with Roman chapter ring and pierced gilt hands, 3in. high. (Christie's)
£1,650

A gilt brass porcelain mounted striking giant carriage clock, the porcelain dial and sides painted with genre scenes of carousing cavaliers, signed H. Desprez, 8½in. high. (Christie's)
£4,950

A French gilt brass and porcelain panelled carriage clock, with replaced lever platform escapement, alarm, push repeat and striking on a gong, 7½in. high. (Phillips)
£1,150

A French gilt brass carriage clock, the dial and side panels decorated with scenes of young couples, 7in. high.
£1,250

A 19th century French brass carriage clock, the lever movement striking on a gong with alarm and push repeat, 7½in. high. £2,000

A porcelain mounted carriage clock, the repeating lever movement stamped Maurice et Cie, 5½in. high.
£1,350

PORCELAIN MOUNTED

A porcelain mounted alarm carriage clock in a gorge case, 5½in. high. £3,500

A porcelain mounted alarm carriage clock, the repeating lever movement with gong striking, 6¼in. high. £1,800

A porcelain panelled carriage clock, the movement with the trademark of J. Dejardin, 7in. high. £3,250

A French brass carriage clock, the movement with lever escapement and gong striking, signed James Murray, Glasgow, contained in a corniche case 6¾in. (Lawrence Fine Arts) £572

A 19th century French gilt brass and porcelain mounted grande sonnerie carriage clock, with trademark P.M., 18cm. high. £6,000

A gilt brass and porcelain panelled carriage timepiece with alarm, in corniche case, the porcelain panels to the sides depicting figures and landscape scenes, 5in. high. (Christie's S. Ken) £935

Late 19th century gilt bronze and jewelled porcelain carriage clock in engraved gorge case, 7in. high. £3,000

A French gilt brass carriage clock, the lever movement striking on a gong, 21cm. high. £1,500

A gilt brass porcelain mounted striking carriage clock with porcelain dial, stamp of Achille Brocot, 6¼in. high. £2,750

ROUND FACE

An alarm carriage clock, the enamel dial signed James Muirhead & Son, Glasgow, 6¾in. high. **£2,400**

Chronometer carriage clock by Dent, London, dial signed, 7in. high. **£12,500**

French gilt brass and glass repeating carriage clock, circa 1900, 7¼in. high. **£1,150**

A gilt brass quarter striking carriage clock with cut bimetallic balance to lever platform, dial signed in Cyrillic *Pavel Buhre*, blued spade hands, within gilt mask, 6¼in. high. (Christie's) **£715**

A 19th century bronze and gilt brass carriage timepiece, the circular movement with going barrel and lever platform escapement, 13.5cm. high. (Phillips) **£540**

A good English gilt brass carriage clock, the twin fusee movement with lever platform escapement, signed Chas Frodsham, London, 8in. high. (Phillips) **£5,000**

Large carriage clock with enamel dial, movement stamped Drocourt, 8½in. high. **£3,500**

A gilt metal striking carriage clock, inscribed Examined by Dent and with presentation inscription dated 1877, 7in. high. **£750**

A quarter-striking carriage clock, the enamel dial signed Dent 33 Cockspur Street, London, 6in. high. **£2,250**

ROUND FACE

A brass grande sonnerie striking carriage clock, gorge case, stamp of Drocourt, 6in. high.   £2,000

A gilt metal striking carriage clock by Paul Garnier, one-piece case with lifting front glass, 5in. high.   £2,000

A brass and glass panelled carriage clock, dial inscribed 'Aird & Thomson, Glasgow', 5½in. high.   £500

A 19th century French gilt brass grande sonnerie carriage clock, the lever movement striking on two gongs with push repeat, 20cm. high.   £2,150

A gilt brass grande sonnerie carriage clock, enamel dial, signed Collin Paris and subsidiary alarm ring below VI within a gilt metal mask, Corinthian case, 7in. high. (Christie's)   £1,320

A lacquered brass striking carriage clock, the ivorine dial with gilt mask, cannelee riche case, stamped for Henri Jacot, 6in. high.   £750

A French miniature brass carriage timepiece, the lever movement bearing *DC* trademark, in a numbered pillared case, 10.5cm. high. (Phillips)   £483

A lacquered brass striking carriage clock with enamel dial with engine-turned gilt mask, gorge case, stamp of Drocourt, 5¾in. high.   £1,000

A 19th century French gilt carriage clock, the lever movement striking on a gong with push repeat, dated *1874*, 7¼in. high. (Phillips)   £720

ROUND FACE

A lacquered brass striking carriage clock, the movement with lever platform, 6½in. high.   £750

An English striking carriage clock, mottled plates signed Chas. Frodsham, 9in. high.   £7,500

A gilt brass striking carriage clock, the backplate stamped J. Klaftenberger, 5¼in. high.   £2,750

A gilt brass grande-sonnerie calendar carriage clock with uncut compensated balance to the silvered lever platform, stamp of Drocourt, 6½in. high.   £5,500

A 19th century French grande sonnerie carriage clock, the movement now with lever platform escapement, signed Paul Garnier, 7in. high. (Phillips)   £1,600

A French 19th century carriage clock, engraved foliate mask, repeating gong striking movement by R & Cº, Paris, 7½in. (Bonhams)   £450

A good 19th century French gilt brass grande sonnerie carriage clock, signed *Klaftenberger* on the edge of the plate, 7in. high. (Phillips)   £3,500

A gilt metal grande sonnerie carriage clock with strike/repeat on gongs with selection lever in the base, 6¼in. high.   £2,000

A late 19th century grand sonnerie carriage clock, with repeat and alarm, the gilt brass dial inscribed *E. Gubelin, Lucerne*, 7½in. high. (Bearne's)   £820

ROUND FACE

A French brass grande sonnerie carriage alarm clock, 7¼in. high. £550

A brass quarter-striking calendar carriage clock, 7in. high. £1,500

A gilt metal striking carriage clock with decorative swagged Arabic chaptered enamel dial, 6½in. high. £700

A giltmetal grande sonnerie striking carriage clock with cut bimetallic balance to silvered lever platform, the backplate with stamp for *Margaine*, 7in. high.
(Christie's) £2,310

A small minute-repeating mantel or travelling time-piece signed Cole London, 3¾in. high. £1,000

A 19th century French gilt brass carriage clock, the lever movement striking on a gong with alarm and push repeat, 8in. high.
(Phillips) £540

A grande sonnerie striking carriage clock, the white enamel dial signed A. Jackemann, Paris, 6in. high. £2,000

Lacquered brass petite sonnerie small sized carriage clock with split bimetallic balance to silvered lever platform, 4¼in. high. £1,250

A French 19th century gilt brass carriage clock, the lever movement striking on a gong and bearing the Drocourt trademark, 7in. high. £1,250

ROUND FACE

A French brass carriage clock, the movement with lever escapement, 6in. high. £500

An English gilt metal carriage clock, movement signed Barwise London, 6in. high. £1,250

A gilt metal striking carriage clock with enamel dial, 5¼in. high. £1,400

A gilt brass grande sonnerie carriage clock with cut bimetallic balance to silvered lever platform, strike on two gongs with three-position selection lever in the base, 5³⁄₄in. high. (Christie's) £4,400

A 19th century French gilt brass carriage clock, signed on the backplate for Ch. Frodsham, Paris, in an engraved one-piece case, 5in. high. (Phillips) £1,250

A chased gilt petite sonnerie carriage clock with calendar, the gilt platform with counterpoised right angle lever escapement, French, circa 1860, 5¹⁄₄in. high. (Christie's New York) £1,459

A gilt brass quarter striking carriage clock with uncut compensated balance to lever platform, 5in. high. £900

French brass repeat alarm carriage clock by Pierre and Alfred Drocourt, 6in. high. £1,000

A 19th century French gilt brass carriage clock, the movement with Soldano lever platform, in an engraved gorge case, 7in. high. (Phillips) £680

ROUND FACE

A small quarter-striking
alarm carriage clock, dial
signed Breguet, 4½in. high,
and a leather travelling case.
£1,250

French brass carriage
clock by Francois-
Arsene Margaine, with
circular silvered dial,
7in. high.   £750

A carriage-style clock, the
movement striking on coiled
gong, with white enamel dial in
bevelled-glazed brass-framed
case, 8in. high.
(Christie's)   £242

French gilt brass car-
riage clock by Pierre
and Alfred Drocourt,
with white enamel
dial, 16cm. high. £1,000

A 19th century French gilt brass
and enamel carriage clock,
striking on a gong, with push
repeat, the silvered chapter
within a gilt mask, 6¾in. high.
(Phillips)   £720

A brass calendar carriage
timepiece, enamel dial
with chapter disc above
gilt mask, 4¾in. high.
£350

An early 19th century brass
timepiece carriage clock, by.
James McCabe, Royal Exchange
London, in plain case, 16cm.
(Phillips)   £1,600

An English brass carriage
timepiece, dial signed
Barwise, London, 7¼in.
£1,000

Grande sonnerie alarm
carriage clock, dial sig-
ned Chas. Frodsham,
London, 6in. high.
£2,500

ROUND TOP

A 19th century English gilt brass travelling clock, the twin fusee movement with maintaining power and lever platform, signed Viner, London, 6½in. high. (Phillips) £1,700

A brass cased quarter striking carriage clock, the backplate signed L. Leroy & Cie, 6in. high. £1,350

A silver calendar carriage clock, the silver dial with gold Breguet hands, the backplate signed Jump, 6¼in. high. £25,000

A silver and shagreen miniature travelling timepiece, the enamel dial signed W. Thornhill & Co., Paris, 3in. high. £375

Breguet Neveu & Compie., No. 3992: a silver quarter striking carriage clock with alarm, 5½in. high. £25,000

A shagreen carriage clock of humpback form, dial signed Jump Paris 93 Mount Street (London), 7in. high. £1,500

SHAPED CASE

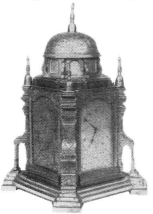

A 19th century French ormolu carriage clock, the lever movement striking on a gong with push repeat and alarm, 8½in. high. £1,200

An early Victorian gilt metal carriage clock, case in the manner of T. Cole, 11½in. high. £3,000

A gilt metal porcelain mounted carriage clock with lever platform, the case with stamp of Japy Freres, 9½in. high. £4,500

SHAPED CASE

An unusual miniature carriage timepiece, late 19th century, the movement with platform lever escapement, signed Bigelow, Kennard & Co., Boston. (Christie's)   £924

A grande sonnerie alarm carriage clock, the movement stamped Fumey, 7½in. high.   £2,000

A gilt brass miniature carriage timepiece with uncut bimetallic balance to silvered lever platform, the caryatid case with harpies to the angles, 2¾in. high. (Christie's)   £1,045

An unusual 19th century French gilt bronze and porcelain mounted carriage clock, bearing the Drocourt trademark on the backplate, in an ornate rococo case, 9in. high. (Phillips)   £4,200

A rare chased gilt carriage clock with singing bird automaton, signed *Japy Freres & Cie.*, surmounted by glazed virtrine with rising handle displaying the bird perched within realistic silk and feather foliage, circa 1860, 12³/₄in. high. (Christie's)   £10,846

A fine chased gilt grande sonnerie carriage clock with moon phase, calendar, thermometer and winding indicator, the movement stamped *H.L.* in lozenge punch, circa 1860, 8in. high. (Christie's New York)   £11,220

A French gilt brass carriage clock, the repeating movement with lever escapement, gong striking and signed John P. Cross, Paris, 6½in. (Lawrence Fine Arts)   £1,375

An ornate gilt repeating carriage clock, signed Bolviller a Paris, 6¼in. high.   £1,000

An unusual 19th century gilt brass French carriage clock, the movement with lever platform escapement, push repeat and alarm, signed *Lucien, A. Paris*, 9½in. high. (Phillips)   £3,600

SILVER CASED

A 19th century Continental silver miniature carriage timepiece, the lever movement with enamel dial, 4in. high, marked London 1895. (Phillips) £400

A silver and enamel miniature one-piece carriage timepiece in the Oriental taste with platform lever escapement, the backplate with stamp of *L'Epeé Made in France 11 jewels*, 3¼in. high. (Christie's) £550

A silver gilt carriage time-piece, the case with coloured stone corner decorations, the lever movement with circular enamel dial, 4in. high. (Phillips) £500

A silver miniature carriage timepiece with cut bimetallic balance to lever platform, the base stamped *Aspreys London* (London 1913); blue leather travelling case, 2⅞in. high. (Christie's) £495

A Victorian parcel-gilt and silver-mounted carriage timepiece, the case with large baluster finial to fish-scale pierced moulded top with two amorous angels seated above, by John Mortimer and John S. Hunt, 1842, 8½in. high. (Christie's) £9,350

A fine parcel gilt silver grande sonnerie carriage clock signed *Tiffany & Co., New York*, the movement probably by Drocourt, circa 1883, 8½in. high. (Christie's) £4,785

A silver and enamel carriage timepiece, decorated in blue enamel with circular enamel dial, signed for H.Gibbs, London, 4½in. high. (Phillips) £360

A silver gilt and enamel miniature 'carriage clock', 1¾in. high. £1,250

A silver-cased minute-repeating carriage clock, inscribed E. White, London, with lever plat-form escapement striking the quarters on two gongs, 3½in. high. (Christie's) £3,080

SILVERED FACE

A fine early English fusee carriage clock with silvered dial, by G. & W. Yonge, London, 5½in. high. £1,500

A 19th century English timepiece, the backplate signed French, Royal Exchange, London, 17.5cm. high. £7,500

An early multi-piece striking carriage clock with narrow lever platform, strike and alarm on bell, 5¾in. high. £800

A 19th century French gilt brass carriage clock, the movement with two plane escapement, signed on the backplate, Paul Garnier, Paris, 6¾in. high. (Phillips) £2,500

A gilt brass quarter chiming giant carraige clock, the triple chain fusee movement with platform lever escapement, bearing the signature Smith & Sons, Clerkenwell, London, 13in. high. (Christie's New York) £11,220

A 19th century French brass carriage clock by Paul Garnier, Paris, with two-plane escapement, striking on a bell with push repeat, signed on the backplate, 6½in. high. (Phillips) £1,350

A 19th century English gilt brass quarter striking carriage clock, the dial signed James McCabe, Royal Exchange, London 2677, 19cm. high. £4,250

An English carriage timepiece, in the manner of Thomas Cole, silver engraved dial with Roman chapter, signed *Hunt & Roskell*, 4⅜in. (Bonhams) £1,800

An unusual gilt brass carriage timepiece, the fusee movement signed Viner on the backplate, rectangular case with turned corner columns, 5¼in. high. (Christie's) £660

TORTOISESHELL

A gold mounted tortoise-
shell miniature carriage
timepiece, maker's mark
CD, 1906, 9.5cm. high.
£1,350

An Art Nouveau tortoiseshell
and silver carriage timepiece,
with uncut bimetallic balance to
silvered lever platform, silvered
Roman chapter disc signed
*George Edward & Sons
Buchanan St. Glasgow*, 4¹/₂in.
high. (Christie's)   £825

A French silver mounted
miniature tortoiseshell carriage
timepiece, inscribed *Edwards
& Sons, 161 Regent St., W.*,
hallmark for 1904. (Lawrence
Fine Arts)   £594

WHITE FACE

A French miniature brass
carriage timepiece, the cylinder
movement with enamel dial in a
corniche case, 9.5cm. high.
(Phillips)   £280

A brass one-piece striking
carriage clock by Paul
Garnier Hger. De La
Marine A Paris, 6¼in. high.
£2,000

Gilt metal petite sonn-
erie carriage clock,
enamel dial inscribed
Dent, London, 6¼in.
high.   £1,000

A 19th century French brass
carriage clock, the lever movement
striking on a gong, with push repeat
and with the Margaine trademark
on the backplate, 7¼in. high.
£750

A 19th century French gilt
brass miniature carriage
timepiece, the lever movement with enamel dial,
3¾in. high, together with
a travelling case.   £1,350

A repeat/alarm carriage clock
in gorge case, the eight-day movement with silvered pointed lever
platform escapement striking on
a bell, 5in. high. (Christie's)
£605

WHITE FACE

A gilt metal striking miniature carriage clock with enamel dial, 3¼in. high.
£1,250

A French carriage clock with lever escapement and repeat mechanism and porcelain dial. £350

A gilt metal striking carriage clock with centre seconds for the Chinese market, 6in. high. £1,000

A French gilt brass carriage clock, with lever platform escapement and push repeat, striking on a gong, with enamel dial signed for *T. Martin*, 7¹/₂in. high.
(Phillips)   £480

A silver jubilee small silver carriage timepiece with gilt lever platform, white enamel Roman dial signed *Chas. Frodsham London* with blued hands, 3¹/₄in. high.
(Christie's)   £605

A French gilt brass grande sonnerie carriage clock, the lever movement striking on two gongs with alarm and push repeat, signed for *Sennet Freres Paris Chnie*, 6³/₄in. high.
(Phillips)   £750

A 19th century French miniature brass carriage timepiece, the lever movement bearing the Margaine trademark, 9.5cm. high.   £600

A French brass carriage timepiece with cylinder movement, in a plain pillared case, 6in. high.
£400

A 19th century French gilt brass carriage clock, the movement with replaced lever platform, 18.5cm. high.
(Phillips)   £500

WHITE FACE

A 19th century French gilt brass carriage clock, bearing the Jacot trademark on the backplate, 6¾in. high. £1,250

Brass one-piece carriage clock, enamel dial signed no. 1 Hy Marc, Paris, 5¾in. high.   £750

A lacquered brass petite sonnerie carriage clock with enamel dial, corniche case, 5¼in. high.   £900

A 19th century French gilt brass miniature timepiece, the enamel dial signed for Payne & Son, London, with Roman and Arabic numerals, 3¾in. high. (Phillips)   £300

A gilt brass striking carriage clock with uncut bimetallic balance to silvered lever platform, white enamel Roman dial with blued moon hands, 5½in. high. (Christie's)   £495

A petite sonnerie and alarm carriage clock in gorge case by Drocourt, the white enamel dial with Roman numerals and Arabic five-minute divisions, 4¾in. high. (Christie's S. Ken.)   £880

A 19th century French brass carriage clock, signed on the backplate Ollivant & Botsford, Paris & Manchester, 17cm. high.   £475

An English petit sonnerie carriage clock with white enamel dial inscribed Lund & Blockley, 6in. high.   £3,000

A 19th century French brass grande sonnerie carriage clock, the lever movement chiming on two gongs, 7in. high. (Phillips)   £1,300

WHITE FACE

A petite sonnerie and alarm carriage clock, the white enamel dial inscribed 'Dent 61, Strand, London'. 18 cm. high.   £1,500

An eight-day repeating carriage clock with alarm, inscribed 'Repasse par Leroy & Fils'. 14 cm.   £1,000

A French miniature brass carriage timepiece, the movement with later lever escapement, 10.7cm. (Lawrence Fine Arts)   £198

A brass grande sonnerie carriage clock with split compensated balance to lever platform, 5¾in. high.   £1,000

A 19th century Austrian grande sonnerie gilt brass carriage clock, the lever movement striking on two gongs, signed J.Jessner in Wien, 6¼in. high. (Phillips)   £1,000

A French brass carriage clock, the repeating movement with lever escapement, contained in a corniche case, 18cm. (Lawrence Fine Arts)   £286

A gilt metal striking one-piece carriage clock, the backplate stamped in an oval Hy. Marc Paris, 6¾in. high.   £1,000

A brass striking carriage clock, enamel dial inscribed Leroy & Fils 57 New Bond Street Made in France, 5½in. high.   £600

A lacquered brass carriage clock, signed on the dial in cyrillic, A. M. Geracimov, St. Petersburg, 8in. high.   £1,250

CARRIAGE CLOCKS

WHITE FACE

A French carriage clock with morocco travelling case and key, by F. A. Margaine, Paris, 6in. high.
£600

A French striking carriage clock, movement with lever escapement and gong strike, in a gilt corniche case, 6¾in. (Bonhams)
£320

A French brass carriage timepiece, the enamel dial signed Leroy & Fils, in a gorge case, 9.5cm. high.
£675

An attractive French gilt brass repeating carriage clock by F. L. Hausburg of Paris, the white enamelled dial with black Roman numerals, 6in. high. (Spencer's)
£520

A 19th century brass carriage clock, the lever movement striking on a gong, bearing the *Margaine* trade mark, with enamel dial, in an engraved gorge case, 7in. high. (Phillips)
£680

A gilt metal striking carriage clock with dial signed Lucien Paris, 6¼in. high.
£900

A brass quarter striking carriage clock signed 7669 Leroy & Fils Palais Royal 13-15 Paris, 5¼in. high.
£1,000

A gilt metal striking carriage clock for the Chinese market, stamp of Japy Freres, 5¾in. high.
£1,000

A French 19th century carriage clock, the gong striking movement, No. 1933, marked with the 'B' trademark, 6¾in. (Bonhams)
£400

WHITE FACE

A 19th century French gilt brass carriage clock, the lever movement striking on a bell with alarm, 6¼in. high. £325

A 19th century French gilt brass carriage clock, the enamel dial signed for J. F. Bautte, Geneve, 17cm. high. £3,000

Late 19th century gilt brass repeating carriage alarm clock with white enamel dial, 7¼in. high. £600

A repeating carriage clock in anglaise case, the eight-day movement with silvered lever platform escapement striking on a gong, 5½in. high. (Christie's) £352

A gilt brass striking carriage clock with brass balance to silvered cylinder platform, strike on bell, corniche case, with brown leather travelling case, 5¾in. high. (Christie's) £330

A 19th century French brass carriage clock, the lever movement with petite sonnerie, the dial signed for Dent London, 7in. high. £1,350

An attractive French repeating carriage clock, the rectangular gilt dial richly engraved with acanthus leaves, 20.4cm. high. (Henry Spencer) £720

A 19th century French brass carriage clock, the lever movement striking on a gong with alarm and bearing the Drocourt trademark, 16.5cm. high. £750

A 19th century brass carriage clock with petit sonnerie and alarm movement, the enamel dial signed Dent, Paris, 4½in. high. £900

WHITE FACE

A 19th century French brass carriage clock, the lever movement with quarter striking on two gongs, 7in. high. £500

A lacquered brass petite sonnerie carriage clock, with the trademark of Francois-Arsene Margaine, 7in. high. £1,500

A gilt-brass carriage clock, inscribed J. C. Vickery, *to their majesties*, with subsidiary alarm dial striking on a bell, 11cm. (Phillips) £200

A gilt brass bottom-wind striking carriage clock with split bimetallic balance to silvered lever platform, dial signed Leroy et fils 5½in. high. £750

A brass grande sonnerie/alarm carriage clock in gorge case, eight-day repeating movement with platform lever escapement striking the hours and quarters with two gongs, 5½in. high. (Christie's S. Ken) £990

A striking carriage clock in Corinthian case, the eight-day movement with lever platform escapement, bearing the trademark LF, Paris, 6¼in. high.(Christie's) £220

A 19th century French gilt brass grande sonnerie carriage clock, with enamel dial in a cannalee case, 7in. high. (Phillips) £1,050

A lacquered brass one-piece striking carriage clock, the backplate stamped Hy. Marc Paris, 5½in. high. £750

A French 19th century gilt brass carriage clock, bearing the Drocourt trademark, and signed for Klaftenberger, Paris, 17cm. high. £500

WHITE FACE

A gilt metal striking carriage clock, stamp of Henri Jacot, 5¾in. high. £1,350

A French brass carriage clock, by Francois Arsene Margaine, 6½in. high. £825

A lacquered brass grande sonnerie calendar carriage clock, signed by Emmanuel, 6¾in. high. £3,500

An English repeating double fusée carriage clock with thermometer and calendar, by Nicole Nielsen & Co. Limd., 6in. high.
(Lawrence) £5,280

An early French 19th century alarm carriage clock, by Paul Garnier, with a silvered engine-turned dial and Roman chapter ring, 6¾in.
(Bonhams) £1,400

A gilt metal one-piece grande sonnerie carriage clock with bridge to helical spring of 'jewelled' lever platform, probably Franche Comte, 5½in. high. £1,750

A French gilt brass and white metal grande son-nerie alarm carriage clock, 7½in. high. £1,350

A 19th century French brass carriage clock, signed on the backplate Bolviller A Paris, 7in. high. £750

A silvered and parcel gilt grande sonnerie calendar carriage clock, 7¼in. high. £3,000

WHITE FACE

Early French brass carriage clock, signed Hy Marc, Paris, 8in. high. £1,000

A gilt metal early multipiece carriage clock signed Leroy a Paris on backplate, 5in. high. £500

A gilt metal striking carriage clock with modern lever platform, stamp of Henri Jacot, 4¾in. high. £660

A French brass carriage clock, the movement with lever escapement, bearing the trade stamps of Hy. Marc and Japy Freres, 6¾in. (Lawrence Fine Arts) £825

Fine Victorian brass and glass cased carriage clock with Corinthian column supports and similar carrying handle, 6in. high. (G. A. Key) £500

An eight-day repeating carriage clock with alarm, the white enamel dial signed *Chas. Frodsham, Clockmaker to the Queen*, 6¼in. high. (Bearne's) £750

A gilt brass quarter striking carriage clock with cut bimetallic balance to lever platform, 6in. high. £800

A Franche Comte gilt metal striking carriage clock for the Chinese market, 6½in. high. £1,500

A lacquered brass grande sonnerie carriage clock with calendar, by Drocourt, No. 12276, 7in. high. £2,750

CARRIAGE CLOCKS

WHITE FACE

A brass carriage clock, by
T. Hyde, Sleaford, in ornate
case. £225

An Austrian brass grande
sonnerie carriage clock with
calendar, 5½in. high. £2,250

A gilt brass grande sonnerie
carriage clock, 7½in. high,
including handle. £1,250

A gilt brass striking calendar
carriage clock, with bi-metallic
balance to silvered lever
platform, strike/repeat/alarm on
gong on backplate with stamp
for Margaine, 6³/₄in. high.
(Christie's) £1,430

A 19th century French gilt brass
quarter striking carriage clock,
the lever movement striking on
gongs, with alarm and push
repeat, signed Barraud and
Lund, in a gorge case, 5¹/₂in.
high.
(Phillips) £700

A French gilt brass carriage
clock, with lever platform and
helical hairspring, push repeat,
alarm, striking on a gong and
signed *Baschet & Baullet, Paris*,
7in. high.
(Phillips) £460

WOODEN CASE

Rosewood carriage clock
by Jas. Murray & Co.,
London, with brass drop
carrying handle, 10³/₄in.
high. £2,250

A Victorian brass inlaid,
rosewood carriage clock,
dial signed Craighead &
Webb, 9¼in. high. £2,250

A satinwood four glass
striking carriage clock, the
dial signed Arnold & Dent
London No 408, 8³/₄in.
high. £5,000

CARTEL CLOCKS

The cartel clock is a French wall clock dating from circa 1750. The casing, of wood or brass, is usually highly ornamental, even flamboyant, with frequent ormolu or vernis Martin embellishment. Common motifs include wings, laurel leaves, cupids and mythological figures. English examples are more often of wood, while French clocks are more often of bronze and gilt or cast brass. Cartel clocks were also made in Holland and Scandinavia.

Late 18th/early 19th century French giltwood cartel clock, 28in. high.   £1,000

Louis XVI ormolu cartel clock, dial signed Imbert, 36½in. high.   £1,500

A late 18th century French cartel clock, urn shaped and festooned with laurels, with a female face above the dial and pineapple finial, the white enamel face signed *Hartingue, Paris*. (Finarte)   £2,626

An Austrian parcel-gilt cartel clock, the circular enamel dial signed *Toban Vellauer a Vienne*, the shaped case surmounted by a vase flanked by seahorses, 30in. high. (Christie's)   £1,540

A Louis XVI ormolu cartel clock with circular enamel dial signed *Baret A Breuvanne*, in a cartouche-shaped case surmounted by a flaming urn, 29in. high. (Christie's)   £3,850

A French cartel clock with eight day movement, 9½in. high.   £250

An 18th century Continental carved giltwood cartel clock, 64cm. high.   £1,250

A wall clock, by Sewill (maker to the Royal Navy), Liverpool, 40in. high.   £375

121

CARTEL CLOCKS

Gilt bronze cartel wall clock in waisted case, circa 1870, 22¾in. high. £900

A Louis XVI ormolu cartel clock, the enamel dial signed Charles Leroy a Paris, 13in. high. £1,850

An ormolu cartel clock of Louis XVI style, the enamel dial signed Guibal, Paris, 26in. high. £750

Régence style gilt-bronze cartel clock, circa 1900, the circular dial cast in low relief with foliate scrolls and shells, 30in. high. (Butterfield & Butterfield) £1,180

A Louis XV ormolu cartel clock with circular glazed enamel Roman-chaptered dial and movement signed *Etienne Le Noir A Paris*, in a raised rockwork and scroll cartouche, 22in. high. (Christie's) £4,950

Austrian giltwood cartel clock, Anton Koppel, Vienna, early 19th century, circular dial with hands for calendar and days of week, 30in. high. (Skinner Inc.) £982

An early 19th century French ormolu cased wall clock with eight-day movement, 30in. high, overall. £1,500

A Louis XVI ormolu cartel clock, the enamel dial signed Brille a Paris, 14in. high. £6,000

A Louis XVI cartel clock, the dial signed Charles Le Roy a Paris, 37in. high. £4,500

Louis XV ormolu cartel clock, signed Joannes Biesta Paris, 33in. high. £3,750

A George III giltwood cartel timepiece with single fusee movement, 35in. high. £800

Gilt bronze cartel wall clock, with pendulum, circa 1850, 32in. high. £1,500

An antique French Louis XVI style gilt-bronze cartel clock with urn-form finial festooned with laurel wreath, inscribed *Lanier*, 28in. high. (Selkirk's) £1,067

A late 19th century French wall clock, the 8 day movement striking on a bell, in bronze casing with red latticework under, signed *Philippe FT 66 Paris Royal 67*. (Auction Team Köln) £445

George III giltwood wall clock, Henry King, Lincoln's Inn, third quarter 18th century, eagle crest above a silvered circular dial, 31in. high. (Skinner Inc.) £494

A George III giltwood cartel clock with later white dial and timepiece movement, 30in. high. £1,350

A George III giltwood cartel clock with associated silvered dial signed Wm. Linderby, London, 34in. high. £4,500

A Continental striking cartel clock with white enamel face, overall length 25½in. £1,000

Regency style gilt bronze cartel clock, dial signed Breguet A Paris, circa 1880, 71cm. high. £1,000

Louis XVI style French bronze cartel clock in reticulated rococo scroll-shaped case, 23in. high. £500

19th century French ormolu wall clock with an 8in. dial and eight day movement. £1,500

Louis XV gilt bronze cartel clock, signed Lepaute Hger. du Roy, circa 1755, 43in. high. £20,000

A George II giltwood cartel clock, signed James Smyth, London, circa 1750, 30in. high. £2,500

Louis XV gilt bronze cartel clock, signed Gilbert a Paris, circa 1760, 29in. high. £10,000

A George III giltwood cartel timepiece, the dial signed Robt. Mawley London, 25½in. high. £3,750

An interesting late 18th century French cartel clock by Etienne Baillon of Paris, the white enamel dial plate with Roman numerals, 27cm. high. (Henry Spencer) £1,200

A wall-hanging cartel clock in a rococo case of gilt bronze, 2ft. 6in. high, by Clouzier of Paris. £7,500

CHRONOMETERS

The chronometer was originally a marine device, with a spring detent escapement developed in the 18th century to keep accurate time at sea for establishing longitude, and was pioneered by John Harrison, an 18th century English horologist. The type was later developed by the Arnolds, Earnshaw and Dent in England, and by Breguet in France.

Marine chronometers come in drum shaped brass cases suspended in gimbals in a wooden box, usually mahogany, with one, two or eight day movements, often with a up and down indicator hand on the dial to show the state of winding.

A marine chronometer in a brass mounted rosewood case, the lid with a separate glass panel, inscribed D. McGregor & Co.   £1,000

A 36-hour marine chronometer by Leroy No. 821, diam. of bezel 82mm.   £900

An eight-day marine chronometer by Hatton & Harris No. 570, diam. of bezel 133mm.   £7,500

An early marine chronometer by John Arnold & Son, with 4½in. circular silvered dial, in mahogany box.   £10,000

A two-day marine chronometer by John Bruce No. 786, diam. of bezel 125mm.   £1,760

A two-day marine chronometer, the silvered dial signed James Muirhead, Glasgow, No. 2169, 100mm. diam. of dial. £7,500

A 20th century two-day marine chronometer, by Thomas Mercer, movement with Earnshaw spring detent escapement, helical spring and bi-metallic balance. (Bonhams)   £530

Late 19th century coromandel and brass inlaid marine chronometer.   £1,250

A two day marine chronometer contained in mahogany deck box, diam. of bezel 115mm.
£5,500

An eight-day marine chronometer by John Poole, in brass bound rosewood case, diam. of bezel 142mm.
£4,500

A small one-day marine chronometer by John Roger Arnold, the dial 64mm. diam.
£3,500

A French two-day marine chronometer, the silvered dial signed *E. DELEPINE No. 1693 A ST NICOLAS, PRÈS DIEPPE*, external brass drop handles, the whole in outer guard box, 6³/₄in. square.
(Christie's)   £2,310

**A thuya wood brass inlaid 8-day Hertfordshire Mercer mantel chronometer, brass bezel to glazed circular silvered engraved dial signed *George Makin & Sons, Ltd. Manchester. 669 Auxillary Compensation*, winding key, 11¹/₂in. high.
(Christie's)   £4,950**

A 19th-century two-day marine chronometer, the top-plate of the movement signed *Poole, LONDON 803*, the silvered dial signed *A. Bruce, MANCHESTER 803*, 6¹/₄in. square.
(Christie's)   £1,650

A two-day marine chronometer in two-tier glazed mahogany box, the 4½in. silvered dial with Arabic numerals, signed Thomas Mercer, No. 28271, in travelling box.   £700

A two-day marine chronometer, the dial signed by Dobbie McInnes Ltd., Glasgow, no. 9615, dial 10cm. diam.   £900

A two-day marine chronometer, the 4in. dial signed Kelvin Bottomley & Baird Ltd., Glasgow, and numbered 9550, in a brass bound mahogany box.
(Phillips)   £950

A brass ship's chronometer in walnut case, signed *Charles Frodsham, London No. 3337*, circa 1862.
(Auktionsverket) £708

A marine chronometer by J. R. Arnold No. 578, diam. of bezel 105mm. £3,750

A two-day marine chrono-meter by James Poole No. 5818, diam. of bezel 125mm. £1,750

A fine semi-miniature marine chronometer, the silvered dial signed *Arnold London*, with Government mark within seconds dial at VI, blued spade hands, flat glass, the top-plate similarly signed, early 19th century, dial diameter 63mm.
(Christie's) £2,750

A rare 19th century black marble mantel chronometer timepiece, signed *Arnold London*, the movement of small size, 41cm. high. (Phillips London) £3,000

English brass and rosewood marine chronometer, Parkinson & Frodsham, Change Alley, London, 1801-1842, in a brass bound rosewood case.
(Skinner Inc.) £971

A two-day marine chronometer, the movement with Earnshaw-type spring detent escapement, signed *Charles Frodsham, London*.
(Phillips) £1,200

A mahogany eight-day mantel chronometer with a 4½in. silvered dial, 8in. high. £2,500

A small two-day marine chronometer by Brock-bank & Atkins, in maho-gany carrying case, diam. of bezel 100mm. £2,250

CANDELABRA

A 19th century French ormolu clock garniture, the shaped case of scroll design, the circular enamel dial with pierced gilt hands, 13³/₄ in. high, together with a matching pair of two armed candelabra.
(Phillips)   £1,600

A 19th century French ormolu clock garniture, the shaped case of scroll and floral design with circular enamel dial, the movement striking on a bell, 25cm. high, together with a matching pair of two-armed candelabra.
(Phillips)   £650

A French porcelain mounted clock garniture, the two-train movement in a drum case, putto decorated dial, 1ft. 3in. high, flanked by a pair of four-light candelabra, decorated with putti and musical trophies.
(Bonhams)   £580

A French ormolu and bronze matched clock garniture comprising a pair of four light candelabra and a mantel clock in the form of a chariot driven by a putto, mid-19th century, the candelabra 24in. high.
(Christie's)   £5,500

Renaissance Revival three-piece brass clock garniture, France, late 19th century, with foliate-pierced urn and pedestal base, by Japy Frères, clock 20in. high.
(Skinner Inc.)   £370

Victorian brass clock garniture, the clock of rococo form with applied and embossed C-scroll and foliate decoration, having a French striking movement. (G. A. Key)
                                                            £200

128

CANDELABRA

A 19th century French ormolu and porcelain clock garniture, with the figures of a couple, the lady selling flowers, on a scroll base, 1ft. 1¹/₂in. high, together with the matching pair of two-branch candelabra.
(Phillips)   £1,500

A 19th century French ormolu clock garniture, 1ft.1½in. high, together with matching pair of two branch candelabra.   £1,500

Extremely fine Napoléon III parcel-gilt and patinated bronze three-piece clock garniture, signed *Raingo Frères*, Paris, third quarter 19th century, the case surmounted by a group of a classically robed reclining woman and three children, 31¹/₂in. wide.
(Butterfield & Butterfield)   £13,497

A French gilt brass and bronzed garniture, comprising a clock surmounted by an urn with foliate swags, the arched case with addorsed dolphins and flaming finials, the dial with twelve enamel numeral plaquettes, late 19th century, 26³/₄in. high.
(Christie's)   £1,980

A pale Royal rouge marble and ormolu three-piece clock set, the lidded urn holding the clock, with two four-branch, four light candelabra, all 34in. high.
£8,500

An ormolu, bronze and white marble garniture de cheminee comprising: a clock with circular glazed enamel dial signed James Aitchison, and a pair of three-light candelabra. (Christie's)   £1,980

CANDELABRA

A gilt metal and cloisonne enamel clock
set in the Gothic style, the dial signed
W. Angus Paris, 17 Lord Street, Liverpool, 20½in. high, the candelabra 17¼in.
high. £2,000

A Victorian mantel clock, with gilt-embellished
black slate dial, in gilt brass-mounted black slate
architectural case, 16½in. wide, and a pair of
five-branch candelabra ensuite, 21½in. high.
(Christie's) £715

A French white marble and gilt metal mounted composite clock garniture, the mantel
clock on column supports with drum shaped
case surmounted by an urn finial and a pair
of twin-branch candelabra, 11in. high.
(Christie's) £418

Fine Louis XV style gilt-bronze and cloisonné
three-piece clock garniture by Vincent and Cie,
retailed by Tiffany and Co., New York, circa
1900, with eight-day time and half-hour strike on
a coiled gong, 28¼in. high.
(Butterfield & Butterfield) £14,172

A 19th century ormolu clock garniture, the
shaped case surmounted by three winged
cherubs and floral swags, the movement
stamped Japy Freres, 1ft. 3¾in. high, together
with a matching pair of two arm candelabra.
(Phillips) £1,300

An ormolu and porcelain garniture, circa
1870, clock 15½in. high, the pair of candelabra, 14in. high. £1,250

CLOCK SETS

CANDELABRA

A 19th century French porcelain and ormolu clock garniture, with two Imari vases on ormolu bases holding candelabra, the clock face set in a similar vase, flanked by putti.
(Finarte)   £2,204

A 19th century French ormolu and porcelain clock garniture, the enamel dial signed Lenoir a Paris, 1ft.8½in. high, together with a matching pair of three branch candelabra.   £2,750

A Louis XV-style mantel clock, in lacquered brass balloon-shaped case cast with acanthus scrolls and flowering foliage, on paw feet, 19½in., and a pair of five branch candelabra ensuite.
(Christie's)   £660

A large Art Deco marble, onyx and bronze clock garniture, the top of the clock's case mounted with a charioteer and horses, and mounted on a stepped base, 62.5cm. high, 44.1cm. across, and a pair of candelabra en suite. (Phillips)   £1,000

A jewelled turquoise ground Sevres pattern porcelain and ormolu clock garniture, with circular dial painted with a turquoise border, the clock 16½in. high.
(Christie's)   £5,280

Brass garniture set, Europe, circa 1915, in the style of Onder den St. Marten, comprising an elongated pendulum clock and matching double arm candlesticks with pierced designs on the front of the cases, 14½in. high.
(Skinner Inc.)   £389

131

CANDELABRA

A 19th century French silver plated three-piece clock garniture, the striking movement by S. Marti & Cie, 16in. high, together with two five-light candelabra, 19in. high. £675

Gilt bronze and blue porcelain clock garniture, dial signed Festeau Le Jeune a Paris, clock 19¼in. high. £3,750

A French ormolu and white marble clock garniture, in rectangular-shaped case, surmounted by a motif of birds, wreath bow and arrow, the eight-day movement striking on a bell, 11in. high; with a matching pair of ormolu and white marble two-light candelabra.
(Christie's S. Ken) £1,100

A French porcelain clock-set comprising a clock-case and two nine-light candelabra, the clock-case formed as a circular drum flanked by two putti, circa 1880, the clock-case 47cm. wide, the candelabra 69cm. high.
(Christie's) £3,850

A French ormolu and porcelain mounted three-piece clock garniture, the clock 13in. high, the side pieces 13¾in. high. £750

19th century Meissen blue and white clock set by Lund & Blockley, 39in. high. £1,350

CANDELABRA

A French gilt brass clock garniture, the two train movement with Brocot type suspension, signed Rollin a Paris, 21in. high.

£1,850

French three-piece brass clock/garniture set, the clock with two cherubs supporting a flower basket, 12in. high.
(Eldred's)   £188

A French ormolu mantel timepiece garniture in drum-shaped case with foliage decoration supported by two putti on scrolled base, 8¼in. high; with a matching pair of single-light candelabra, 7¾in. high.
(Christie's S. Ken)   £1,320

A bronzed and gilt metal clock garniture, the clock with circular gilt foliate stamped dial set in a horizontal cylindrical drum as a houdah, surmounted by a chinoiserie figure holding a feather fan, 23in. high, flanked by a pair of two branch candelabra.
(Spencer's)   £2,700

A French gilt marble and gilt metal garniture, with matching three-arm candelabra, 18in. high.   £1,500

A 19th century French ormolu clock garniture, the clock contained in a drum, 2ft.9in. high, together with matching pair of seven branch candelabra, 2ft.10in. high.   £2,750

CANDLESTICKS

A Jacob Petit garniture of a clock and a pair of candlesticks all moulded with rococo scrolls, shells and leaf motifs, 39.5cm.

£900

An unusual 19th century enamelled and gilt brass 'Gothic' chamber clock and candlesticks, clock 22in. high.   £4,750

A 19th century gilt brass and champlevé enamel mantel timepiece garniture, the rectangular case surmounted by a pineapple finial, 8¼in. high, together with a matching pair of candlesticks.
(Phillips)   £750

A 19th century ormolu and porcelain mantel clock, the decorated dial with Roman numerals, the twin train movement stamped *Ch. Vcne*, together with a pair of associated candlesticks, 16in. high.
(Phillips)   £820

A pink marble and ormolu clock garniture, the clock with enamel dial inscribed *Made in France for Jas Crighton & Co., Edinburgh*, the clock 8¾in. high.
(Christie's)   £550

A small French champleve enamel clock garniture, the movement with Brocot suspension and gong striking, the gilt dial with Arabic numerals, 28cm. (Lawrence Fine Arts)
                                                    £1,100

FIGURAL

Late 19th century French black marble and bronze clock garniture, height of clock 21in., height of statues 18½in. £900

Mid 19th century French bronze and marble garniture, signed Crouillard, 21in. high. £600

A 19th century French gilt and patinated bronze three piece clock garniture, of small proportions, the movement stamped 'H & F Paris'; the gilded case in the form of a staved barrel lying on its side draped with a fruiting vine and flanked by two scantily clad, animated, patinated bronze putti, 19cm. high. (Henry Spencer) £520

An Art Nouveau-style mantel clock, with cream enamel dial in gilt brass-mounted green onyx architectural case, surmounted by a spelter figure of a female mandolin player, 31½in. high, and a pair of side ornaments ensuite. (Christie's) £660

A 19th century French enamel clock, surmounted by a foliate finial, 35cm. high, together with the matching pair of candlesticks, each sconce held aloft by a putto. (Phillips) £1,400

Victorian spelter and gilt metal clock garniture, the French drum cased clock having striking movement and surmounted by an angelic figure. (G. A. Key) £175

135

OBELISKS

Egyptian Revival marble and onyx three-piece clock garniture, circa 1880, the black marble mantel clock applied with bronze Egyptian figures and surmounted by a bronze sphinx, time and strike movement, impressed *R & C/ Paris*, 18¹/₂in. high.
(Skinner Inc.) £548

An Egyptian Revival red and black marble garniture, comprising two obelisks on moulded plinths, the clock, en suite, surmounted by sphinx, the white enamel dial, signed *Savage, Lyman & Co., Montreal*, French, circa 1875, 16in. high.
(Christie's New York) £3,366

TAZZAS

A black marble French clock garniture, the black enamel dial ring with gold Roman numerals, signed *Requier a Lisieux*, the decorated brass chapter ring with bevelled glazing, circa 1880, 42cm. high.
(Auction Team Köln) £328

A Charles X Siena marble and bronze mounted composite clock garniture, the rectangular shaped case surmounted by a bronze group depicting 'The Oath of Horatii', 19¼in. high, and a pair of tazze on square plinths, 11¼in. high. (Christie's)
£1,890

A French 'silver'-mounted turquoise porcelain clock garniture, Napoléon III, Paris, circa 1870, the movement in a four-column temple case, clock 40cm. high.
(Sotheby's) £3,080

A 19th century French black and red marble garniture de cheminée, the 8 day Paris movement sounding the half hours on a bell, with porcelain dial, 47cm. high.
(Duran) £528

A Sevres pattern pink-ground porcelain and gilt bronze composite garniture-de-cheminee, circa 1880, the clock 34cm. wide, the vases 26.5cm. high. £1,250

Porcelain and gilt bronze composed clock garniture, movement by Achille Brocot, 1870's, 41cm. high. £1,000

A clock garniture in the Louis XVI style, signed in the centre 'Goldsmiths' Alliance Ltd./Cornhill, London', 12½in. high. (Bearne's) £400

Oriental inspired French 19th century cloisonne enamel clock garniture by Japy Freres. £3,000

A 19th century French porcelain and gilt metal garniture de cheminee, the clock with glass dome and stand, 44cm. high. £500

Louis XVI style gilt bronze and enamel three-piece clock set. £4,250

Louis XVI style three-piece gilt bronze
and Sevres jewelled porcelain annular
clock set.   £10,000

A champleve enamel Mexican onyx and gilt
metal garniture, circa 1900, the clock 13½in.
high, the pair of urns 11in. high.   £1,250

An ormolu and Paris porcelain clock garniture
comprising: a pair of cassolettes, each with a
lid with a pineapple finial, and a mantel clock,
the rectangular dial indistinctly inscribed
ROB^T. H. HALFORD, the bell-striking going
barrel movement similarly signed, late 19th
century, the clock 18in. high, the cassolettes
15in. high.
(Christie's)   £2,420

An ormolu and white marble clock garniture
comprising: a pair of brules parfums, each
with a domed top cast with foliage, and a
mantel clock with circular enamel dial
inscribed *TIFFANY & CO.* and twin going
barrel striking on gong movement, the brules
parfums 13½in. high, the clock 14in. high.
(Christie's)   £3,850

A 19th century Empire style French clock
garniture, the clock and matching urns of
ormolu mounted Sèvres type porcelain, the 8 day
movement striking the half hours on a bell.
(Duran)   £1,528

French Greek Revival black marble and
metal clock garniture, late 19th century, the
clock with bust of Pericles on a black marble
case, impressed *H & F Paris,* 23in. high.
(Skinner Inc.)   £229

URNS

A gilt bronze and porcelain clock garniture, dial signed Connell, clock 14½in. high, circa 1880. £2,000

A gilt bronze onyx and champleve enamel clock garniture, the clock 13in. high, circa 1900. £750

A French gilt brass and porcelain mounted striking clock garniture, the balustraded case with foliage fruiting finials, detached acanthus and Corinthian capped columns, the two similarly painted urns en suite on similar bases, 16½in. high.
(Christie's) £1,100

A French 19th century clock garniture, the mantel clock in architectural gothic case, stamped Villamesens, Paris, with gilt cast pendulum, 20¼in. high, and a pair of similarly decorated cassolettes, on cylindrical plinths and square bases, 11½in. high.
(Christie's) £880

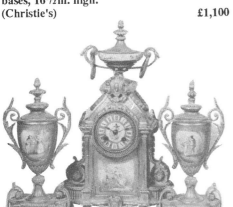

A French porcelain and ormolu clock garniture, two-train movement by Henri Marc, with dial decorated with birds, flanked by a pair of bulbous urns, 11½in. high.
(Bonhams) £1,300

An Austrian porcelain three-piece clock set, the clock case moulded with arches and painted with classical figures, 47cm. high, a two-handled pedestal jar and cover on either side.
(Bearne's) £640

URNS

A French porcelain clock garniture by Jacob Petit, the rococo moulded clock painted with panels of flowers on a gold decorated green ground, 32cm high.
(Bearne's) £820

A gilt spelter and porcelain composed garniture, the clock 22in. high, circa 1880, the pair of 'Sevres' covered urns, circa 1860, 15½in. high. £1,200

A 19th century ormolu and porcelain mounted mantel clock case, of arched form surmounted by an oval enamel panel, with foliate swags, on four turned feet and mounted with twelve floral panels, together with two associated side pieces.
(Phillips) £550

A French 19th century porcelain and ormolu clock garniture, painted dial, black Roman numeral reserves, colourful centre scene with figures looking into a pond, bell striking movement signed *Japy Freres*, 20in.
(Bonhams) £1,200

An impressive French ormolu mounted and Sèvres style porcelain clock garniture, the clock with Japy Frères movement, 23in. high.
(G. A. Key) £2,800

19th century brass and blue and white china clock set in the Renaissance manner, the side urns of baluster form with figure designs.
(G.A.Key) £460

URNS

An ormolu mounted Imari porcelain clock vase garniture, the circular enamel face indistinctly signed, 20in. high. £2,400

An Empire ormolu mounted bronzed mantel clock with a seated figure of Ceres, and a pair of urn-shaped cassolettes, 41cm. high. £2,500

A French gilt brass and champlevé enamel clock garniture, the arched case of four glass form, surmounted by a twin handled urn and four finials, 1ft. 8in. high, together with a matching pairs of urns. (Phillips) £1,600

A French 19th century ormolu and porcelain mounted clock garniture, the eight-day movement striking on a bell, bearing the maker's stamp *Hy. Marc, Paris*, 13in. high; with a matching pair of porcelain and ormolu urn shaped sidepieces, 8in. high. (Christie's S. Ken) £880

An attractive French gilt metal and pink and grey striated marble garniture de cheminée, the clock with convex circular white enamelled dial and black Arabic numerals, 24in. high. (Spencer's) £480

A French 19th century fine porcelain mounted and ormolu mantel clock, the porcelain dial signed *Le Roy e fil, Paris*, together with a pair of matched jewelled porcelain urns, 17in. (Bonhams) £2,500

URNS

A gilt bronze and champleve enamel clock
garniture, the clock 14in. high, the urns
12½in. high.   £1,350

A French gilt brass clock garniture , the
movement with Brocot type suspension,
14½in. high.   £750

A French ormolu and Sèvres-pattern blue
ground garniture, the mantel clock of square
outline surmounted by an urn with flaming
finial, a female mask head to each corner, the
dial decorated with a cherub, late 19th century,
18in. high.
(Christie's)   £3,300

A 19th century French ormolu and porcelain
mounted clock garniture, the clock case
surmounted by a twin-handled urn flanked by
mask heads, 1ft. 2½in. high, together with a
pair of associated vases.
(Phillips)   £1,250

A 19th century French ormolu clock set,
20in. high.   £2,250

A good ormolu and porcelain garniture, 18in.
high.   £2,250

URNS

A white marble and gilt metal three-piece clock set, by J. Marti & Cie., the clock 23in. high, the urns 17in. high. £1,500

A Mexican onyx and champleve enamel four-glass clock garniture, circa 1900, the clock 20in. high, the urns, 14in. high. £950

A French veined rouge marble and ormolu mounted clock garniture, the mantel clock in four-glass case flanked by cylindrical columns, 18½in. high; and a pair of matching ornamental vases, 14½in. high. (Christie's) £825

A French ormolu and Sèvres-pattern turquoise ground garniture, the clock surmounted by an urn, with a mask-head and swag handle to each side, decorated with a woman and putti, late 19th century, 19in. high. (Christie's) £3,520

A French veined marble garniture, 17in. high. £650

19th century Sevres porcelain garniture de cheminee, by S. Wartenberg, Paris. £3,000

URNS

Mid 19th century black marble garniture de cheminee with ormolu mounts and Continental movement. (British Antique Exporters) £250

A Second Empire ormolu and green marble clock set on the theme of the Oath of the Horatii, the side pieces formed as ewers. £4,377

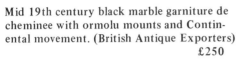

A French porcelain mounted gilt spelter clock garniture, the movement with Brocot suspension, outside locking plate and bell striking. (Lawrence Fine Arts) £990

A French 19th century brass, enamel and porcelain mounted clock garniture, signed Lefranc, 1ft.3in. high, together with a pair of side urns. £2,500

A late 19th century marble and gilt metal clock garniture, the painted enamel face surmounted by gilt metal basket of flowers, supported on two columns, the base with turned feet, with two gilt metal mounted urns. (Phillips) £360

A 19th century French ormolu and porcelain clock garniture, the shaped case surmounted by two putti and a tortoise flanked by two flaming urns, with inset panels, 1ft. 4in. high, together with an associated pair of vases. (Phillips) £800

CUCKOO CLOCKS

German Black Forest carved cuckoo clock.   £40

A 19th century Black Forest Trumpeter wall clock, the carved case decorated with a stag's head and a door below opening to reveal two trumpeters, 2ft. 10in. high. (Phillips)   £2,400

A finely carved Black Forest cuckoo clock decorated with a stag and dead game.   £700

A fine Black Forest clock with two train movement striking in a wire gong and with cuckoo, 48in. high.   £1,700

A Black Forest carved wood striking cuckoo clock of standard form, the dial with Roman chapter ring, pierced bone hands, a cuckoo and seated boy appearing on the hour behind shutters, 30in. high. (Christie's)   £902

A small 1950's decorated carved wood clock with two cuckoos and a weight driven movement.   £35

Black Forest shelf mounted German cuckoo clock with spring driven movement, striking on a gong and cuckoos.   £300

Combined cuckoo and weather clock, complete with thermometer.   £25

A small 1980's Black Forest cuckoo clock with weight driven movement.   £20

A gilt brass timepiece table compendium, with trade label of John Cockburn, Richmond, base 9in. wide. £4,500

1950s round Cartier desk clock, with lapis and gold face and gold and green enamel hands, signed *Cartier nn 8364–5728*. (Finarte) £4,605

A late 19th century French timepiece with 3½in. plain glass dial, 9½in. high. £450

A Bulle Clockette electric desk clock in red-brown bakelite case, the silvered dial behind arched glass door, 21cm. high, 1910/20. (Auction Team Köln) £94

A chromium plated and gilt desk timepiece modelled as an Edwardian tourer, 8½in. high. (Christie's) £450

A finely decorated and cast gilt French desk clock with hand painted porcelain inlay, the 8 day non striking movement signed *Japy Freres, France*, 45cm. diameter, circa 1890. (Auction Team Köln) £154

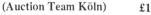 

A brass digital desk clock with calendar attachment, the American movement signed *The Plato Clock*, 15cm. high, circa 1900. (Auction Team Köln) £140

A Seth Thomas American desk clock, the 8-day movement striking on a gong, in walnut case with galleried pediment, the painted metal dial with Roman numerals, circa 1880/90. (Auction Team Köln) £169

A German oak and walnut cased desk clock with calendar automaton, the 8-day movement with half hour striking on a gong, circa 1890, 51cm. high. (Auction Team Köln) £1,640

German cast metal desk clock with a hunter and his bag, German 1-day movement, silvered dial, 30cm. high, circa 1930.
(Auction Team Köln) £94

A Swiss hexagonal silver 8-day desk clock, enamelled in blue, signed on box *St. Pauls Lodge num. 43, Ladies Night 1928*, 9cm. high.
(Duran) £222

A hardstone and enamel timepiece, unmarked, circa 1900, 16.5 cm. high. £3,500

A brass desk timepiece with barometer and thermometer, the rectangular case surmounted by a handle with compass below, 8in. high.
(Phillips) £420

An unusual presentation deskwatch with battery operated winding in mottled green enamelled brass case with applied Rolex name and crest and the words Timed to the second, 90mm.diam.
(Christies) £3,450

A guilloche enamel desk clock, the split seed-pearl bezel enclosing a white enamel dial with black Arabic chapters, white metal, marked Faberge, 1899-1908, 5in. high. (Christie's) £14,300

A gilt timepiece and barometer desk set in oval case surmounted by a carrying handle, with timepiece movement and platform escapement, 6¾in. high.
(Christie's) £352

Late 19th century circular silver mounted hardstone desk clock by Faberge, St. Petersburg, 12.3cm. £1,700

A Viennese enamel desk clock, mid 19th century, the whole supported by Hercules, decorated with polychrome classical scenes over a pink ground, 8in. high.
(Skinner Inc.) £887

A gilt-metal desk time-
piece, dial signed Hunt
& Roskell London, 5in.
high, with a velvet lined
travelling case.   £1,250

A gilt metal desk timepiece
in the manner of Thos. Cole,
the dial signed Dent, 34
Cockspur St., 6in. high. £750

Late 19th century French
champleve and ormolu desk
timepiece, 8in. high.   £475

American 'Beehive' desk clock,
the mahogany case in the form
of a beehive, the door with
glazed Spanish landscape scene,
8 day movement by the
Waterbury Clock Co. striking
on a gong, 48cm. high, circa
1880.
(Auction Team Köln)   £131

Hand painted, floral decorated
Ansonia porcelain desk clock,
signed *La Savoie von F M, Bonn,
Germany*, the American 8 day
movement striking the half
hours on a gong, 29cm. high,
circa 1900.
(Auction Team Köln)   £187

An owl desk clock with blinking
eyes, in wooden case with pewter
and silvered front, the 1 day
movement by Junghans, the
paper numeral ring with Arabic
numerals, 17cm. high, circa
1900.
(Auction Team Köln)   £351

A Viennese silver, enamel
and gemset desk clock on
oval base with two dolphin
supports, 4¼in. high. £750

A silver-gilt and enamel
desk timepiece made by
Third Artel, St. Petersburg,
1908-17, 11.1cm. high.
                    £4,000

A gilt metal desk timepiece
of long duration and in the
manner of Thos. Cole, 7½in.
high.   £1,750

LANTERN CLOCKS

The lantern clock, often erroneously called the Cromwellian clock, was introduced in England in the early 17th century and continued in production for about a hundred years. All the earliest examples were weight driven with a balance wheel escapement. As they quickly became popular, the movements began to be encased in brass, and brass soon replaced iron for the various wheels. The case was formed by a pillar at each corner with plates between, these plates often being finely engraved. Another common adornment was fretwork, particularly at the top of the front and side to conceal the space between the top of the case and the bell, which would be surmounted by a single finial. The frets can be a useful guide to determining the age of the clock. A shield and mantling design was among the earliest to be used, while scrolling and monsters' heads became common in the first half of the 17th century. The crossed dolphin design evolved from the monsters' heads after 1640 and remained the favourite until the clocks went out of fashion.

During the late 17th and early 18th century the diameter of the dial increased, without any corresponding enlargement of the case, so the former would protrude noticeably on each side.

Lantern clocks could be fitted with alarms, and those that were can be identified by a small dial behind the hand of the hour numbers in Arabic figures. From around 1670 the pendulum came to replace the balance wheel and a cord spring in a barrel and the key-wound fusée began to replace the traditional cord and weight drive. A thirty hour movement is general and was never exceeded, while some of the earliest examples might run for 12 or 15 hours.

Lantern clocks have been widely copied to the present day.

A late 17th century brass "winged" lantern clock with pierced dolphin fret above the Roman chapter ring, 14½in. high. (Christie's) £1,068

Midlands Clockmaking, a small and rare alarm lantern timepiece, 8½in. high. £7,500

An early 18th century brass lantern clock of typical form, the engraved centrefield inscribed Humphrey Marsh, Highworth, fecit, number 105, with a single steel hand, 16in. high. (Christie's S. Ken.) £1,320

An interesting late 17th century English brass lantern clock with pierced and engraved decoration of entwined dolphins and foliage, 34cm. high. (Henry Spencer) £950

A brass lantern clock of typical form, the rectangular case with turned pillars at the corners, 15¹/₂in. high. (Christie's S. Ken.) £660

Late 17th century small alarm lantern timepiece, dial signed Joseph Knibb Londini, 6½in. high. £4,500

ARCHED DIAL

A George II small brass lantern clock with silent escapement, chapter ring signed John Fletcher, 9in. high. £1,500

A brass lantern clock for the Turkish market, signed John Ellis, London, 36cm. high. £1,250

A brass lantern clock with pendulum verge escapement, signed Stephen Tracy, London, 15in. high. £1,000

A George III brass lantern alarm timepiece, signed Jno Silke Elmsted, the movement with anchor escapement, 8½in. high.
(Phillips) £1,250

A George I miniature brass lantern timepiece with alarm, the arched dial signed *Massey London* on a disc within foliate engraving, lacking gallery frets and one side door, 8in. high.
(Christie's) £1,265

A brass lantern clock, signed in the arch *Jos. Hocker, Reading*, with a French twin train carriage clock movement, 21.5cm. high.
(Phillips) £300

Mid 18th century brass lantern clock for the Turkish market, signed Isaac Rogers, London, 14in. high. £900

A Georgian brass miniature lantern clock made for the Turkish market, signed Robt. Ward, London, 5½in. high. £2,000

A Georgian brass lantern clock, made for the Turkish market, signed Jno. Parks, London, 1ft.2½in. high. £900

JAPANESE

A Japanese striking lantern clock with alarm, 15in. high.   £3,750

A Japanese brass lantern clock, the posted frame 30-hour iron movement with double foliot verge escapement, 11½in. high. £2,000

A 19th century Japanese lantern clock with red enamel dial, 28cm. high.   £3,000

An early lantern clock, yagura-dokei, the brown-lacquered brass case etched with a hemp-leaf pattern, on four stump feet, unsigned, circa 1700, 45cm. high. (Christie's)   £4,950

A Japanese brass lantern clock, the posted frame movement with verge and single foliot escapement and European hour count-wheel strike on bell above, 7¾in. high. (Christie's)   £1,540

A Japanese striking lantern clock with alarm, the case of standard form with twin foliot verge movement, black painted dial with Japanese chapters, lacking hand, 9½in. high. (Christie's)   £1,650

A silver and gilt inlaid strik-ing Japanese lantern clock, 19th century, 250mm. high.   £3,250

A Japanese gilt brass miniature lantern clock, 5¾in. high.   £1,800

A Japanese double foliot brass lantern clock with alarm, 31½in. high.   £6,000

A brass lantern clock, signed
Chr. Gould, Londoni Fecit.,
late 17th century, 15in. high.
£3,250

Wing alarm lantern clock,
circa 1700, 15½in. high.
£2,250

An early 18th century brass
lantern clock, dial signed
Smorthwait in Colchester,
37cm. high.   £1,800

A fine Charles II gilt brass
lantern clock of small size
with rare indirect wind line-
and-barrel drive within standard
frame, signed Thomas Ford de
Bucks Fecit, 12½in. high.
(Christie's)   £5,500

An early lantern clock,
the 7in. dial signed
Thomas Knifton at the
(crossed keys) Loth-
bury Fecit, 12in. high.
£3,250

Nicholas Coxeter Londini Fecit,
a Charles II lantern clock with
alarm, the movement with large
diameter balance to verge
escapement, countwheel strike
on bell above, 15½in. high.
(Christie's)   £3,520

Benjamin Hill in Fleete Streete, a
late 17th century brass lantern
clock, the frame surmounted by
a later bell and cage with turned
corner posts, 1ft. 3in. high.
(Phillips)   £1,900

A wing lantern clock, the 6in.
dial signed John Ebsworth at
ye (sign of the crossed keys)
in Lothbury Londini Fecit,
15½in. high, with a wood
bracket.   £3,250

A brass lantern clock, the posted
movement surmounted by a bell,
the dial signed Thos Mortlock,
Stradishall, the twin-train movement with anchor escapement,
14½in. high.
(Phillips)   £1,600

An Italian brass and iron lantern clock, probably circa 1700, 35cm. high. £4,500

A wing alarm lantern clock, the 7½in. dial with alarm disc, 15in. high. £3,000

Late 17th century lantern clock, the 6¾in. dial signed John Knibb Oxon, 16in. high. £1,500

A Viennese gilt metal miniature striking lantern clock, the movement with tic-tac escapement, the gilt case with trellis-work engraving to side doors, 6in. high. (Christie's) £2,420

A miniature winged brass lantern clock with verge escapement and pendulum bob in the form of an anchor, 9½in. (Phillips) £1,300

A silver and giltmetal miniature lantern clock of standard form, the dial engraved with scrolling foliage bearing inscription Fromanteel, 6in. high. (Christies) £6,600

A lantern clock, the broad chapter ring signed Thatcher Cranbrook, 13½in. high. £2,250

A late Stuart brass striking winged lantern clock of standard form, with verge escapement and arrowhead pendulum, 15¼in. high. (Christie's) £1,870

18th century brass lantern clock, with engraved decoration, probably English, 14in. high. (Eldred's) £546

A late 17th century brass lantern clock, the dial signed Edward Stanton, London, 39cm. high.
£2,000

18th century lantern clock with painted enclosed iron casing, striking on two bells, German, possibly Simmental, 33cm. high. (Galerie Koller) £5,394

A 17th century Stuart brass and steel lantern clock, by J. Ebsworth in Bethlehem, London, fecit, 16in. high.
£1,350

A brass striking lantern clock, the case of typical form with florally engraved dial centre signed *Morguet A H'Oudain*, with galleried front fret, 12³/₄in. high.
(Christie's) £600

A 17th century brass lantern clock, the posted frame surmounted by a bell with engraved dial plate signed *John Pennock in Lothbury, Londini*, 1ft. 5in. high.
(Phillips) £1,200

A brass lantern clock with adapted thirty hour movement, incorporating a mid-17th century dial with floral engraving, signed *John Langley*, 10in. high.
(Phillips) £450

A brass lantern clock, the case of typical form, the twin fusée movement striking the quarters on two bells, 41cm. high.
(Phillips) £800

Pierced and engraved brass lantern clock, circa 1700, possibly western Switzerland, 26cm. high.
(Galerie Koller) £1,162

A brass lantern clock, the posted frame surmounted by a bell, the engraved brass dial signed *Peter Amyot, Norwich*, 24cm. high.
(Phillips) £300

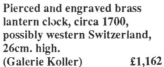

A brass lantern clock, the dial with brass chapter and engraved centre signed Tho Muddle, Rotherfield, 1ft. 3½in. high. (Phillips) £620

An Eureka Clock Company electric timepiece, the circular brass chapter ring with black Roman numerals, 41cm. high. (Henry Spencer) £580

A brass lantern clock by Edward Clement, circa 1791, with single hand, (no pendulum or weight), 13¼in. high. £1,350

Robert Robinson, Londini, a 17th century brass lantern clock, the signed florally engraved dial,with silvered chapter ring and alarm set disc to the centre, 1ft. ½in. high. (Phillips) £1,400

A Louis XV quarter chiming lantern clock, with circular chased gilt dial signed below Le Bel a Orbec, the three train movement with verge escapement, 1ft.8½in. high. (Phillips) £1,200

A late 17th century brass lantern clock, the frame surmounted by a later bell, the signed florally engraved dial inscribed *S F * K*, with brass chapter, 1ft. 4in. high. (Phillips) £5,000

Reproduction brass mantel clock in the form of a lantern clock, striking movement, 15in. high. (G. A. Key) £420

Italian lantern clock, the brass dial with Roman and Arabic numerals, circa 1700, 27cm. high. (Galerie Koller) £1,660

Henry Ireland, Londini (circa 1654–75), a brass cased lantern clock, converted to anchor escapement, 38cm. high. (Bearne's) £1,900

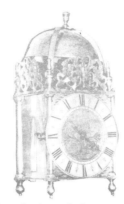

Late 17th century lantern clock, 5¾in. dial signed Henry Jones in ye Temple, 15½in. high.   £2,400

Brass lantern clock, on an oak bracket, the clock inscribed *Roger Moore, Ipswich.* (G.A. Key)   £750

An English brass lantern clock, signed Tho. Power Weallingborow, 15¼in. high.   £2,750

An early brass lantern clock, signed on the fret, Richard Beck, near Ye French Church, Londini, mid-17th century, 17½in. high.   £3,750

A brass miniature lantern clock, signed D. Robinson Northampton on the chapter ring, 9in. high. (Christie's)   £2,750

A late Stuart brass quarter chiming carillon lantern clock, dial signed Edw. Hemins of Bister, 15in. high.   £5,000

A brass lantern clock of standard form with verge and balance escapement, outside countwheel, strike on bell above the cast dolphin frets, 14¼in. high. (Christie's)   £715

Thomas Loumes, at the Mermayd in Lothbury, a 17th century brass lantern clock, the case surmounted by a bell with turned corner posts, 1ft. 1½in. high. (Phillips)   £2,600

A gilt brass striking lantern clock of standard form with anchor escapement and countwheel strike on bell above, the dial signed *John Lisborrow Ashen,* 15in. high. (Christie's)   £1,320

A brass lantern clock with alarm, unsigned, 17th century, with restorations, 14½in. high. £2,500

A French brass lantern clock, the circular chased dial with enamel numerals, 41cm. high. £900

Lantern clock, dial signed Nicholas Coxeter, London, circa 1680, 16½in. high. £3,000

A brass lantern clock, the dial with brass chapter signed Wilmshurst, Odiham, 1ft.3in. high, together with an oak wall bracket. £1,500

Lantern clock, late 17th century, by Nicholas Coxeter at the Three Chaires in Lothbury, London, 15in. high.
(Brian Loomes) £2,500

A brass lantern clock, the dial with brass chapter and engraved centre signed *Tho Muddle, Rotherfield*, 1ft 3¹/₂in. high.
(Phillips) £700

Brass lantern clock by J. Windmills, London, with silvered chapter ring, Roman numerals and anchor escapement, early 18th century, 36cm. high.
(Auktionsverket) £258

A rare quarter chiming lantern clock, the going train with verge escapement and later pendulum suspension, signed *D. Lesturgeon, London*, circa 1700, 7in. wide.
(Christie's New York) £1,459

A Chares II brass striking lantern clock, with original verge escapement and bob pendulum, the florally engraved dial signed *Tho. Wintworth, Sarum Fecit*, 14³/₄in. high.
(Christie's) £2,860

A brass lantern clock, 39.5cm. high (probably 17th century). £3,000

A N. European striking lantern clock, dated 1672, 8in. high. £3,000

A brass lantern clock, dial signed Lawrence Debnam in Froome, 34cm. high. £1,500

A brass lantern clock by William Selwood, the circular foliate cast dial with Roman numerals, inscribed *William Selwood at ye Maremaid in Louthbury*, 15in. high. (Christie's) £2,860

A brass lantern clock, the frame surmounted by a bell, the 17th century engraved brass dial inscribed *John Hilderson, Londini Fecit*, with brass chapter ring and single steel hand, 1ft. 2½in. high. (Phillips) £800

A Charles II brass lantern clock, Charles Fox at the Fox in Lothbury, London, the bell surmounted by an urn finial over pierced frets, circa 1670, 14½in. high. (Christie's) £2,803

A Charles II brass lantern clock of standard form, the florally engraved dial signed Henry Burges Fecit, 14½in. high. (Christie's) £1,650

English lantern clock, signed R T Evans, Halstead with 8-day Vicentini movement, short pendulum, striking on a bell, late 19th century, 40cm. high. (Duran, Madrid) £884

A small lantern/alarum time-piece, the movement with verge escapement and bob pendulum, signed *Kefford, Royston,* 25cm. (Lawrence Fine Arts) £2,200

A lantern clock with a 6½in. dial engraved with a ring of tulips, 15in. high.   £900

An English lantern clock, dial signed Nicholas Coxeter, 14½in. high.   £5,500

An 18th century Continental brass lantern clock of small size, 27cm. high.   £1,750

A brass lantern clock with alarm of standard form, now with early anchor escapement and countwheel strike on bell above, narrow silvered chapter ring, 15¹/₂in. high. (Christie's)   £1,540

A brass lantern clock, the substantial movement with verge and double foliot escapement, European-hour countwheel strike on pork-pie bell above, 18th century, overall 120cm. high. (Christie's)   £5,280

An unusual silver lantern timepiece, perhaps German, the movement with verge escapement and verge alarm, the dial plate engraved with tulips, 9in. high. (Phillips Sevenoaks)   £2,600

Lantern clock, late 17th century, by James Delaunce of Frome, converted later to twin fusee eight-day key-wound movement, 15in. high (Brian Loomes)   £1,200

Late gothic lantern clock with wrought iron dial painted with Mary and Christ in heaven, Roman numerals, striking on two bells, circa 1580, 40cm. high. (Galerie Koller)   £5,187

A Charles II brass miniature lantern timepiece case signed *Windmills London* on the foliate engraved dial centre with alarm disc, 9¹/₄in. high. (Christie's)   £715

The longcase clock, often referred to as the grandfather clock, emerged shortly after the invention of the pendulum and of the anchor escapement in 1670, since the narrow arc of swing of this escapement made it possible to enclose the weights and pendulum in a narrow trunk.

The type derives from the lantern clock, probably as a means of protecting the weights and pendulums, which had hitherto swung free on the wall. The earliest examples were slender, and were rarely more than 7ft. tall. They usually had square hoods, often with barley twist capitals and stable-looking base sections. As luxury items they boasted carcases of oak veneered first in ebony and later in yew, walnut, kingwood or laburnum. Later in the 17th century Dutch floral marquetry became fashionable.

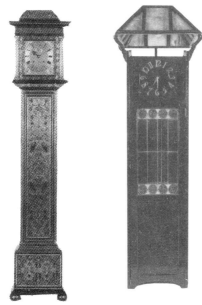

A boulle month calendar longcase clock, dial signed Daniel Quare, 7ft. 5in. high.
£25,000

An Arts and Crafts black painted oak electric longcase clock, with a stained and leaded glass door, 76in. high.
(Christie's) £330

An olivewood longcase clock, dial signed Joseph Knibb, 6ft.4in. high.
£27,500

Height and style continued to vary with fashion – as higher ceilings came in, the clocks became taller, often by the addition of a flattened dome, or 'cushion top' above the hood, which in turn was often adorned with brass finials. Some too have fret cut friezes at the top of the hood to allow the chimes to be clearly heard. These appeared after 1696, when Edward Barlow introduced the first chiming mechanism. In 1710, Tompion

An unusual Art Deco ebonised and chromium plated cocktail cabinet, fashioned as a longcase clock, having a 'Temco' electric timepiece, 170cm. high. (Phillips) £1,400

An unusual weight driven calendar clock with astronomical indications, signed *G. Croenen Inu. & Fecit, anno 1813*, 19th century, 65in. high excluding dome. (Christie's) £15,950

An eight day long case clock, the silvered and brass square dial inscribed *John Nethercott, Chipping Norton*, 7ft. 5in. high. (Tennants) £500

introduced the arched dial, and by 1720 this was in widespread use. Early faces were made of brass adorned with floral and scroll engraving. By the 1680s, these had increased to 10in. square, while from the beginning of the 18th century, 12in. dials were common, following the introduction of the arch. The earliest spandrels, or ornamental corner pieces on the dial, were of cupids' heads between curved wings. Later, scrollwork became popular, and by 1700 this often incorporated a female mask.

Later in the 18th century, clock cases became plainer, as bracket clocks superseded the longcase in popularity. By 1750, however, the widespread use of mahogany, and the wonderful designs of, for example, Sheraton and Chippendale, had restored the longcase to popularity.

While height has little to do with the value of a clock, slender examples have always been more favoured. Better clocks tend to have at least eight day movements, and some will run for months or even a year. Country made examples, on the other hand, often had thirty hour movements, which were well within the scope of the local blacksmith, who would produce them for locally made carcases. After 1790, as quantity took over from quality in many cases, the painted wood or iron dial was introduced.

There are some interesting features to look for, which, though by no means infallible, can be useful for dating a clock. The fleur de lys, for example, used to mark the half hours, was seldom employed after the 1740s, the same period that larger Arabic numerals replaced the Roman as minute markers. After 1750, an engraved brass or silvered face without a chapter ring was often used and, from 1775, a cast brass pre-enamelled copper face was introduced.

An ebony veneered month longcase clock, the 10in. dial signed Joseph Knibb, 6ft.7in. high. £30,000

A 1930's longcase clock, movement engraved 'Johnston Crawford Production No. 1', 176.5cm. high. £1,500

Federal birch inlaid tall case clock, New England, circa 1780, 90in. high. £3,000

A celebrated Queen Anne astronomical longcase clock of long duration signed Edward Cockey, Warminster, in an ebonised, parcel-gilt and silvered case, 10ft.2in. high. (Christie's) £66,000

Queen Anne maple tall clock, Benjamin Cheney, East Hartford, Connecticut, circa 1760, 89½in. high. (Skinner) £9,506

A 30 hour longcase clock, the 10in. square brass dial signed at the base Thomas Tompion Londini, with winged cherub's head spandrels and silvered chapter ring, 7ft 8in. high. (Phillips) £8,000

CHERRY WOOD

A Federal cherry in-
laid tall case clock,
by J. Loring, Mass.,
circa 1800, 87in.
high.   £6,000

Cherry tall case clock,
by Jacob Hosteter,
94½in. high. £1,750

Federal cherry inlaid
tall case clock, back
of dial inscribed 'Wm.
Prescott', circa 1790,
91¾in. high.£12,000

A Federal cherrywood
tallcase clock, dial
signed by Samuel
Shourds, circa 1770,
89¼in. high. £2,500

A fine Federal inlaid
and figured
cherrywood tall case
clock, Elisha Cheney,
Middletown,
Connecticut, circa
1800, 7ft. 5¼in. high.
(Sotheby's)   £20,511

A Chippendale
cherrywood tall-case
clock, dial signed
Nathan Dean,
Plainfield, Connecticut,
late 18th century,
86½in. high.
(Christie's)   £2,424

A fine Chippendale
carved cherrywood
tall-case clock, Stephen
Sibley, Great
Barrington,
Massachusetts, circa
1795, 7ft. 7in. high.
(Sotheby's)   £4,632

A Federal inlaid
cherrywood tall-case
clock by Christian
Eby, Manheim,
Pennsylvania, circa
1810, 107½in. high.
(Christie's)   £27,720

CHERRY WOOD

A Federal cherry inlaid tall case clock, E. New Hampshire, circa 1800, 94in. high. £6,000

A Federal cherry inlaid dwarf time-piece, Mass., circa 1810, 43in. high. £3,000

A Federal cherry-wood inlaid tall-case clock, 1800/10, 93½in. high. £3,250

A Federal cherry-wood tall case clock, circa 1810-30. £2,250

A Chippendale carved cherrywood tall-case clock, dial signed *Isaac Brokaw*, case attributed to Matthew Egerton, New Brunswick, New Jersey, circa 1790–1810. (Christie's) £15,730

A rare Federal inlaid cherrywood long case clock, dial signed *Caleb Davis,* Wood-stock, Virginia, circa 1804, 97in. high. (Christie's New York) £5,188

An early 19th century American cherrywood longcase clock, the 11½in. arched painted wood dial signed *L. Watson, Cincinnati,* with subsidiaries for seconds and date, 7ft. 6in. high. (Phillips) £2,000

Federal cherry inlaid tall case clock, Concord, Massachusetts, 1800–1815, 90in. high. (Skinner Inc.) £2,569

163

LACQUERED

A George II green japanned chiming longcase clock, the dial signed John Taylor London, 8ft. 3in. high. £3,750

A black lacquered month going longcase clock, signed John Blake, 7ft. 7in. high. £2,000

Queen Anne japanned tall case clock, Gawen Brown (1749–1773), Boston, circa 1760, 87in. high. (Skinner Inc.) £2,400

A George II black-japanned month longcase clock, dial signed Fra Robinson, 8ft. high. £4,000

William Webster, Exchange Alley, London, an 18th century chinoiserie lacquer longcase clock with eight-day movement striking on a bell, 104in. high. (Bearne's) £1,500

A green lacquer longcase clock, signed on a raised silvered disc *Danl. Torin, London*, strike/silent ring in the arch flanked by dolphin spandrels, 88¹/₂ in. high. (Christie's S. Ken) £2,200

A George III black and gold lacquer longcase clock, inscribed *Frances Durrell, London*, the hood with brass finials, 7ft. 8in. high. (Woolley & Wallis) £2,000

An unusual lacquered 30-hour longcase clock with stylised pagoda top surmounted by a gilt cockerel finial, the rectangular door painted with religious scenes, 85in. high. (Christie's) £1,155

LACQUERED

A George II green and chinoiserie lacquered longcase clock, by Wm. Lambert, London, 7ft.2in. high.   £1,500

A George III dark green japanned longcase clock, dial signed Thomas A. Deptford, 7ft.6in. high.   £3,000

A japanned long-case clock, dial signed Chr. Gould London, 5ft.10in. high.   £15,000

A green japanned longcase clock, the brass dial signed Jos. Windmills, London, 8ft.4in. high.   £3,000

An 18th century green japanned longcase clock, the 29cm broken arched brass dial with the inscription John Long, of London to the chapter ring, 232cm high. (Henry Spencer)   £800

Walter Harris, London, George II eight-day lacquered longcase clock with 12in. arched brass dial, 84in. high. (Bearne's)   £1,400

George III scarlet japanned chinoiserie decorated tall case clock, James Jackson, London, third quarter 18th century, 90in. high. (Skinner Inc.)   £1,800

A George II long case clock, the eight-day movement with brass and silvered dial signed *Wm Chase Derby*, circa 1740, 7ft. 5^{1}/2in. high. (Tennants)   £2,200

MAHOGANY

A late Georgian mahogany longcase clock, dial signed Robert Martin, Glasgow, 6ft. 11in. high. £1,250

A George III mahogany 8-day striking longcase clock, dial inscribed Jno. Morse, 6ft.9in. high. £3,600

A Georgian mahogany longcase clock, the dial with subsidiary seconds, 8ft. high. £4,500

A George III longcase clock, the dial inscribed Jno. Williams, London, 90¾in. high. £2,000

Late George III inlaid mahogany longcase clock, the dial signed *Barry, Leigh,* **first quarter 19th century, 7ft. 11½in. high. (Butterfield & Butterfield)** £2,049

A George III mahogany longcase regulator, signed *Richd Pendleton Pentonville,* the later flat steel pendulum with mercury bob, 1.81m. high. (Phillips) £9,200

A mahogany longcase clock, hood with swan neck pediment surmounted by three gilt eagle finials, signed *Thomas Brown, Chester,* **93½in. high. (Christie's S. Ken)** £2,420

An early Victorian mahogany longcase clock, inscribed George Lumsden, Pittenweems, and decorated with shipping scenes, 225cm. (Phillips) £1,600

MAHOGANY

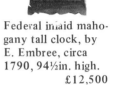

A George III maho-
gany veneered 8-day
striking longcase
clock, inscribed
James Vigne, London,
8ft.2in. high. £4,250

A George III maho-
gany longcase clock,
the dial signed Chas.
Cabrier, 7ft.11in.
high.   £6,500

A Georgian maho-
gany longcase clock,
signed on a cartouche
John Hart, Yarmouth,
7ft.6in. high. £3,000

Federal inlaid maho-
gany tall clock, by
E. Embree, circa
1790, 94½in. high.
              £12,500

An 18th century
quarter chiming
mahogany longcase
clock, signed Richard
Style London, the later
four pillar movement
chiming the quarters,
8ft. 3¼in. high.
(Phillips)   £2,300

A late Victorian
mahogany longcase
clock, the broken
pediment above an
arched and glazed
hood enclosing a brass
dial, 93in. high.
(Christie's)   £2,035

MAHOGANY

A George III mahogany longcase clock, signed G. Forster, Sittingbourne, 7ft. 5in. high.   £2,750

A mahogany longcase clock by Nathaniel Brown, Manchester, 95½in. high.   £4,000

A mahogany grandmother longcase clock with 7in. brass dial, 59½in. high.   £2,500

A mahogany longcase clock, the brass dial inscribed Maple & Co. Ltd., London, 7ft. 11in. high.   £1,000

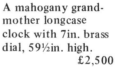

Late Federal mahogany and mahogany veneer long case clock, William Brenneiser, Lancaster County, Pennsylvania, 1780-1830, 99½in. high. (Skinner Inc.)   £1,677

Bertler & Eggert, Bristol, an unusual George III longcase clock, the eight-day movement striking on a bell, 87in. high. (Bearne's)   £1,600

A George III mahogany longcase clock, the arched hood with pierced fret and moulded cornice, signed *Paul Griffis, London*, 7ft. 8in. high. (Phillips)   £2,800

An Edwardian carved mahogany and inlaid nine tube chiming longcase clock, with decorative carved pediment, 108in. high. (Christie's S. Ken)   £2,640

MAHOGANY

An 18th century longcase clock, inscribed JN Greaves, Newcastle, 89in. high. £2,500

Mid 18th century George III mahogany tall case clock, signed 'Isaac Hewlett, Bristol', 93.1/8in. high. £5,000

A 19th century chiming longcased clock in 'Jumbo' mahogany case, 7ft. 10in. high. £2,000

A Federal mahogany tall case clock, inscribed O. Hopkins, 1756, 95in. high. £1,000

A 19th century mahogany longcase clock, the 12in. arched painted dial with subsidiary seconds and date aperture, signed *Lawley & Co.*, 7ft. 2in. high. (Phillips) £1,500

American mahogany tall case clock with chimes, circa 1880, leaf carved swan's neck pediment over arched dial with painted moon phase, silvered chapter ring, 9ft. 5in. high. (Skinner Inc.) £2,556

A mahogany long case clock with rack striking eight day movement, signed *Abrm. Larnill, Frome*, 93in. high. (Lawrence Fine Art) £1,540

An early 19th century eight-day longcase clock, the 12in. enamel square dial with painted shell spandrels, 199cm. high. (Allen & Harris) £460

MAHOGANY

A longcase clock by Edward Hurst, painted dial with cottage scene in inlaid mahogany case, 85in. high. £1,000

A Georgian mahogany quarter chiming longcase clock, the dial signed Wm. Dutton, London, 2.09m. high. £9,000

A George I longcase clock with eight-day striking movement by T. Martin, London, 85½in. high. £2,250

A late 18th century eight day long case clock, the silvered and brass dial signed *S. Collier Eccles*, circa 1790, 7ft. 5in. high. (Tennants) £3,500

Mahogany tall case clock, William Claggett (1695–1749), Newport, Rhode Island, (1725–40), 88¼in. high. (Skinner Inc.) £13,440

A Federal ivory-inlaid mahogany bow-front tall case clock, John Esterlie, Maytown, Pennsylvania, circa 1815, 8ft. 4¼in. high. (Sotheby's) £5,955

A Federal inlaid mahogany tall-case clock, Baltimore, Maryland, early 19th century, 8ft. 6in. high. (Sotheby's) £3,639

Federal mahogany inlaid tall case clock, William Cummens, Roxbury, Massachusetts, circa 1800, 89in. high. (Skinner Inc.) £12,204

MAHOGANY

A Chippendale mahogany tall case clock, works by Thos. Stretch, Phila., circa 1750-65, 92½in. high. £12,500

A Chippendale mahogany tallcase clock, dial signed by Joseph and John Hollingshead, circa 1780, 98in. high. £12,500

A Federal inlaid mahogany tallcase clock, dial signed Alex. J. Willard, early 19th century, 86¾in. high. £3,000

A late 18th century George III mahogany longcase clock, inscribed Robert Hood, London, 94in. high. £12,500

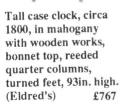

Tall case clock, circa 1800, in mahogany with wooden works, bonnet top, reeded quarter columns, turned feet, 93in. high. (Eldred's) £767

A mahogany and boxwood strung longcase clock with flat moulded pediment, signed J. Charlton, Durham, 83in. high. (Christie's S. Ken.) £770

A Federal carved mahogany tall-case clock, by Isaac Reed, Frankford, Pennsylvania, circa 1800, 91½in. high. (Christie's) £5,742

An antique Scottish George III mahogany longcase clock, maker's name *John Peatt, Crieff*, (circa 1800), 6ft. 11in. high. (Selkirk's) £1,460

MAHOGANY

Federal mahogany inlaid tall case clock, circa 1790, 98in. high.   £3,250

A Federal inlaid mahogany tallcase clock, dial signed by Aaron Willard, circa 1805-10, 94½in. high. £15,000

A tallcase clock, dial signed S. Brenneiser, Penn., circa 1810. £5,000

George III mahogany longcase clock with swan-neck pediment, 7ft.10in. high.   £950

A Federal inlaid mahogany tall-case clock, Aaron Willard, Roxbury, Massachusetts, circa 1805, the hood with three brass ball-and-spire finials, 91in. high. (Christie's)   £14,469

Chippendale mahogany tall case clock, Pennsylvania, late 18th century, inscribed *Geo Lively, Baltimore*, 7ft. 7in. high. (Butterfield & Butterfield)   £1,445

A George III mahogany longcase clock, the 12in. arched brass dial with silvered chapter ring, subsidiary seconds and date aperture, signed *Joshua Arnold, London*, with painted seascape in the arch, 8ft. 2½in. high. (Phillips)   £2,900

A George III Scottish flame mahogany longcase clock, signed *Sam. Collier Eccles* on the arch above the painted moonphase, the four pillar rack striking movement with anchor escapement, 7ft. 7½in. high. (Christie's) £1,320

172

MAHOGANY

An 18th century mahogany longcase clock, by Charles Haley. £2,000

W.B. Cornforth Macclesfield, a good early 19th century mahogany longcase clock, 93in. high. (Phillips) £1,300

A George III mahogany longcase clock, the 13in. brass dial signed Samuel Young, Bonebury, 7ft.9in. high. £4.250

A Federal inlaid mahogany tallcase clock, dial signed by Aaron Willard, 1805-10, 88½in. high. £20,000

A nine-bell chiming mahogany and boxwood inlay longcase clock, signed *J.L. Bath*, the three-train movement striking the quarters on eight bells and the hours on a ninth, 95in. high. (Christie's S. Ken) £2,200

A Victorian mahogany longcase clock, the painted dial signed *Simcock Warrington* with subsidiary dials for seconds and calendar aperture, 7ft ½ in. high. (Christie's) £1,540

A George III mahogany and inlaid longcase clock, signed on a cartouche *Benjn Heeley, Deptford*, and with strike silent subsidiary, 7ft. 2in. high. (Phillips) £3,500

A George III mahogany longcase clock, the silvered centre with subsidiaries for seconds and date signed *Joseph Hatton, Tooley Street, Southwark*, 8ft. 1in. high. (Phillips) £2,500

MAHOGANY

Early 19th century
longcase clock with
eight-day move-
ment, 82in. high.
£1,000

A 19th century
style mahogany
longcase clock,
8ft.4in. high.£5,000

Art Nouveau mahogany tall
case clock, late 19th century,
by Gerr Suss, Hamburg,
96½in. high.   £1,500

A George III figured
mahogany longcase
clock with eight-day
movement, by J.
Lomax of Blackburn,
7ft.4in. high. £1,500

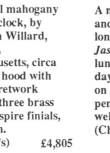

A Chippendale
mahogany tall-case
clock, dial engraved
*Benjamin Morris, Hill
Town*, Bucks County,
Pennsylvania, 1760–
1780, the hood with
moulded swan's-neck
pediment terminating
in carved rosettes,
92¹/₂in. high
(Christie's)   £7,892

A Federal mahogany
tall-case clock, by
Benjamin Willard,
Roxbury,
Massachusetts, circa
1775, the hood with
pierced fretwork
centring three brass
ball-and-spire finials,
93in. high.
(Christie's)   £4,805

A mahogany, boxwood
and fruitwood inlay
longcase clock, signed
Jas. Cawfon, with
lunar calendar, eight-
day movement striking
on a bell, with
pendulum and two
weights, 93in. high.
(Christie's S. Ken)
                £1,980

A 19th century maho-
gany longcase clock,
the pagoda topped
hood decorated with
three ball and spire
finials, signed on a
circular cartouche
in the arch, Pridgin,
Hull, 8ft. 1in. high.
(Phillips)   £2,300

LONGCASE CLOCKS

MAHOGANY

A Georgian mahogany longcase clock, signed Williams, Preston, 7ft. 6½in. high. £3,750

Late 19th century mahogany 8-day rack striking longcase clock, by Seddon & Moss, £5,000

A mahogany cased reproduction long-cased clock. £2,400

An 18th century mahogany longcase clock, signed G. Binch, Manchester, 94in. high. £1,500

A George III mahogany longcase clock, the arched hood with three ball and spire finials flanked by fluted columns, signed *Tho' Smart, Ryder Street, St. James*, 7ft. 6½in. high. (Phillips) £2,400

A Federal inlaid mahogany and flame birch tall-case clock, works by Aaron Willard, case attributed to John or Thomas Seymour, Boston, circa 1800, 103³/₄in. high. (Christie's) £38,280

A Georgian mahogany longcase clock, the pagoda topped hood with pierced brass fret, signed on a cartouche David Rivers, London, 7ft. 11in. high. (Phillips) £2,200

A rare and impressive mid 18th century month going astronomical quarter chiming longcase clock by Thomas Ogden, Halifax, the hood with swan-neck pediment, 107in. high. (Christie's S. Ken) £11,000

MARQUETRY

An early 18th century walnut and floral marquetry longcase clock, signed Cartwright, 7ft.2in. high. £7,500

A late 17th century walnut and panel marquetry longcase clock, signed Jos. Buckingham in ye Minories, 2.16m. high. £8,000

A William III walnut and marquetry longcase clock, the 12in. sq. dial signed John Marshall, 7ft.1in. high. £12,500

A George I Vernis Martin longcase clock, the 12½in. dial signed Wm. Stephens, Godalming, 7ft. high. £3,000

A Queen Anne longcase clock, movement with five ringed pillars, the dial signed Samuel Stevens London, 6ft. 8in. high. £4,500

Fine Louis XV style gilt-bronze-mounted parquetry regulateur, late 19th century, 8ft. 5in. high. (Butterfield & Butterfield) £7,564

John Wise, London, eight-day marquetry longcase clock with 11in. square brass dial, 87in. high, with brass cased weights. (Bearne's) £2,300

A Charles II parquetry longcase clock by Johannes Fromanteel, London, circa 1680, 75in. high. (Christie's) £12,122

LONGCASE CLOCKS

MARQUETRY

A late Stuart Provincial walnut longcase clock, dial signed Thos. Cruttenden in Yorke, 6ft. 11½in. high.
£3,250

A Dutch walnut marquetry longcase clock, the 11in. dial signed Joans. Klock Amsterdam, 8ft.2in. high.
£4,500

A William and Mary walnut and marquetry month going longcase clock, the 11¼in. dial signed Wm. Jourdain, 7ft. 3in. high. £12,500

An early 18th century walnut and panel marquetry longcase clock, the 11in. square brass dial signed Thos. Stubbs, London, 2.10m. high. £15,000

An 18th century Dutch walnut and marquetry musical longcase clock, Jan Bernink, Amsterdam, 7ft. 4in. high. (Spencer's)
£2,300

A William and Mary walnut and marquetry longcase clock, the 12in. sq. dial signed Jn Gavell, London on the silvered chapter ring, 7ft. high.
(Christie's) £5,500

Dutch rococo marquetry longcase clock, the dial signed *H. Smitt, Amsterdam*, 7ft. 10in. high. (Butterfield & Butterfield)
£2,994

A William and Mary floral marquetry longcase clock, signed *Wm. Cattle in fleet Street Londini fecit* at VI o'clock, 1680s, 78½in. high.
(Christie's) £11,484

MARQUETRY

A late Stuart walnut and marquetry longcase clock with 11in. sq. dial, 7ft.0½in. high. £12,500

An 18th century walnut longcase clock, by Windmills, London, 7ft.7in. high. £1,800

Edwardian mahogany and marquetry longcase clock banded in satinwood, 96in. high. £2,250

A late Stuart walnut and marquetry longcase clock, dial signed Peter Mallett, London, 7ft.6in. high. £10,000

A Charles II longcase clock movement signed *John Williamson Londini fecit* on the 10in. square dial, in purpose-made walnut and olivewood parquetry convex moulded case, 7ft. high. (Christie's) £4,400

Louis XVI fruitwood and parquetry longcase clock, the nine and one half inch brass arched dial repoussé with cherub's head spandrels, 7ft. 11in. high. (Butterfield & Butterfield) £4,496

A William III floral marquetry longcase clock signed *John Motley, Londini Fecit*, the movement with five ringed pillars, later dead beat escapement with V-anchor, circa 1695, 78in. high. (Christie's New York) £3,927

A Charles II burr walnut and marquetry month-going longcase clock, the 10in.sq. dial signed John Ebsworth Londini fecit on a lambrequin in the tulip engraved centre, restoration, 6ft.6in. high. (Christie's) £16,500

MARQUETRY

A marquetry long-case clock, dial sig-ned Chr. Gould Londini Fecit, 6ft. 9in. high. £10,000

Mid 18th century Dutch floral marquetry longcase clock, signed Lourens Eichelar, 8ft. 5in. high. £6,000

A Charles II walnut and parquetry long-case clock, 10in. dial signed C. Gretton, London, 6ft.3in. high. £10,000

A 17th century wal-nut marquetry long-case clock, inscribed Thos. Taylor in Hol-born, London, 85in. high. £7,000

An early 18th century walnut and panel mar-quetry longcase clock, the 11in. square brass dial with silvered chapter ring signed Nat Hodges, Londini Fecit, 6ft.8½in. high. (with some restora-tions) (Phillips) £8,000

A Queen Anne burr walnut and marquetry longcase clock, the dial signed Dan le Count London on the silvered chapter ring, now rack strike and anchor escapement, 7ft.1in. high. (Christie's) £5,280

A walnut and mar-quetry longcase clock, the 10in. sq. dial sig-ned Joseph Stripling in a lambrequin in the florally engraved centre, the movement with anchor escape-ment, 7ft. high. (Christie's) £4,620

An early 18th century walnut and floral marquetry longcase clock, the 11in. square brass dial with silvered chapter ring, signed *Natha. Pyne Londini fecit*, with subsidiary seconds, date aperture and with ringed winding holes, 6ft. 5½in. high. (Phillips) £4,200

MUSICAL

A musical mahogany longcase clock, movement stamped Elliot's patent, circa 1880, 91in. high. £2,250

A carved walnut musical clock with ten Symphonion metal discs, 7ft.5in. high. £6,500

Early 19th century mahogany organ clock, dial signed Edwd. Wicksteed London, 6ft.5½in. high. £3,250

Late 18th century walnut musical longcase clock with automaton, by J.M. Juntes, Amsterdam, 9ft. 2½in. high. £10,780

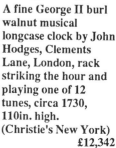

A George III mahogany musical longcase clock for the German market, the dial signed Jos. Herring, 8ft.11in. high overall.£12,500

An 11¾in. Symphonion longcase clock with twin combs, two-train clock and walnut case, 78½in. high. (Christie's) £7,700

An early 20th century musical longcase clock, bearing the date 1925, the three-train movement with deadbeat escapement. (Phillips) £1,600

A fine George II burl walnut musical longcase clock by John Hodges, Clements Lane, London, rack striking the hour and playing one of 12 tunes, circa 1730, 110in. high. (Christie's New York) £12,342

MUSICAL

A Georgian mahogany musical quarter chiming longcase clock, signed J. Cooke, Cambridge, 8ft.2½in. high.   £4,000

A Polyphon style No. 62 ('Geisha') longcase clock with 15¾in. double comb movement in base, 108in. high. (Christie's) £18,700

A George III mahogany musical longcase clock, Robert Wood, London, 8ft. 5in. high (Spencer's)   £3,400

Fine 'Mikado' polyphon hall clock, 104½in. high. (Christie's)   £23,100

A late 19th century German walnut polyphon musical disc clock. £6,000

A Black Forest organ clock, the 24-key movement with thirty-six wood pipes, eight-air barrel and painted dial, 97in. high.   £3,250

A Dutch burr walnut musical longcase clock, signed N. Wyland, Amsterdam, mid 18th century, 113in. high.   £4,750

A large Regina oak longcase 15½in. disc. musical box clock, with eighty-six discs, 252 cm. high, circa 1900.   £5,000

OAK

American Moorish-style carved oak hall clock, circa 1900, 112in. high. £3,750

17th century oak longcase grandmother clock with single hour hand. £1,100

Late 19th century oak longcase clock, 99in. high. £1,500

Continental oak longcase clock, inscribed J. J. L. Batz., 8ft.5in. high. £1,500

An L. & J. G. Stickley tall case clock, signed with red Handcraft decal, circa 1908, 81in. high. £12,500

Late 18th century 30-hour oak long-cased clock, maker John Kent, Monmouth, circa 1790. £700

Gustav Stickley tall case clock, c. 1902, with copper numerals within tall slightly flared case, $70^{3}/_{4}$in. high (Skinner Inc) £4,658

An Art Nouveau oak longcase clock, by J. Gruber, 253cm. high. £3,000

OAK

A carved oak longcase clock, signed Edw. Whitehead, Wetherby, 86in. high. £950

A small oak 30-hour striking longcase clock, the 11in. brass dial by Sam Hanley, circa 1750. £1,500

Mid 19th century oak longcase clock, inscribed Tempus Fugit, 90in. high. £1,250

An oak longcase clock, the dial signed Creighton B-Mena No. 120, 91in. high. £800

A late 18th century oak longcase clock, the hood with swan neck pediment, plaque to the centre inscribed *Vincent Menil, Amsterdam,* the eight day movement with anchor escapement, 7ft.8in. high. (Phillips Sevenoaks) £3,400

An 18th century oak longcase clock, the 12in. arched brass dial with brass chapter, subsidiary seconds and date aperture, signed *Robert Cox, Christchurch,* 7ft. 5in. high. (Phillips) £1,000

A George III oak grandmother longcase clock, the case on bracket feet, signed *Thos. Grimes London,* the four pillar rack striking movement with anchor escapement, 5ft. 9in. high. (Christie's) £550

Thomas Bartholomew, London, eight-day chiming clock with 14½in. arched brass dial, 110in. high. (Bearne's) £2,200

OAK

An oak longcase clock, signed Thos. Brown, Birmingham, 6ft.11½in. high.£1,000

A Gustav Stickley oak tall case clock, circa 1902-04, 71in. high.   £7,500

George III oak longcase clock, by J. Ivory, Dundee, 7ft. 6in. high.   £1,000

A carved oak longcase clock, with 3 weights, key and winder, circa 1880, 98in. high. £3,000

An oak long case clock, the eight day movement with inside count wheel, signed on the chapter ring Josiah Stringer, 7ft. 4in. (Lawrence Fine Art) £2,530

Arts and Crafts oak tall case clock, circa 1910, brass numerals and dial over leaded glass cabinet door, 75½in. high. (Skinner Inc.)   £541

A George II oak longcase clock, by Arthur Hurt, Ashford, mid 18th century (reduced in height), 77½in. high. (Skinner Inc.)   £473

George III bleached oak tall case clock, Thos. Gordon, Edinburgh, late 18th century, 93in. high. (Skinner Inc.)   £688

A George III oak and
mahogany longcase
clock, by Willm.
Latham Macclesfield,
circa 1775, rack
striking on the hour,
80in. high.
(Skinner Inc.)   £946

A George III long-
case clock, the arch
painted with scene
of a girl and her dog,
7ft. 3in. high. (Green-
slades)   £638

An oak and mahogany
long case clock, the
eight day movement
rack striking, signed
on the chapter ring
W. G. Hyde, 7ft. 9in.
(Lawrence Fine Arts)
                    £858

George III oak and
mahogany cross-
banded longcase
clock , circa 1785,
7ft. 4in. high. £1,250

An eight-day oak and
mahogany longcase
clock, the 13in. painted
dial signed *Oldham,*
Southam, subsidiary
seconds and date dials,
7ft. 1in. high.
(Bonhams)   £880

A George III
mahogany and oak
longcase clock, 12in.
painted dial, faded
signature *Barry,*
Lichfield, with seconds
dial, calendar
aperture, painted
floral spandrels and
arch, 7ft. 2in. high.
(Bonhams)   £1,100

John Warrone, Kirby
Moorside, a good
George III oak and
mahogany longcase
clock of slender
proportions, 96in.
high.
(Phillips)   £1,600

An oak and mahogany
veneer eight-day
longcase clock, 11$\frac{1}{2}$in.
arched brass dial
signed John Safley,
Nicolson's Street,
matted centre, silvered
chapter, seconds dial
with masonic
engraving, 7ft. 4in.
high.
(Bonhams)   £800

OAK & MAHOGANY

An oak longcase clock, signed J. Green, Nantwich, 7ft. high. £1,500

Late 18th century oak and crossbanded longcase clock, by D. Collier, Gatley, 80in. high. £2,000

A longcase clock with eight-day movement by D. Jones, 7ft.2in. high. £750

An early 19th century longcase clock, the 8-day movement by R.Roberts, Bangor, 7ft.9in.high. (Greenslades) £1,460

A 19th century oak and mahogany longcase clock, the 12in. arch painted dial, with subsidiary seconds and date aperture signed, *Garrat, Peterborough*, with moonphase in the arch, 6ft. 7½in. high. (Phillips) £1,050

A George III mahogany and oak longcase clock, with a 12½in. arched dial signed in the engraved center *N. Davidson*, 7ft. high. (Bonhams) £1,000

A George III mahogany and oak longcase clock, 14in. painted dial signed *W. Nicholas, Birmingham*, with seconds and calendar dials, 7ft. 5in. high. (Bonhams) £700

Thos. Bembow, Newport, a late 18th century oak and mahogany longcase clock, the trunk with quarter reeded brass capped pilasters, 94in. high. (Phillips) £1,200

186

Early 19th century
painted and carved
tallcase clock, Penn.,
98in. high. £12,500

An Edwardian pain-
ted satinwood long-
case clock, the chap-
ter ring signed Wm.
Eastwood, 8ft.2in.
high.   £3,000

Early 19th century
Federal painted tall-
case clock, possibly
Berks County, Penn.,
96in. high.   £2,000

Fine putty painted
long case clock, Silas
Hoadley, Plymouth,
Connecticut, circa
1830, the case painted
in tones of red orange
and mustard on ivory,
85in. high. (Skinner
Inc.)   £5,325

Swedish neoclassical
painted thirty-hour
longcase clock, late
18th century, now
painted Venetian red
with pale grey detail,
8ft. 7in. high.
(Butterfield &
Butterfield)   £2,891

A carved and painted
longcase clock in the
form of a woman
standing with arms
akimbo, with glazed
convex painted dial
signed Joh Ylie
Konnig Tlmola, late
19th century, 7ft.
high. (Christie's)
                £4,620

An Edwardian
satinwood and painted
miniature longcase
clock, the pagoda
topped hood flanked
by turned columns, 5ft.
high.
(Phillips)   £3,860

A grain painted tall
timepiece, Pennsyl-
vania, circa 1820, the
hood with moulded
swan's neck cresting
with rosette carved
terminals, 105in. high.
(Skinner Inc.)   £625

PINE

Early 19th century painted pine tall case clock by A. Edwards, Mass., 91in. high. £1,000

A painted pine tall case clock, by Silas Hoadley, Conn., circa 1825, 93½in. high. £7,500

A Chippendale pine tall case clock, by B. Bagnall, Boston, 1710-40, 98in. high. £7,500

Country painted pine tall clock, by Simeon Crane, Mass., circa 1810, 86¼in. high. £5,500

Antique American tall case clock in pine with wood works, by Riley Whiting of Winchester, Connecticut, 82in. high.
(Eldred's) £631

George III pine tall case clock, circa 1780, 92in. high. £900

A Federal pine grain painted tall case clock, by S. Hoadley, Conn., circa 1830, 86in. high. £12,500

A pine polychrome decorated tall case clock, Connecticut, circa 1830, 85in. high. £6,000

REGULATORS

A 19th century Vienna walnut regulator longcase clock, 6ft.10in. high. £2,000

A Victorian mahogany longcase regulator, the dial signed P. G. Dodd & Son, 6ft.3in. high. £3,000

A mahogany longcase regulator clock with 14in. dial, signed P. G. Wilson, Inverness, 6ft. 7½in. high. £1,350

A George III mahogany regulator, the 10in. dial signed Holmes, London, 5ft.11½in. high. £7,500

A month-going longcase regulator with equation of time, the dial signed *George Graham, London*, the dial and movement circa 1750, 75in. high. (Christie's New York) £16,830

A 19th century mahogany regulator, by Hepting, Stirling, 75in. high. £1,000

An American carved walnut longcase regulator, signed Howard & Davis, Makers — Boston, circa 1851, 8ft.0½in. high.£20,000

A 19th century mahogany regulator, the dial signed James, Saffron Walden, 1.87m. high. £4,250

REGULATORS

A mahogany long-
case regulator, the
Franklin type dial
signed Vulliamy
Pall Mall London,
5ft.11in. high.
£10,000

A figured mahogany
longcase striking
regulator, signed
Whistler, 6ft.7in.
high.   £3,250

A mahogany month
regulator, the 12in.
silvered dial signed
John Arnold Lon-
don, 6ft.4in. high.
£35,000

A Regency mahogany
longcase regulator,
the 12in. dial signed
Grimalde London,
6ft.1in. high. £9,000

Henry Pearce,
Grantham, a mid-19th
century eight-day
regulator longcase
clock with circular
silvered minutes dial,
83in. high.
(Bearne's)   £1,600

A mahogany longcase
sidereal regulator with
break circuit work,
signed Wm. Bond &
Sons, Boston, circa
1858, 64½in. high.
£20,000

A 19th century maho-
gany regulator with
12in. circular painted
dial, 2.09m. high.
£3,500

A Scottish mahogany
regulator, the 10¼in.
dial signed Alexander
Ferguson Cupar Fife,
4ft.1in. high.
£4,250

ROUND FACE

A walnut longcase clock, signed W. Donald, Glasgow, 7ft.1½in. high. £1,250

A Victorian mahogany eight-day striking longcase clock, circa 1850.   £900

A Louis XV design longcased clock by Gilbert, Belfast.   £4,250

An unusual George III longcase clock by Thos. Wilson, 100in. high. (Bearne's)   £1,000

A Scottish Regency mahogany longcase clock in the gothic taste, the 12in. circular engraved silvered dial signed *W. Young Dundee* with subsidiary seconds and calendar rings, 7ft. 1in. high.

(Christie's)   £1,980

A Louis XV kingwood and ormolu mounted longcase clock, the 10in. circular convex enamel dial signed J.S. Chauvet a Paris, 6ft. 7in. high. (Phillips)   £8,000

An Austrian long case timepiece of Empire style, the anchor movement with enamelled dial, in polygonal drum case, circa 1810, 6ft. 11in. high. (Tennants)   £800

A Regency mahogany longcase clock, the arched hood surmounted by a spire and turned wood finial, the 12in. convex painted dial signed Barraud, Cornhill, London, 87½in. high. (Phillips)   £2,800

ROUND FACE

An early 19th century Scottish longcase clock, inscribed *Geo. White, Glasgow,* 7ft. 2in. high. (Woolley & Wallis) £680

A Regency mahogany longcase clock, the 12in. silvered dial signed Grant, London, 7ft. high.   £5,500

Scottish 19th century mahogany longcase clock by D. Robinson, Airdrie, 7ft. tall. £1,500

An early 19th century Irish mahogany longcase clock, dial signed Edwd. Smith, 6ft. 6in. high. £1,750

A Dent Victorian oak cased railway longcase regulator clock, the 12½in. engraved silvered dial signed *Dent, London, Clockmaker to the Queen,* date circa 1855. (Bonhams)   £2,200

An early Victorian Scottish mahogany longcase clock, the drumhead hood with glazed bezel to circular silvered engraved dial signed *Whitelaw Edinburgh,* 6ft. 6in. high. (Christie's) £1,100

A 19th century mahogany longcase clock, the 12in. circular painted dial now signed *John Grant,* the five pillar movement with anchor escapement, 6ft. 9in. high. (Phillips) £2,200

A Regency mahogany longcase clock, inscribed Christopher Lawson, Edinburgh, with subsidiary seconds dial, the drum hood over moulded plinth, 214cm. (Phillips)   £950

A magnificent and highly important George III mahogany parcel-gilt musical and astronomical longcase clock and barometer, unsigned, circa 1770, three train movement, the going train having deadbeat escapement.
(Christie's) £78,500

A George II walnut longcase clock; circa 1745/7, the boxwood and ebony lined case on double-footed plinth, the 12in. square dial signed *Geo: Graham London* beneath the brass chapter ring, 7ft. 1in. high.
(Christie's) £29,700

ROUND FACE

A 19th century mahogany longcase clock, the dial signed Barraud, Cornhill, London, 1.98m. high. £900

A good William IV mahogany and ebony strung regulator, the tapering case surmounted by a gadrooned caddy, signed *James Condliff*, 7ft. high. (Phillips) £7,150

A 19th century mahogany longcase clock, the dial signed Brysons, Edinburgh, 6ft.6in. high. £1,250

A late 18th century Sheraton-style balloon longcase clock with year movement, 7ft. high. £5,000

A 19th century Scottish longcase clock, by Winter, Edinburgh, 87½in. high, circa 1840. (Tennants) £900

A Scottish longcase clock, signed A. McMillan, Glasgow, the mahogany hood on tapering column trunk. (David Lay) £950

Italian Renaissance style walnut tall case clock, A. Cheloni, Firenze, 1889, 110in. high. (Skinner Inc.) £5,047

An early Victorian Scottish burr walnut longcase clock, the repainted dial signed *J. Welsh. Motherwell* with Roman chapter ring, 7ft. 2in. high. (Christie's) £1,100

ROUND FACE

An Irish George IV longcase clock, signed Donegan, Dublin, the mahogany case with carved hood. (David Lay) £500

A George III oak cased 8-day striking longcase clock, the dial signed J. Marr of Retford. £1,000

19th century pollard oak cased regulator clock with glass sides and white enamel face. £1,000

An Austrian beech-wood longcase clock painted to simulate mahogany, circa 1900, 207.9cm. high. £800

An ormolu mounted amaranth and tulipwood long-case regulator clock, dial signed Leroy a Paris, 88in. high. £7,500

A late Regency maho-gany longcase clock, the drum head with relief husk border over tapered trunk, inscribed Whitelaw, Edinburgh, 200cm. (Phillips) £1,700

An early Victorian mahogany longcase clock, inscribed J. D. Reid, Airdrie, with subsidiary seconds and calendar dials, 230cm. (Phillips) £750

An early 19th century mahogany longcase clock, inscribed J. Durward, Edinburgh, the eight-day movement striking on a single bell, 201cm. (Phillips) £750

William III walnut and marquetry longcase clock, the case on later bracket foot with inhabited floral marquetry to the plinth and in panels to the rectangular trunk door, the 11in. square dial signed *Josh. Alsope cast Smith Field* on the silvered chapter ring, 7ft. 1in. high. (Christie's) £10,450

A George II walnut longcase clock, the feather-banded case on skirted plinth and with arched trunk door, the arched dial signed *Thomas Grace London* on a silvered disc in the arch, silvered chapter ring with lozenge half-hour markers, 7ft. 7in. high. (Christie's) £2,750

A fine Queen Anne marquetry inlaid walnut and ebony month-going longcase clock, the 12in. square dial signed *Dan Quare London*, six ringed and latched pillar movement with anchor escapement and inside countwheel strike on bell, 8ft. 3in. high.
(Christie's)   £17,250

A Regency mahogany longcase regulator, the 12in. diameter circular silvered engraved dial signed *Matthews Leighton*, the six pillar movement with maintaining power, deadbeat escapement with woodrod pendulum and brass-cased weight, 6ft. 3¹/₂in. high.
(Christie's)   £4,025

WALNUT

An 18th century walnut longcase clock, by Marm'd. Storr. £3,000

Federal walnut tall case clock, possibly Penn., circa 1820. 81in. high. £1,850

A Pennsylvania Chippendale inlaid walnut tallcase clock, 88in. high. £3,500

A late 17th century longcase clock, by R. Seignior, London, 6ft.8in. high. £5,000

George II walnut eight-day longcase clock by Joseph or Joshua Morgan, London, second quarter 18th century, 7ft. 9½in. high. (Butterfield & Butterfield) £4,387

Tho. Tompion London No. 542, a Queen Anne burr walnut longcase clock, the finely veneered case with plain foot and concave mouldings, the flat top hood with brass capped quarter columns, 6ft.8in. high. (Christie's) £44,000

A fine third quarter of the 18th century automata and quarter-striking inlaid burr-walnut longcase clock by Jan Henkels, Amsterdam, 100in. high. (Christie's S. Ken) £7,700

A George I burr walnut longcase clock, the crossbanded case with double-footed plinth, dial signed Willm. Manlove London on a silvered arc in the matted centre with subsidiary seconds, 8ft.5in. high. (Christie's) £4,400

WALNUT

An 18th century walnut and mahogany longcase clock by Bronne, Liverpool. £1,250

Walnut tall case clock, New England, circa 1780, 88in. high, back of dial inscribed 'G.R.'. £2,000

An 18th century walnut cased clock by Jno. Baylis of Bromyard. £2,400

An 18th century walnut longcase clock, brass dial signed Hen. Massey, London, 2.46m. high. £2,750

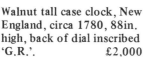

A George I burr walnut longcase clock, the 13½in. square dial signed *Jas. Booth, Dublin* on the broad silvered chapter ring, four pillar movement with inside countwheel strike and anchor escapement, 8ft. high. (Christie's) £3,300

A Charles II burr walnut month going longcase clock, the 9½in. sq. dial with winged cherub spandrels and signed Joseph Knibb Londini fecit in florid script at the base, circa 1673-5, 6ft.8in. high. (Christie's) £60,500

A walnut longcase clock with automaton by Nicholas Weilandt, Amsterdam, the movement with anchor escapement, Dutch striking on two bells, third quarter 18th century, 98½in. high. (Christie's New York) £5,049

A Charles II walnut longcase clock with bun feet to crossbanded convex moulded case, the silvered chapter ring signed Cha. Gretton London, case extensively restored, 6ft.3½in. high. (Christie's) £12,100

A William and Mary seaweed marquetry
longcase clock, the 11in. square dial signed *John
Cotton London*, the four pillar rack striking
movement with anchor escapement, 7ft. 5in.
high.
(Christie's)   £3,450

A fine Regency mahogany longcase regulator,
the circular silvered engraved regulator dial
signed *Webster London No. 6096*, the movement
with four double-screwed pillars, jewelled
deadbeat escapement, 6ft. 5in. high.
(Christie's)   £6,900

An important Louis Philippe mahogany six-month going longcase regulateur, the 10³/₄in. diameter silvered dial signed *Ame. Jacob*, anchor escapement planted on the backplate, stamped *sousciption Aimé Jacob No. 17*, 7ft. 1in. high (Christie's)   **£54,300**

William Scafe, London, a fine Queen Anne lacquered longcase clock, the dial signed *William Scafe London*, the five pillar rack striking movement with anchor escapement and strike on bell, 9ft. 2in. high. (Christie's)   **£5,175**

WALNUT

A Dutch burr-walnut month calendar longcase clock, dial signed Fromanteel & Clarke, 7ft.8in. high. £6,000

A 19th century burr walnut and mahogany longcase clock, maker's name John Elliott, London, 7ft.6in. high. £3,000

An early 18th century walnut quarter chiming longcase clock, by Claude Du Chesne, London, 8ft.1in. high. £12,500

A Chippendale carved walnut tall case clock, Pennsylvania, circa 1770, 8ft. 1¼in. high. (Sotheby's) £2,647

An early 20th century burr walnut quarter-chiming grandmother clock, the arch moulded top above plain trunk, 69in. high. (Christie's S. Ken.) £1,100

A Chippendale walnut tall-case clock, Pennsylvania, dated 1804, the base with applied shell-carved 'turtle' panel, 7ft. 8½in. high. (Sotheby's) £7,278

An unusual 18th century Continental walnut longcase clock, inscribed on a cartouche in the arch *William Jordain, London*, 7ft. 4in. high. (Phillips) £4,800

A Dutch striking burl walnut longcase clock, signed *Thos. Monkhouse, London,* mid 18th century, 110½in. high. (Christie's) £5,104

WALNUT

An Irish inlaid walnut longcase clock, the 13½in. dial signed Tho. Parker Dublin, 7ft.4in. high. £3,500

A George II burr walnut calendar longcase clock, the dial signed George Merttins, Londini, 8ft. high. £6,250

A Chippendale walnut tall case clock, dial signed by Johnson, London, case probably Penn., 1770-90, 92in. high. £2,000

An 18th century walnut month going longcase clock, the dial signed Christophe Gould Londini fecit, 6ft.10in. high. £5,000

Federal walnut inlaid tallcase clock, Pennsylvania, circa 1770–1810, 7ft. 11in. high. (Butterfield & Butterfield) £3,206

A Charles II walnut longcase clock, circa 1685, the 10in. square dial signed *John Knibb Oxon fecit*, 6ft. 6in. high. (Christie's) £52,800

A Chippendale carved walnut tall case clock, Pennsylvania, 1870–1890, the hood with carved swan's neck pediment, 92in. high. (Christie's) £2,884

Dutch baroque walnut tall case clock, 18th century, pagoda top with carved frieze, arched dial with painted moon phase, 97in. high. (Skinner Inc.) £2,603

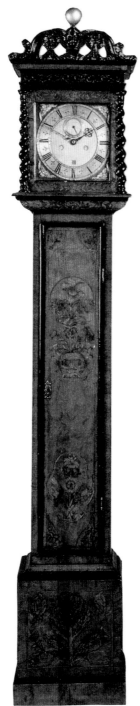

A Charles II walnut and marquetry longcase clock, the convex moulded case now on skirted plinth inlaid with floral marquetry, the 10in. square dial signed *Edw: Stanton Londini* on the silvered chapter ring, finely matted centre with calendar aperture and large diameter seconds ring, 7ft. 1in. high.
(Christie's) £12,650

A George III mahogany longcase clock, the unusual case on bracket feet with raised shaped panel to plinth flanked by reeded stop-chamfered angles, the dial signed *Richd. Peyton Gloucestershire* on the silvered chapter ring with subsidiary seconds ring and calendar aperture to the foliate engraved centre, 7ft. 5½in. high.
(Christie's) £3,850

A fine and rare Regency mahogany sidereal and mean time month-going longcase regulator, the 12³/₄in. diameter silvered engraved dial signed *Margetts London*, the massive five pinned pillar movement previously with dust covers, the anchor inverted and beating half-seconds with short lead bob gridiron pendulum, 6ft. 2¹/₂in. high.
(Christie's) £33,350

A Victorian walnut year-going longcase regulator with calendar, the narrow case on skirted plinth with glazed rectangular trunk door flanked by turned ³/₄ columns, the 11in. by 12¹/₄in. engraved silvered dial signed *William Schoof, London* with Roman and Arabic chapters, 6ft. 11in. high.
(Christie's) £7,150

WALNUT

An 18th century walnut longcase clock, the 11in. square dial signed Jnº. Wise, London, 2.10m. high. £2,400

A Chippendale walnut tall case clock, dial signed by Thos. Crow, Delaware, circa 1770, 89¼in. high. £6,000

A walnut month going equation longcase clock, signed Geo. Graham, London, 240cm. high. £100,000

A Pennsylvania Chippendale walnut tall-case clock, the dial signed C. Warner, 91in. high. £3,250

An early 18th century walnut and mulberry longcase clock, signed 'Joseph Knibb, Londini Fecit', the eight day movement with outside count wheel striking on a bell, 192cm high. (Henry Spencer) £3,400

A good early 18th century Dutch walnut longcase clock by Willem Redi of Amsterdam, with black Roman numerals and Arabic minutes, 245cm high. (Henry Spencer) £7,500

George I Circassian walnut eight-day longcase clock, labelled *Joseph and Thomas Windmills, London,* circa 1714, 6ft. 10¹/₂in. high. (Butterfield & Butterfield) £8,773

A mid 18th century inlaid walnut longcase clock, inscribed Stenard, Henley, the trunk with arched door, parquetry inlaid with herringbone, 6ft.8in. high. (Hobbs & Chambers) £5,000

WALNUT

A mid Georgian ormolu mounted walnut clock by Jno. Melling, Chester, 88½in. high. £12,500

A German Renaissance Revival carved walnut and elm Standuhr, two-train chiming movement, 8ft. 5in. high. (Selkirk's) £1,966

A Georgian walnut and inlaid longcase clock, signed Jon. Sales, Dublin, 8ft. 5½in. high. £3,250

Dutch baroque burl walnut tall case clock, *Corn.ˢ Engering A. Dort Recht*, mid 18th century, 107in. high. (Skinner Inc.) £7,415

An early 18th century walnut longcase clock, with silvered chapter ring, signed *Wm. Crow, London*, with subsidiary seconds and date aperture, 6ft. 10in. high. (Phillips) £1,500

An 18th century walnut longcase clock, the hood with stepped dome top, the 12in. arched brass dial signed Martin Jackson, London, 8ft. high. (Phillips) £3,800

A mid 18th century Provençal walnut longcase clock, the lyre shaped case carved with foliate and shell motifs, 267cm. high. (Finarte) £1,286

An 18th century walnut longcase clock, signed *Peter King, Longacre*, with subsidiary seconds and date aperture, 7ft. 6in. high. (Phillips) £1,800

An Empire ormolu striking table clock, symbolising the Sciences, floral bezel to the annular white enamel Roman dial, the twin going barrel movement with outside countwheel strike on bell (lacking), 16in. high. (Christie's) £1,760

A Viennese ormolu and porcelain mounted mantel timepiece, the Arabic enamel dial painted with garlands of flowers and with brilliant-set milled bezel, the typical going barrel movement with anchor escapement, 9½in. high. (Christie's) £1,540

A French gilt and silvered brass perpetual calendar four glass mantel clock, the case with fluted Corinthian columns to the four angles, the going barrel movement with steel suspended mercury pendulum and strike on bell, 14¼in. high. (Christie's) £3,300

Cartier .10162, a fine silver and enamel quarter striking travelling clock, with agate ring handle to top with cabochon push-repeat button, convex glazed white enamel bezel to the white enamel Roman and Arabic dial signed *Cartier Paris Londres*, 4in. high. (Christie's) £12,650

A Louis Philippe ormolu striking long duration skeleton clock, the white enamel Roman dial with pierced blued trefoil hands, the centre with visible motion work, the twin going barrel movement with Brocot escapement, 21½in. high.
(Christie's) **£1,320**

An Empire ormolu and green veined marble striking table clock, the white enamel Roman and Arabic dial signed *a Paris*, the twin going barrel movement with anchor escapement, 17½in. high.
(Christie's) **£3,080**

A magnificent William and Mary ormolu-mounted ebony grand sonnerie table clock, the dial signed *Thomas Tompion Londini Fecit*, massive triple fusee movement, verge escapement, steel single-cocked levers, the backplate engraved with scrolling foliage with acanthus strap-work, 26¾in. high.
(Christie's) **£298,500**

An Empire ormolu and cut glass striking musical table clock, the twin going barrel movement with anchor escapement and gridiron pendulum with cut glass bob, hour trip for the pin-barrel musical movement in the mahogany oval base, the sides with three levers with brass plaque engraved *Jouer/Aretter/Changes*, 20in. high.
(Christie's) **£2,200**

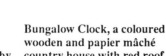

French brass and champlevé enamel mantel clock, retailed by A. Stowell, Boston, 19th century, domed top over a glazed case, 16in. high.
(Skinner Inc.)   £1,026

Bungalow Clock, a coloured wooden and papier mâché country house with red roof and incorporating a clock, made in the half round by the Lux Clock Mfg. Co., New York, 15cm. high.
(Auction Team Köln)   £32

A Louis XV ormolu mounted kingwood mantel clock, the glazed enamel dial signed Baret a Brevanne, 17½in. high.
(Christie's)   £495

A French porcelain panelled mantel clock, the movement with Brocot suspension, the dial decorated in the Japanese manner with herons, butterflies and other birds, 13in.
(Lawrence Fine Arts)   £682

A Japanese gilt-brass and padouk wood striking mantel clock of standard form with four baluster pillar movement, 5¼in. high.
(Christie's)   £2,185

An early Victorian maple wood lancet mantel timepiece, the dial with inscription Thos. Cole, London, 10in. high.   £2,000

A large free standing mantel clock with Ship's Bell strike on gong, silvered dial with raised Arabic hour numerals signed *Chelsea Ship's Bell*, 14in. wide.
(Christie's)   £550

Classical Revival gilt gesso mantel timepiece, probably Atkins Clock Company, Connecticut, circa 1840, 18½in. high. (Skinner Inc.)   £798

A leather covered travelling timepiece, the later lever movement signed Le Coultre Co., the ivory dial signed Cartier, France, 'Eight Days', 4in. high.
(Phillips)   £260

A Charles X mantel clock with 3½in., diameter silvered dial, Roman numerals and eight-day movement, 20½in. high. (Bearne's) £450

A Vitascope bakelite clock, the pink body enclosing a marine scene of a ship on rough seas, 32cm. high. (Bonhams) £240

A small timepiece contained in an amboyna veneered lancet case with brass outline, by Thos. Cole, 10in. high. £1,850

A mid Victorian burr elm Gothic mantel clock, inscribed Webster, Cornhill, London, the base with trefoil panels supporting obelisk pilasters, height 62cm. (Phillips) £600

'Metropole', a Memphis clock, designed by George J. Sowden, 1982, wood and plastic laminate, finished in shades of grey, green, yellow and mauve, with metal plaque, *Memphis, Made in Italy*. (Christie's) £1,430

A 19th century satinwood mantel clock, the rectangular case surmounted by a sphinx, the florally engraved square gilt brass dial signed *Walter Yonge*, 10½in. high. (Phillips) £2,200

A wooden Ansonia child's clock, with pointed roof and painted with fairy tale characters, with American 30-hour movement, 23cm. high. (Auction Team Köln) £28

An unusual Continental fruitwood and enamel mantel timepiece, the verge fusée watch movement with bridge cock, signed *Pre. Rigaud, Geneve*, 8½in. high. (Christie's S. Ken) £880

A 19th century mantel clock, the front incorporating a rectangular porcelain panel painted with an Arab street scene, 11¾in. high overall. (Bearne's) £680

A Biedermeier ormolu grande sonnerie mantel clock, the four pillar movement with bridge cock verge escapement, chain fusee for the going, 7in. high.
(Christie's)   £1,430

A Regency ebonised mantel timepiece, the brass line-inlaid case on bun feet with out-set angles, the arched silvered engraved dial signed *James McCabe Royal Exchange London*, 8¼in. high.
(Christie's)   £1,650

A Viennese gem-set silver-gilt mantel timepiece, the rocaille base supporting a tree bearing fruits being picked by a ruby-set boy, the bridgecock verge movement signed *Sebastian Manhart*, 9in. high.
(Christie's)   £1,760

A Louis XVI white and black marble and ormolu mounted striking mantel clock, the white enamel Arabic dial signed *Ridel a Paris*, the twin going barrel movement with verge escapement, 22in. high.
(Christie's)   £2,530

A Directoire bronze and ormolu striking mantel clock, the white enamel Arabic dial signed *Develberie. A. Paris*, the twin going barrel movement with anchor escapement, 15³/₄in. high. (Christie's) **£2,420**

A Regency ormolu and black marble timepiece, the five-pillar chain fusee movement with anchor escapement, backplate signed *Grimalde & Johnson, Strand, London*, 17¹/₄in. high. (Christie's) **£1,650**

A Directoire ormolu striking mantel clock, the white enamel dial signed *Robin aux Galeries du Louvre*, the circular twin going barrel movement with anchor escapement, signed *Robin A Paris*, 12¹/₂in. high. (Christie's) **£2,420**

A tortoiseshell gold-mounted mantel timepiece, the going barrel movement with bi-metallic balance to lever platform, the back door with engraved dedication dated *12th January, 1911*; hallmarked, *London 1909*, 4³/₄in. high. (Christie's) **£1,265**

ART DECO

A chromium plated Smiths electric mystery clock, inscribed Smith Electric, with dagger hands, 8in. high. (Christie's) £286

A French Art Deco gilt bronze timepiece, the circular dial with gilded hands, 26.5cm. high, the case marked *G. Dunaime.* (Phillips) £1,150

Ferranti electric clock, 1930s, with amber dial. (Muir Hewitt) £20

A German 'Secessionist' plated timepiece, the circular dial with gilded hands mounted in a face with pointed and pierced top, 44.5cm. high. (Phillips) £680

A silvered bronze mantel clock, by Edgar Brandt, 30.6cm. high. £4,500

An unusual French marine clock, modelled in the form of a shell with propeller fuse, inscribed *DUGHS CASTELNAUDARY*, 22in. high. (Christie's S. Ken) £462

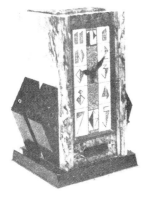

An Alfred Dunhill Art Deco marble mantel clock and cigarette case, 23.7cm. high. £1,000

An Art Deco style circular pink mirror glass electric mantel clock. £300

Art Deco hardstone and cloisonne enamel desk clock, with 13J Swiss movement, 4in high. £900

ART DECO

Chrome plate electric clock by Smiths.
(Muir Hewitt)   £45

A square Nephrite travelling timepiece with gold mounts, by Cartier, circa 1920, 6.7cm.
£2,000

A gold, rock crystal, onyx and enamel clock by Tiffany & Co.   £3,500

An unusual Jaeger LeCoultre table clock in Art Deco style, the straight line eight day movement jewelled to the centre with monometallic balance, 7½in. diam. (Christie's)   £242

A French Art Deco Van Cleef & Arpels small mantel timepiece, the lapis lazuli body with diamond chip surround and diamond set hands, 4in. high. (Tennants)   £20,000

A Jaeger-Le Coultre eight day mantel clock, with Roman chapters, the transparent glass discus-shaped body with chrome rim and foot, 23.3cm. diam. (Christie's)   £528

Early 20th century grey marble and glass Art Deco mantel clock, France, 11in. high.   £300

A gilt-brass mantel timepiece with alarm, the rectangular dial signed *Cartier 8 days alarm Swiss* with raised blued Arabic chapters, the movement signed *Concord Watch Co.*, 3½in. high. (Christie's)   **£1,320**

A silvered bronze Art Deco table clock, signed R. Terras, 34.5cm. high. (Christie's)
£990

An Austrian engraved brass striking pendule de voyage, the triple going barrel movement with bridge-cock verge escapement, strike/repeat on two gongs on plain backplate, 6¹/₂in. high. (Christie's)   **£1,540**

A Second Empire ormolu and bronze striking four-glass table clock, the twin going barrel movement with Brocot escapement and spring suspended foliate pendulum, 19³/₄in. high. (Christie's)   **£1,540**

A spherical striking skeleton clock, the five pillar twin chain fusee movement with verge escapement and original pendulum, the meridian ring signed *Barraud Cornhill London*, 12in. high. (Christie's)   **£6,050**

A Swedish gilt-wood striking cartel clock, painted dial signed *Carl Bergsten Skara*, the five pillar movement with anchor escapement with silk-suspended pendulum, 31in. high. (Christie's)   **£1,840**

A Viennese quarter striking picture clock, the painting on copper depicting a harvest scene with the sea and mountains in the background, circa 1860, 35¹/₄ x 36¹/₂in.
(Christie's)   £2,200

A Viennese musical picture clock, the oil painting on canvas depicting a harvest scene, the tower inset with the clock, playing two tunes with manual release, 44 x 36¹/₂in.
(Christie's)   £1,650

ART DECO

A Marchak & Linzeler
Art Deco boudoir clock,
circa 1925, 8cm. £3,000

An enamelled Art Deco timepiece,
retailed through Fortnum & Mason,
London, 23.5cm. wide, when open,
with Swiss 8-day movement. £1,250

A P. M. Faure glass clock
case on stepped base,
circa 1930, 16cm. £225

An Art Deco marble and enamel
timepiece, the corners set with
cloisonne enamel panels
decorated in black, brown,
yellow, beige and white, 26.2cm.
high. (Phillips)   £260

1930s chrome and black electric
clock.
(Muir Hewitt)   £50

A hammered brass and chro-
med metal mantel clock,
probably Wiener Werkstatte,
circa 1905/10, 26.5cm. £1,000

An Ato Art Deco table clock
with a pair of bronze owls
perched on top, 41.5cm.
high. (Christie's)   £495

Art Deco green onyx cased clock
flanked by two ivory figures,
14½in. wide.   £2,250

Early 19th century
French Art Deco mantel
clock with white marble
pediment.   £425

ART NOUVEAU

Art Nouveau porcelain mantel clock, elongated 'A' shape with green glaze and eight-day time and strike movement.
£225

Patinated metal clock, Amsterdam School, (1915–30), bulbous teardrop shape with round dial, 11in. high. (Skinner Inc.) £294

A decorative Art Nouveau plaster clock case, signed 'Simon', circa 1900, 97.75cm. high. £1,000

A Junghans Mysterieuse pendulum clock with a cast pewter female figure on a black wooden base, the white enamel dial with Arabic numerals, 35cm. high, circa 1900. (Auction Team Köln) £422

Edwardian mahogany cased mantel clock with Art Nouveau shell inlay and striking movement behind an enamel dial. (G. A. Key) £155

An electroplated pewter presentation clockcase, surmounted by an Art Nouveau maiden standing contraposto, her arms raised against an elaborate pierced trellis superstructure, 50cm. high. (Christie's) £770

An eight-day time and strike clock with J. Pradier bronze, 11in. long. £1,000

Goldscheider pottery clock with oxidised metal circular dial, 20in. high. £375

A carved wood Art Nouveau mantel clock, by the Chelsea Clock Co., Boston, circa 1920, 18¼in. high. £750

A Regency ormolu mantel timepiece, in the French taste, the elaborate case cast with scrolling foliage and surmounted by a spray of flowers, the circular white enamel Roman and Arabic dial signed *Viner, London*, 13in. high.
(Christie's) £880

An Empire ormolu and bronze mantel timepiece, with later white enamel Roman dial signed *Ryan Armadh 100*, the going barrel movement with anchor escapement and silk suspended pendulum, 10in. high.
(Christie's) £2,200

A burr walnut and brass-inlaid Hertfordshire Mercer mantel chronometer, the engraved silvered Roman dial signed *Hardy Bros. 32 Old Burlington St. London W1*, the single chain fusee gilt movement with maintaining power, Earnshaw escapement, 11¼in. high.
(Christie's) £4,830

A Louis XVI white marble and ormolu striking mantel clock, the white enamel Arabic dial signed *Macors AParis*, the twin going barrel movement with later anchor escapement, backplate signed *Antoine Coliau AParis*, 17½in. high.
(Christie's) £1,955

A Directoire veined marble ormolu mounted striking mantel clock, the drum-head movement surmounted by a figure of Minerva, the large twin going barrel movement with anchor escapement, outside countwheel strike on bell on backplate signed *Liolane AParis*, 22¼in. high. (Christie's) **£2,200**

An Empire ormolu striking mantel clock emblematic of Time, with floral bezel to the white enamel Roman dial signed *Goret Dangreville a abbeville*, the twin going barrel movement with anchor escapement and silk suspended pendulum, 15½in. high. (Christie's) **£2,530**

A Victorian ormolu-mounted ebonised quarter chiming mantel clock, the engraved dial signed *French Royal Exchange London* within a reserve beneath the Roman chapter ring, the triple chain fusee movement chiming on eight bells with hour strike on gong, 13in. high. (Christie's) **£17,250**

A Louis XVI marble and ormolu mounted striking mantel clock, the glazed circular white enamel dial signed *Le Coeur l'aine A Paris*, the twin going barrel movement with anchor escapement and silk suspended sunburst pendulum, 22in. high. (Christie's) **£5,500**

ARTS & CRAFTS

An Arts & Crafts mahogany mantel clock with bevelled glass, circa 1900, 12in. high. £450

An Arts and Crafts silvered metal mantel clock, the embossed circular dial with Arabic chapters, with stud decoration, 14½in. high. £220

An Arts and Crafts pewter mantel clock, cast in relief with a tall stemmed rose tree enclosing circular dial, 33.5cm. high.
(Christie's) £935

An Aesthetic movement Elkington & Co. black marble mantel clock, with porcelain panels painted with stylised daisies, inscribed *Elkington & Co.*, 31.8cm. high.
(Christie's) £1,100

An Arts & Crafts square oak mantel clock, by Seth Thomas Clock Co., 20th century, 12½in. high, 10½in. wide. £950

A Scottish Arts and Crafts ebony and silver timepiece with rectangular case in dark wood with flat metal top, signed 'J. H. McNair', 23.8cm. high.
(Phillips) £8,000

An Arts and Crafts copper and brass mantel clock, the pagoda style top with strapwork embellishment, 42cm. high.
(Phillips) £520

Victorian oak hanging wall clock with pendulum, 1900. £125

Late 19th century ebonised mantel clock in the Arts and Crafts style with porcelain face and eight day movement.
(British Antique Exporters) £150

BALLOON CASE

A 19th century mahogany mantel timepiece, of balloon form, the circular painted dial signed Daldorph, Croydon, the fusee movement with anchor escapement. (Phillips) £220

Fine Regency period satinwood balloon cased mantel clock with sunburst inlay, and pineapple finial, 17in. high. (G. A. Key) £900

A Scottish Regency mahogany balloon mantel regulator of large size, with handles to sides and on brass ball feet, the backplate signed *Ian. Dalgleish Edinburgh*, 25¹/₂in. high. (Christie's) £1,320

BAROMETER CLOCKS

A gilt brass combination timepiece aneroid barometer and thermometer, the timepiece with platform lever escapement, 11in. high. (Lawrence Fine Art) £440

A 19th century brass double-dialled barometer and timepiece in the form of a ship's wheel surmounted by a gimballed compass, signed *La Fontaine Opticien*, 11¹/₂in. high. (Christie's S. Ken) £1,100

A French boudoir combined timepiece, barometer and thermometer with cream enamel dials and silvered-metal scale, 12in. high. (Bearne's) £290

CAST IRON

Cast iron mantel clock with painted dial and eight-day time and strike movement, America, circa 1860, 20in. high. £300

A cast iron front mantel clock, polychrome painted, America, circa 1890, 11¾in. high. £100

A cast iron and mother-of-pearl shelf clock by Terry & Andrews, with painted dial, circa 1855, 15¾in. high. £200

An Empire green painted and ormolu striking portico clock, the twin going barrel movement with anchor escapement and outside countwheel strike on bell on backplate stamped *L Marti et Cie*, 16¼in. high.
(Christie's)   £1,210

A Victorian engraved giltmetal, malachite and lapis luzuli miniature chiffonier mantel timepiece, with four pillar single chain fusee 8-day movement, original double-ended cruciform key, by Thomas Cole, circa 1850–55; 5½in. high.
(Christie's)   £11,000

An unusual Victorian engraved giltmetal striking large desk clock in the manner of Thomas Cole, the engraved silvered Roman dial signed *J. W. Benson 25 Old Bond Street*, the faceted glazed twin chain fusee movement with cut bimetallic balance to gilt lever platform, 13in. high.
(Christie's)   £2,090

A Regency rosewood striking four-glass mantel clock, foliate engraved gilt Roman dial with pierced blued hands and strike/silent lever above XII, plain balance to gilt lever platform of the five-pillar twin chain fusee movement with strike/trip repeat on gong on backplate engraved *Payne 163 New Bond St. London*, 9in. high.
(Christie's)   £2,970

CALENDAR

Rosewood cased double dial calendar clock, by L.G. & W.W. Carter Bristol, Connecticut, circa 1865, 30¼in. high. £700

A Victorian eight-day calendar clock by B. Jacobs, Hull, 15¾in. wide.   £600

Late 19th century French porcelain mounted ormolu mantel clock with perpetual calendar, 17in. high. £3,500

A late 19th century oak double dial calendar shelf clock, by Waterbury Clock Co., 29in. high.   £625

French calendar mantel clock by A. Redier, in a rectangular ebonised wood case, circa 1880, 13¼in. high.
                £500

Rosewood double dial calendar timepiece, Seth Thomas Clock Co., Thomaston, Connecticut, mid 19th century, eight-day movement, 27½in. high. (Skinner Inc.)   £370

A Belgian incised black slate perpetual calendar mantel clock, 16¾in. high. £1,250

A French black marble perpetual calendar mantel clock, the movement bell striking, the two piece white enamel dial with Roman numerals, dated 1884, 22½in. high.
(Lawrence Fine Art)   £1,078

An oak double dial calendar clock, by Waterbury Clock Co., circa 1900, 29in. long.   £1,250

CALENDAR

An Ithaca walnut calendar clock, 1866, 45in. long.
£1,500

A French red marble perpetual calendar mantel clock and barometer, 18½in. high. £1,000

Late 19th century oak double dial calendar shelf clock, by Waterbury Clock Co., 24in. high. £650

An unusual 19th century ebonised mantel clock, with perpetual calendar and equation of time by William Jones, Gloucester, painted white dial with Roman numerals.
(Bonhams) £1,900

A fine modern perpetual calendar and moonphase chronometer four-glass clock by Sinclair Harding, Cheltenham, in ebony and gilt brass glazed case, 14in. high.
(Christie's S. Ken) £6,050

An ormolu grande sonnerie mantel clock with calendar, the moulded ebonised base raised on toupie feet, with applied gryphons and scrolls, Vienna, circa 1810, 19in. high.
(Christie's) £4,147

Welsh calendar clock with case painted to simulate rosewood, spring driven pendulum movement, 33in. high.
(Eldred's) £384

A walnut mantel clock, the movement of the Black Forest type with wooden plates, 17in. high. £525

A grain-painted astronomical calendar clock, by Gabs Patent Welch Spring & Co., circa 1880, 30½in. long.
£3,750

CALENDAR

A gilt bronze perpetual calendar mantel clock, circa 1860, 21in. high.
£3,150

An attractive late 19th century French black slate mantel clock/ perpetual calendar/aneroid barometer, 18in. high. (Spencer's) £900

A Restoration rosewood month calendar mantel regulator with a glass dome, 24in. high.
£32,500

A rare American globe calendar clock, signed *Patent 1860 improved by Leonard Thorn*, on moulded circular base engraved with year calendar, 13½in. high. (Christie's New York) £5,610

James Fr. Cole London, an important and early silver-cased, minute repeating, perpetual calendar, astronomical travelling timepiece with alarm, London 1823, unnumbered, 6in. high. (Christie's) £170,500

A black slate perpetual calendar and equation striking mantel clock, the twin going barrel movement striking on bell on backplate stamped *Drielsma Liverpool*, 16½in. high. (Christie's) £880

A French brass four-glass clock with perpetual calendar, the calendar dial signed Achille Brocot, 13in. high.
£4,250

A French black marble and porphyry perpetual calendar mantel clock, signed Francis Glading, 15¼in. high. £1,500

An ormolu and white marble four glass clock with perpetual calendar and moonphase dial below time dial, 16¾in. high.
£5,000

DOULTON

The Menagerie, a Doulton stoneware clock case in the form of a circus building, with incised wild animals, circa 1875, 9¾in. high. £3,250

A small circular Doulton clockcase in buff stoneware with applied rough cast chips, circa 1890, 7¼in. high. £300

An early architectural Doulton clockcase glazed ochre and blue, with incised blue, green, and purple leaves, o.m., 1875, 14½in. high. £1,250

A monumental Doulton clockcase glazed in shades of blue and brown with carved and incised details and applied bead work, c. m., 1879, 15½in. high. £1,500

The Fables Clock, the stoneware case modelled with the interior of a house and numerous figures and animals, the base inscribed: H. Doulton & Co., Lambeth, and G. Tinworth, circa 1882, 11¼in. high. £3,500

A Doulton Punch and Judy clockcase, the buff stoneware with a bright blue glaze, c.m.l. & c., circa 1905, 11½in. high. £1,000

A Doulton stoneware bracket clockcase by Eliza Simmance, inspired by 18th century models, r.m. & e., circa 1895, 14½in. high. £1,500

An architectural Doulton clockcase glazed in dark brown, blue and green, r. m., 1884, 10¼in. high. £1,000

A Doulton Lambeth clock case of rectangular section inset with a circular dial, 14in. high. £750

EBONISED

French inlaid ebonised mantel clock, signed L'aine a Paris, 22in.high.
£475

Chrome and black painted wood electric clock by Smiths. (Muir Hewitt) £40

Mid 18th century ebony veneered mantel clock, dial engraved Willm. Addis, London, 26in. high. £2,000

An early Georgian ebonised mantel clock, by William Webster, the brass dial with silvered chapter ring, inscribed *William Webster, Exchange Alley, London*, 14¹/₂in. high. (Christie's) £1,760

An 18th century French ebonised and ormolu mantel clock, the dial with Roman numerals in enamel cartouches, above an applied bronze scene of the Banquet of the Gods, 38cm. high. (Finarte) £1,682

A black wood rectangular mantel clock by Ehrhardt & Söhne Schwäbisch Gmünd, with brass and marquetry dial, circa 1910, 20cm. high. (Kunsthaus am Museum) £371

A 19th century ebonised mantel clock, the dial signed James McCabe, Royal Exchange, London, 1717, 26cm. high. £2,000

A Royal Presentation ormolu mounted ebony grande sonnerie spring clock by Thos. Tompion, London, No. 278, circa 1700, 28in. high. £250,000

A 19th century ebonised mantel timepiece, the enamel dial signed Archd Haswell, London, the fusee movement with anchor escapement, 26cm. high. (Phillips) £740

EBONISED

An ebony and ivory inlaid
mantel clock, designed by
Josef M. Olbrich, circa 1902.
£16,500

An early ebony-veneered
pendulum clock by A.
Fromanteel, 7¾in. high.
£50,000

A George III chiming mantel
clock with brass dial and ormolu
embellishments, 27in. high.
£3,750

A Regency mahogany, ebonised
brass-inlaid timepiece, the circular white painted dial with
Roman numerals, eight day
single fusee movement, 15½in.
high. (Christie's)   £660

An Edwardian ebonized and gilt
metal mounted quarter-chiming
bracket clock with stepped flat
top surmounted by flame finials,
the massive three-chain
movement chiming on eight bells
and four gongs, 22in. high.
(Christie's S. Ken)   £1,100

A Victorian three-train ebonised
mantel clock, the fusée anchor
movement with brass and
silvered dial inscribed *Deacon,
Swindon*, 29½in. high.
(Tennants)   £1,000

An ebonised travelling
or mantel timepiece, the
3in. silvered dial signed
De La Salle & Christie,
7in. high.   £1,000

A Louis XV-style ebonised
and ormolu mounted bracket
clock with fusee movement,
3ft.11in. overall.   £650

An ebonised Haagse clock,
signed, circa 1660,
36.7cm. high.   £7,500

FIGURAL

A 19th century French bronze, porcelain and gilt mantel time-piece, the movement mounted in a circular case on the back of an elephant, 8½in. high. (Phillips) £520

A French ormolu and bronze mantel clock, two-train movement by S. Martin with silk suspension, embossed gilt dial with white enamel numeral reserves, 1ft. 11in. wide. (Bonhams) £900

A 19th century ormolu and porcelain mounted mantel clock, the rectangular case surmounted by a figure of a boy riding a dolphin, 12in. high. (Phillips) £620

A French gilt metal striking mantel clock with blue porcelain face, 28in. high. £1,000

19th century French black marble and Barbedienne gilt bronze mantel clock, signed, 30in. high. £1,000

A bronze and ormolu mantel clock of Louis XVI design with horizontal movement contained in an urn. £5,000

A Charles X ormolu and bronze mantel clock with silvered dial, 16in. high. £1,500

Mid 19th century ormolu mantel clock with circular dial, 17½in. high. £800

An Empire bronze and gilt-bronze mantel clock, circa 1815, 31½in. high. £1,500

231

FIGURAL

A 19th century French ormolu and white marble mantel clock, the movement contained within a bronzed sphere, 1ft. 5in. high. (Phillips) £980

An Empire ormolu mantel clock, the movement signed James McCabe, London 2133, 12½in. high. £2,400

An Empire ormolu mantel clock with enamel dial signed Leroy Hr. du Roi a Paris, 14½in. high. £1,000

An attractive late 19th century French gilt metal mantel clock, the circular white enamelled dial with black Roman numerals, inscribed *Hry Marc a Paris*, 19in. high. (Spencer's) £360

French bronze mantel clock, late 19th century, time and strike movement striking the half hour impressed *Raingo Freres, Paris,* (finish rubbed) 21in. high. (Skinner Inc.) £645

A French gilt-metal and white marble mantel clock with circular white enamel dial and Roman numerals, late 19th century, 16in. high. (Bearne's) £480

A French 19th century white marble and ormolu mounted mantel clock of Louis XVI design, signed Crosnier à Paris, 20¼in. high. (Christie's S. Ken.) £935

A Louis Philippe gilt bronze mantel clock with eight-day striking movement and a glass dome, 16½in. high. £600

Louis XV ormolu and patinated bronze figural mantel clock, the dial signed *Antoine Thiout*, mid-18th century, 21¾in. high. (Butterfield & Butterfield) £4,728

FIGURAL

A Charles X ormolu mantel clock with circular dial signed 'Guyerde(?) aine Paris', 12in. wide. £1,000

A French Empire ormolu mantel clock, the movement mounted on a chariot, 44cm. high. £1,800

A gilt bronze mantel clock, the dial with silvered chapter ring, 18½in. high, circa 1850. £600

A 19th Century bronze and ormolu mantel clock, the case surmounted by the figure of Venus with winged Cupid in a cage, 2ft. 12in. high. (Phillips) £2,800

Fine Austrian automatic repeating mantel clock, 19th century, the ormolu face with two cherubs below a mask which has movable eyes, 27½in. high. (Eldred's) £1,298

A French Empire mantel clock, the eight-day movement striking the hours and half-hours and with white enamel dial, 16in. high. (Bearne's) £1,550

A Second Empire ormolu and bronze mantel clock, the chased dial signed Michelez Eleve de Breguet, with a frieze of emblematic putti, 19in. high. (Christie's) £1,430

A French ormolu and bronze mantel clock, the circular glazed enamelled dial signed Brenzes...? the case signed Aug. Moreau, 9in. high. (Christie's) £825

A 19th century ormolu mantel clock, 3in. enamel dial with Roman numerals, bell striking movement with silk suspension, 17in. (Bonhams) £280

FIGURAL

A gilt bronze mantel clock by Raingo Freres, circa 1870, 19¾in. high. £1,500

An Empire ormolu 'Atala and Chactas' mantel clock, 42cm. high. £2,500

A Louis XVI ormolu mantel clock, the dial signed Le Neveu a Paris, 12in. wide. £1,000

A 19th century Black Forest 'clock-vendor' time-piece, circa 1850, 15in. high. £2,000

A Sevres pattern gilt bronze mantel clock, the movement by Gasnier a Paris, circa 1875, 41cm. wide. £1,250

A fin de siecle 'bras en l'air' mantel clock with a gilt metal female figure against an enamel background, 17in. high. £3,000

Mid 19th century silvered bronze and ormolu mantel clock, the backplate signed Leroy a Paris , 26½in. high. £1,000

Louis XVI style gilt-bronze and white marble figural mantel clock by S. Marti et Cie, Paris, late 19th century, 12¹/₂in. high. (Butterfield & Butterfield) £1,687

A 19th century French ormolu and bronze mantel clock, the dial with enamel numerals, 58cm. high. £1,000

FIGURAL

An 18th century elephant mantel clock, signed Vulliamy London, probably French, 19½in. high.
£2,400

An Empire ormolu mantel clock, the silk-suspended countwheel striking movement with enamel dial, 19in. wide.
£2,400

A gilt and patinated bronze mantel clock with silvered dial, 23in. high, circa 1830.
£675

A French Louis XV style bronze and ormolu mantel clock, the enamel dial signed Thuillier A Paris, 1ft.3½in.
£2,000

An Empire ormolu mantel clock flanked by the figures of Apollo and Venus, the rectangular base applied with a mythological scene in bas relief, 54cm. high.
(Finarte)
£3,673

A late 19th century French mantel timepiece, the circular ormolu dial with Roman numerals, within a cartouche shaped champevé enamel case, 10½in. high.
(Christie's)
£495

A Regency English bronze and gilt bronze mantel timepiece, 30cm. high.
£675

A 19th century French ormolu mantel clock, the circular case surmounted by an urn and raised on the back of a stallion, 1ft. 1in. high.
(Phillips)
£380

An Empire bronze and ormolu mantel clock, the enamel dial signed Lemoine a Paris, 24¼in. high.
£2,400

FIGURAL

Late 19th century bronze and marble mantel clock, 23½in. high. £500

An early 19th century ormolu mantel clock, 1ft.9in. high. £1,000

A 19th century French Empire style 8-day striking mantel clock, 17in. high. £500

A 19th century ormolu mantel clock, the base decorated with putti in a palm leaf border, surmounted by a female figure holding a cornucopia, 68cm. high.
(Finarte) £1,215

A gilt metal figural stackfreed clock, the figure, in classical armour, standing next to an engraved shaft supporting a wreath and scroll mount to silver time ball, circa 1580, 11¾in. high.
(Christie's) £6,380

An ormolu mantel clock with enamel circlet dial, signed Bausse Rue de Richilieu, in globe shaped case supported by the winged figure of Aurora, 20½in. high. (Christie's) £1,760

A French ormolu and bronze mantel clock flanked by seated cherubs, mid 19th century, 30¾in. high, 26½in. wide
(Christie's) £2,200

A French porcelain mounted gilt brass mantel clock, with the trade stamp of Miroy Freres, 14½in. high. £325

A 19th century French ormolu mantel clock with circular enamel dial, 35cm. high, together with a base. £600

FIGURAL

A Restoration ormolu mantel clock with silk-suspended pendulum, 40cm. high.
£650

19th century French gilt metal mantel clock on rococo plinth.   £750

An ormolu and marble mantel clock, French, 12in. high, circa 1860.   £1,250

A French gilt bronze and bronze sculptural mantel clock with pietra dura panels, with Brocot suspension, bell striking and bearing the stamp of Vincenti, 16½in. high.
(Lawrence Fine Art)   £1,100

A substantial 19th century French ormolu mantel clock, the case lavishly decorated with foliage and sun rays and with three naked winged putti, 2ft.9½in. high. (Phillips) £2,900

A 19th century French bronze and ormolu mantel clock, the rectangular case with acanthine borders, surmounted by the figure of an infant bacchanal, 19in. high.
(Christie's)   £935

An ormolu and bronze mantel clock the glazed enamel dial signed Duot a Paris, the pedestal case surmounted by Cupid, 15½in. high. (Christie's)£1,430

A 19th century French ormolu and porcelain mantel clock, the case surmounted by an urn and flanked by naked putti, 1ft 2in. high. (Phillips)   £800

A 19th century French bronze and parcel gilt mantel clock with Cupid surmount, the twin train movement striking on a bell, 13½in. high.
(Christie's)   £330

FIGURAL

An Empire ormolu mantel clock, the steel dial signed Leroy & fils Hrs du roi, 25in. high. £1,500

A fin-de siècle ormolu and porcelain mounted mantel clock, white enamel Roman and Arabic dial signed *Jas. Muirhead Glasgow* with pierced gilt hands, the twin going barrel movement with anchor escapement and strike on bell, 17³/₄in. high. (Christie's) £2,530

A gilt bronze and porcelain mantel clock, the dial with Arabic numerals, 28½in. high. £5,000

Louis XV style parcel-gilt and patinated bronze figural clock, 19th century, raised on a support cast with palm fronds, a seated putto at its base holding a tablet, flanked by two putti, 25¹/₂in. high. (Butterfield & Butterfield) £1,891

A George III giltwood mantel clock, the associated George I watch movement by William Webster, 13in. high. £1,500

An Empire-style French gilt bronze mantel clock, decorated with a mythological goddess, the 8-day movement with half-hour strike on a bell, with gilt dial and Roman numerals, 1860, 36cm. high. (Auction Team Köln) £454

A Regency ormolu-mounted griotte marble mantel clock by Benjamin Lewis Vulliamy, the milled circularRoman-chaptered dial in a serpent bezel, 16in. wide. (Christie's) £4,620

A French 19th century ormolu bracket clock, the elaborate rococo style case cast with scrolls, flowers, and seated satyrs, on low matching plinth, 3ft. high. (Russell Baldwin & Bright) £500

An early 19th century ormolu and white mantel timepiece, surmounted by an ormolu figure of a boy and swan, the single fusee movement lacking pendulum, 11¹/₂in. high. (Christie's S. Ken) £1,210

FIGURAL

An Empire ormolu mantel clock, the dial signed F. B. Adams, London, 17in. high.
£1,250

A 19th century English ormolu and bronze mantel timepiece, the fusee movement with anchor escapement, signed on a cartouche *Baetens, 23 Gerrard Street, Soho, London*, 11³/₄in. high.
(Phillips)   £1,800

Late 19th century bronze and ormolu figural mantel clock, France, 28½in. high.
£2,100

A French Directoire ormolu and marble mantel clock, the case depicting 'La Lecture', the female figure seated before a draped table with a lamp, 1ft. 1in. high.
(Phillips)   £2,100

A French 19th century bronze ormolu and red marble mantel clock, the enamel dial signed Guibal A Paris, 57cm. high.   £2,250

A 19th century ormolu and white marble mantel clock, the circular case decorated to the side with a winged putto reading and with foliage and a globe, signed *Mannheim à Paris*, 12½in. high.
(Phillips)   £700

Charles X gilt-bronze figural clock, circa 1830, the engine-turned circular clock face within an ivy frame set in a rectangular case surmounted by a ewer, 14³/₄in. high.
(Butterfield & Butterfield)   £787

A Second Empire yellow marble, ormolu and bronze striking mantel clock, the case with ormolu foliate mounts and surmounted by a bronze lion, 15in. high.
(Christie's)   £550

A gilt and ormolu French mantel clock, with a female figure leaning on a rocky mound, the dial with Roman numerals and signed *Bioula a Amien*, mid 19th century.
(Herholdt Jensen)   £361

FIGURAL

An Empire ormolu mantel clock cast as an organ-grinder, 33cm. high. £750

A Regency bronze and gilt bronze mantel timepiece, 31cm. high. £1,500

French bronze mantel clock, circa 1860, on scrolled base, 14in. high. £500

A late 19th century mantel clock, with back plate signed 'J.W.Benson, London', surmounted by a bronze group of a young man and woman holding a tambourine, 22¼in. high. (Bearne's) £600

French ormolu clock, the 8-day movement striking the half hours on a bell, the movement signed *Pierre LeRoy*, the white enamel dial with Roman numerals and minutes in Arabic numerals, 43cm. high, circa 1770.
(Auction Team Köln) £2,155

Napoleon III gilt-bronze figural mantel clock, Japy Frères, third quarter 19th century, surmounted by a group of a young girl and hound on a knoll, 19in. high.
(Butterfield & Butterfield) £1,028

A Charles X ormolu and malachite mantel clock, the dial flanked by the brothers Horatii taking their oath, after J-L David, 21½in. wide. £6,000

A French gilt bronze and bronze Elephant mantel clock, the movement with Brocot suspension, 22½in. high.
(Lawrence Fine Art) £1,760

A 19th century French ormolu and bronze mantel clock, the gilt dial with enamel numerals, 1ft.10in. high. £1,250

FIGURAL

A Charles X ormolu mantel clock with silk-suspended pendulum, 20.5cm. high. £650

A French mid 19th century mantel clock with eight-day movement stamped Japy Freres, 12in. wide. £1,000

A late Empire bronze ormolu and griotte marble mantel clock, 17½in. wide. £1,500

A Second Empire ormolu striking mantel clock, the case on milled sconce feet, the pedestal flanked by a column with incense urn atop and an angel strumming a lyre, 14in. high.
(Christie's) £990

An American Sambo figural clock, the cast iron coloured figure of a Negro playing his banjo, with American 30-hour movement, 39cm. high, circa 1875.
(Auction Team Köln) £1,030

An Empire ormolu and patinated bronze figural large mantel clock, first quarter 19th century, signed LeRoy h'ger du Roi à Paris, the movement with anchor escapement, 30in. high.
(Christie's) £5,030

A Louis XVI ormolu and bronze mantel clock, the two-train movement with silk suspension in a drum case mounted on a bronze horse, 1ft. 1in. high.
(Bonhams) £5,200

A Louis XVI ormolu and white marble clock, the glazed enamel dial signed *Guydamour a Paris,* with drum shaped case flanked by Venus and Cupid, 18½in. high.
(Christie's) £3,300

A 19th century French ormolu mantel clock, the case with a figure of a dancing female to the side holding a harp, 12½in. high.
(Phillips) £520

FIGURAL

An early 19th century
French mantel clock
with eight-day movement,
21½ x 24in.   £750

A French 19th century gilt metal
and porcelain mantel clock,
painted dial, signed *Archer Jack,
Paris & Cheltenham*, 10in.
(Bonhams)   £520

An Empire ormolu mantel
clock with circular enamel dial
set within a plinth with Apollo
and his lyre, 20½in. high. £1,500

A good Louis XVI white marble
and ormolu calendar mantel
clock, circular white enamel dial
signed *Furet a Paris*, the top
surmounted by a seated female
figure embraced by a winged
cherub, 1ft. 9in. high.
(Bonhams)   £4,000

A 19th century French ormolu
and white marble mantel clock,
the circular case with a winged
cherub to the side, 12in. high.
(Phillips)   £1,250

An Empire ormolu striking
mantel clock, the circular
Roman dial signed *Caillard à
Paris* with blued moon hands,
twin going barrel movement
with anchor escapement and silk
suspended pendulum, 21in. high.
(Christie's)   £1,320

A French 19th century ormolu
and white marble mantel clock,
the globe case surmounted by
putti, bands and signs of the
Zodiac, signed *E. Vittoz, Paris*,
25½in. high.
(Christie's S. Ken)   £1,210

Mid 19th century French
ormolu and marble figural
mantel clock, signed Caran-
das, A Versailles, 18½in.
high.   £600

A French ormolu and rouge
marble mantel clock in drum-
shaped case, with ribbon-tie
cresting, eight-day movement
striking on a bell, 15¼in. high.
(Christie's S. Ken)   £1,540

FIGURAL

A Charles X ormolu and bronze mantel clock with silvered dial, 15in. high. £1,850

A late 19th century French burnished gilt metal mantel clock by Henri Marc of Paris, 16in. high. (Spencer's) £600

A French mantel clock with eight-day striking movement, 13in. high. £450

A Louis XVI ormolu bronze and rouge marble striking mantel clock, the glazed circular enamel Arabic dial signed *Schmit à Paris*, the movement with outside countwheel strike and later Brocot escapement, 12¼in. high. (Christie's) **£1,100**

An Empire ormolu and marble striking mantel clock with green marble base on toupie feet, a lady seated in a bergère reading at a draped table on paw feet with oil lamp atop, signed *Leroy & Fils Hgers. du Roi A Paris No. 1065*, 12¾in. high. (Christie's) £2,530

An Empire ormolu striking mantel clock, the glazed engine-turned Roman dial with blued moon hands and foliate bezel, the twin going barrel movement with anchor escapement and silk suspended pendulum, 22½in. high. (Christie's) £1,210

A 19th century bronze and ormolu mantel clock, the circular case surmounted by the figure of Cupid and raised on the back of an elephant, signed *Thuret à Paris*, 1ft. 5¼in. high. (Phillips) £2,500

A Louis Philippe ormolu, bronze and white marble mantel clock, with enamel circlet dial, 14in. high. £1,000

A 19th century French ormolu and porcelain mantel clock, the shaped case surmounted by two seated putti on a naturalised ground, the circular enamel dial signed for *Bennett*, 1ft. 7in. high. (Phillips) £2,300

FIGURAL

Mid 19th century Charles X ormolu mantel clock, with eight-day time and strike, 23¼in. high. £500

A Regency bronze and ormolu mantel clock with enamel dial, 14½in. wide.
£3,500

An Empire ormolu negro clock with silk-suspended pendulum, 37cm. high.
£3,000

A French 19th century ormolu and bronze mantel clock formed as a classical maiden, standing and leaning pensively on a classical urn, 22½in. high.
(Christie's S. Ken.)   £1,045

An Empire bronze mantel clock, early 19th century, the circular enamelled dial surmounted by a bust of Socrates, 25in. high.
(Skinner Inc.)   £1,183

A Charles X bronze and ormolu mantel clock with circular dial surmounted by Cato amidst the ruins of Carthage, 17½in. wide.
£1,750

An Empire ormolu mantel clock, first quarter 19th century, signed LeRoy h'r, Palais Royal, 15³/₄in. high.
(Christie's)   £3,018

A 19th century French white marble, ormolu and bronze mantel clock, surmounted by two naked putti, signed *Aubanel & Rochat, A. Paris*, 1ft. 6in. high.
(Phillips)   £450

A Charles X ormolu mantel clock with enamel dial surmounted by a bust of Aristotle flanked by a cherub, 19½in. high.   £1,500

FIGURAL

An early 19th century
French mantel clock,
with eight-day move-
ment, 12 x 14½in.
£600

Empire ormolu mantel clock,
19th century, circular dial
inscribed *Manneville Rue St.
Honore a Paris*, 18½in. high.
(Skinner Inc.) £1,620

An early 19th century
ormolu mounted bronze
mantel timepiece, signed
Geo. Young, London,
12in. high. £1,000

An ormolu mantel clock, supported by a satyr seated on a
tree stump, mid 19th century,
the clock signed Paul Buhre,
St. Petersbourg, 29¼in.
(Christie's) £2,200

An 18th century French
ormolu and white marble
mantel clock, the circular
enamel dial signed *Le Masurier
a Paris,* 35cm. high. (Phillips
London) £450

A French ormolu mantel clock,
the two train movement with silk
suspension, outside locking plate
and bell striking, 20¾in. high.
(Lawrence Fine Art) £715

An early 19th century timepiece inkstand, the movement
with engine-turned gilt face by
Edward Lock, 19cm. high,
18cm. wide. £500

Mantel clock on D-shaped
marble base, the clock
face surmounted by a
bronzed group of lovers.
£600

A Louis Philippe ormolu
mantel clock, the silvered
dial signed A. C. Decauville
A Paris, 24½in. high.
£2,000

Late 19th century champ-
leve, glass and brass mantel
clock, France, 10¾in. high.
£800

A French late 19th century
champleve, bronze and glass
mantel clock, 15½in. high.
£1,250

An oval four-glass lacquered
brass 8-day striking mantel
clock with enamel dial, 9½in.
tall. £375

A 19th century French gilt brass
mantel clock, of four glass form,
the circular enamel dial signed
Callier, Horloger de la Marine
Imperiale, 22 Bould Montmarte
22, 14in. high. (Phillips) £680

An early Victorian four-glass
mantel timepiece, engraved
silvered dial signed *W. Davis &
Sons*, the four pillar single chain
fusee movement with anchor
escapement, 8¾in. high.
(Christie's) £858

A 19th century French bronze
and glass mantel clock, 8 day
Paris movement sounding the
half hours on a bell and with
Brocot escapement, 30cm. high.
(Duran) £417

A rosewood four glass mantel
timepiece, silvered chapter ring
signed Vulliamy London, chain
fusee movement, 7¼in. high.
(Christie's) £5,280

A French four glass and
gilt brass mantel clock, the
two-train movement with
Brocot suspension, 14¼in.
high. £650

A 19th century French ormolu
and enamel four glass mantel
clock, decorated Corinthian
columns, 12in. high. (Phillips)
£900

246

FOUR GLASS

A 19th century French gilt brass and champlevé enamel four glass mantel clock, 38cm. high. (Henry Spencer) **£780**

A French brass and enamel four glass clock with singing bird automaton, 30½in. high. **£4,250**

Ansonia brass mantel clock, dial with Arabic numerals. **£600**

An interesting English fruitwood four-glass chronometer mantel timepiece by Viner, London, the unusual eight-day chain fusee movement with three plates and four screwed pillars, 7¼in. high. (Christie's S. Ken) **£3,300**

A gilt quarter striking mantel clock on moulded base, the case glazed with four bevelled panels, the rounded angles, supporting plain cornice, English/French, mid 19th century, 15in. high. (Christie's) **£1,595**

An early Victorian rosewood four-glass striking mantel clock, the engraved silvered dial with foliate engraved spandrels and silvered bezel, the five pillar twin chain fusee movement with anchor escapement, 13in. high. (Christie's) **£1,100**

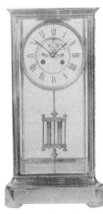

A glass and ormolu oval four-glass clock with gong strike, the chapter ring signed Franz Wiess & Sohne, Wien, 13in. high. **£2,500**

A French four-glass clock, the dial with enamelled swags above a mercury double chamber pendulum, the top and base of onyx, 27cm. high. **£700**

A 19th century French brass mantel clock, the enamel dial signed for Payne, Tunbridge Wells, 1ft.8in. high. **£1,800**

FOUR GLASS

A French four glass regulateur de table, the twin going barrel movement striking on bell with 3-rod grid iron pendulum, 22in. high. (Christie's) £2,640

An unusual French four-glass mantel clock, two-train movement by Vincenti & Cie, white enamel dial with red numerals, 1ft. 5¹/₂in. high. (Bonhams) £700

A French gilt brass four glass mantel clock, with decorated enamel dial and twin glass mercury pendulum, 10¹/₄in. high. (Phillips) £520

A good French ormolu mantel regulator, signed Lepaute, the movement with pin wheel escapement mounted on the backplate, 1ft.3in. high. (Phillips) £8,500

A Victorian satinwood four glass mantel timepiece, dial signed Webster, Queen Victoria Street, London, 17273, 7¾in. high. £2,500

Seth Thomas brass mantel clock, 20th century, with convex front and conforming glazed sides, mercury pendulum and key, 11in. high. (Skinner Inc.) £169

A 19th century French brass, enamel and green onyx mantel clock, of four glass form, on a green onyx base, 9¾in. high. (Phillips) £500

A French four glass and brass mantel clock, the movement with Brocot type escapement, stamped H. P. & Co., 13¾in. high. £600

A 19th century French gilt brass and champleve enamel four glass mantel clock, 25cm. high. £750

FOUR GLASS

A gilt and enamel French four glass clock, surmounted by a multi-coloured enamelled dome, the pendulum with a portrait of a lady, 16½in. high. (Christie's) £715

William IV period mahogany four glass mantel clock, by W. J. Thomas, London, 12½in. high. £950

An ormolu and cloisonné enamel four glass mantel clock, the twin-train movement with off-white enamel dial, decorated with floral swags, on paw feet, 17½in. high. (Christie's) £682

A good 19th century French mantel regulator, the gilt brass case of four glass form, signed Chs Oudin, with an annular dial below, 1ft 7in. high. (Phillips) £4,800

A late French 19th century four glass regulator clock, 4in. white enamel dial signed, *L. Leroy & Cie HGERS Dela Marine, Paris 7 Boulᵖ De La Madeleine*, 13in. (Bonhams) £400

A 19th century French green onyx, gilt brass and enamel mantel clock, 10in. high. (Phillips) £360

A French champleve enamel four glass clock, the 8-day movement striking on bell, 13in. high. £900

A 19th century rosewood cased four-glass mantel clock, dial signed French, Royal Exchange, London, 9¼ x 6¼in. £3,000

Early 20th century green onyx, glass and brass mantel clock, by Ansonia Clock Co., Conn., 11in. high. £375

FOUR PILLAR

A French Empire gilt bronze mounted black marble mantel clock, 16in. £400

A French Siena marble and ormolu mounted mantel clock, the drum-shaped case with lyre finial, 15½in. high. (Christie's) £275

A Louis XVI ormolu mounted marble pendule a cercle tournant, signed Ant. Coliau a Paris, 15½in. high. £4,500

French mahogany hall clock with four columns on a rectangular base, the enamel face in a palmetto surround, circa 1830, 44cm. high. (Kunsthaus am Museum) £714

A French ormolu mounted grey and white marble mantel clock, the white enamel dial with Roman numerals, pierced gilt hands and signed *Chopin a Paris*, 24½in. high. (Lawrence Fine Art) £605

A French mahogany portico clock, the gilt dial with Roman numerals and engine-turned centrefield signed *Bernard et fils, Bordeaux*, the eight-day movement with outside countwheel strike on a bell, 18½in. high. (Christie's S. Ken) £528

An Empire mahogany and ormolu pendulum mantel clock of architectural design, the circular dial with Roman numerals on a white enamel face, 53cm. wide (Finarte) £2,066

A Louis XVI white marble and ormolu mantel clock, the enamel dial inscribed A Paris, 1ft.10½in. high. £1,500

A white marble and ormolu portico clock, circa 1830, the white enamel annular dial signed Leroy a Paris, 19½in. high. £1,250

INDUSTRIAL

An unusual French brass and black marble automaton band saw mantel timepiece, two-train movement by C.L.T. Paris, 1ft. 4in. high.
(Bonhams) £2,100

A gilt bronze mantel clock in the form of a pump with white enamel face, 7¼in. high. £1,250

A late Victorian novelty clock in the form of a ship, the pendulum surmounted by a figure of a helmsman at the wheel. £1,000

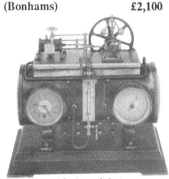

An unusual industrial steam engine incorporating a timepiece and barometer with thermometer, the horizontal boiler surmounted by the horizontal single cylinder steam engine with governor and flywheel driven by a separate spring barrel, 11in. high.
(Christie's S. Ken) £2,750

A gilt and patinated bronze industrial clock, signed *Japy Frères*, in the form of a trip hammer on oblong base, the hammer serving as the pendulum, circa 1880, 17¼in. high.
(Christie's New York) £1,571

An interesting late 19th century industrial mantel timepiece in the form of a watermill, the large paddle wheel driven by a separate movement rotating in a simulated waterway, inscribed *M. Grumberg, Bombay & Paris*, 15in. high.
(Christie's S. Ken) £5,500

An automaton clock in the form of a waterwheel in brickwork surround, 16in. high. £6,000

Mid 19th century red marble and patinated gilt bronze industrial clock, French, 17in. high. £2,250

Late 19th century gilt and patinated bronze and marble industrial clock, probably French, 14½in. high. £1,600

LALIQUE

A Lalique opalescent glass clock, 12.5cm., 1930's. £650

Moineaux, a Lalique frosted glass clock of domed outline, the central dial enclosed by nestling sparrows. (Phillips) £1,000

A Lalique clear glass clock of flat square form, 'Inseparables', 4¼in. square. £800

'Inseparables', a Lalique opalescent clock, the clear and opalescent glass moulded with two pairs of budgerigars among prunus blossom, 11.2cm. high. (Christie's) £1,980

'Deux Figurines', a Lalique moulded and engraved glass clock, of arched form, the clear and satin-finished glass moulded in intaglio with two scantily clad maidens, 38.7cm. high. (Christie's) £17,600

'Sirènes', a Lalique frosted opalescent glass desk clock, the square frame moulded in relief with sea sprites, 11.5cm. high. (Christie's) £1,485

Cinq Hirondelles, a Lalique glass timepiece, moulded with five swallows in flight amid branches of blossom, 15cm. high. (Phillips) £1,600

A Lalique clock, the satin-finished glass moulded with two pairs of love-birds in blossoming branches, with brown stained decoration, 21.8cm. wide. (Christie's) £880

René Lalique Deux Figurines clock, with recessed moulded design of two women in diaphanous gowns, 14in. high. (Skinner Inc.) £5,590

LIBERTY

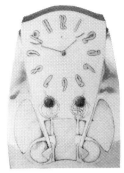

A Liberty & Co. 'Cymric', copper, mother-of-pearl and lapis clock, Birmingham 1903. £8,000

A Liberty & Co. pewter and enamel clock, with scrolling decoration and four turquoise enamelled hearts, the circular face with Arabic chapters, 10.3cm. high.
(Christie's) £220

Liberty & Co., an "English Pewter" plain arch mantel time-piece with enamelled dial.
(David Lay) £150

A Liberty & Co. oak and enamel mantel clock designed by Archibald Knox, the circular dial with a red scrolling design on a mottled blue and green ground, 29.3cm. high. (Christie's) £1,320

A Liberty & Co. lightly hammered silver mantel clock, with panels of repoussé decoration, the circular clock face with Arabic chapters, stamped *L&Co* with Birmingham hallmarks for 1911, 14.5cm. high, 760 grams gross.
(Christie's) £990

A Liberty and Co. hammered pewter clock, the body decorated with stylised tree and foliate panels, the copper clock face with black enamel Roman chapters and turquoise enamel centre, 18.2cm high.
(Christie's) £660

A Liberty & Co. Tudric pewter clock designed by Archibald Knox, decorated with rectangular panels of abalone, circular dial with Roman chapters, circa 1902, 16.7cm. high.
(Christie's) £1,540

A Liberty & Co. pewter and enamel clock of domed rectangular outline, the circular dial centred in blue and turquoise enamels, 18cm. high, factory marks and *'01156'* to base.
(Phillips) £520

A Liberty & Co. 'Cymric' silver and enamelled timepiece, embellished with a tree motif against a ground of coloured enamels, Birmingham marks for 1903, 11.5cm. high.
(Phillips) £5,200

LIBERTY

A Liberty pewter and enamel table clock designed by Archibald Knox, circa 1900, 14.2cm. high. £1,850

A silver and enamel desk clock by Liberty & Co., Birmingham 1911. £750

A Liberty & Co. 'Tudric' pewter and enamel clock, circa 1905, 20.5cm. £1,000

A Liberty & Co. Tudric pewter clock, the stepped rectangular form with overhanging top, moulded with panels of foliate decoration, 18.3cm. high. (Christie's) £286

A Liberty & Co. pewter carriage clock, the copper dial with black enamel chapters, on a mottled blue and green enamelled ground, stamped *English Pewter, Made by Liberty & Co.*, 12.2cm. high. (Christie's) £605

A Liberty & Co. Tudric pewter timepiece designed by Archibald Knox, embellished in relief with stylised plant forms, two buds set with blue enamel, 14cm. high. (Phillips) £2,600

A Liberty & Co. pewter, copper and turquoise enamel clock, marked Tudric 0150, circa 1900, 33cm. high. £900

A Liberty & Co. Tudric pewter 'Architectural' mantel clock, circa 1920, 7¼in. high. £800

A Liberty & Co pewter timepiece, designed by Archibald Knox, with copper coloured numerals, 8in. high. (Christie's) £2,090

LIGHTHOUSE CLOCKS

The lighthouse clock is an American shelf clock, some 16in. high, which resembles a miniature lighthouse. The type was patented by Simon Willard, the Massachusetts clockmaker, in 1822. It is comprised of three sections, the top part consisting of the dial with alarm movement, protected by a dome shaped lid, then there is a circular trunk, widening slightly towards the bottom, which rests on a round or octagonal base. The type was copied in Germany.

Eddystone lighthouse mahogany and mahogany veneer timepiece, by Simon Willard & Son, 30in. high.   £50,000

An unusual French 19th century bronze and gilt brass mantel timepiece, the case in the form of a light-house, with circular enamel dial, 10in. high. (Phillips) £1,000

A Federal mahogany veneer lighthouse clock, by Simon Willard, Mass., circa 1825, 27½in. high.   £75,000

Late 19th century lacquered brass and painted metal lighthouse clock, probably French, 22in. high.   £2,000

19th century metal night clock in the form of a lighthouse, with revolving dial, 21in. high.   £450

LONGCASE MINIATURES

Late 18th/early 19th century miniature Continental painted tall clock case, 17in. high.   £650

A Foley 'Intarsio' earthenware clock case in the form of a miniature long-case clock, circa 1900, 33.8cm. high. £750

Late 19th century ebonised wood miniature tall clock, by G. Hubbell & Son, 24in. high.   £1,250

LYRE CLOCKS

The lyre clock was a wall or shelf clock which first appeared in France in the late 18th century. It is named from its lyre shaped frame, often of bronze or ormolu mounted marble, which could be decorated with enamel or diamanté. The dial was mounted in the lower part, with the gridiron pendulum suspended above to simulate lyre strings. The bob was connected to the escapement and sometimes formed a ring set with paste brilliants around the dial.

An 8 day version was also produced in America by firms in Massachusetts between circa 1820–40.

A Regency rosewood striking mantel clock of lyre form, circular 3in. white enamel dial signed *Thwaites & Reed, London*, 8in. high.
(Bonhams) £1,150

A 19th century French white marble and ormolu mounted lyre clock, 1ft.4in. high. £1,350

Louis XVI style gilt-bronze mounted white alabaster lyre clock, Japy Frères, late 19th century, the white enamelled dial painted with floral festoons, 24in. high.
(Butterfield & Butterfield) £1,156

A 19th century Viennese enamel and silver-mounted timepiece of lyre shape, painted with scenes of Omphale, Queen of Lydia, with Hercules spinning yarn, 11$\frac{1}{2}$in. high, overall.
(Christie's S. Ken) £2,750

A 19th century French mahogany and ormolu mounted mantel clock of lyre shape, the twin train movement striking on a bell, 19$\frac{1}{2}$in. high.
(Christie's) £1,320

An Empire ormolu and bronze mantel clock of lyre shape supported upon seated griffins, 10$\frac{1}{2}$in. high. £1,500

A 19th century French ormolu mantel clock, the case in the form of a lyre, 38cm. high, on an oval ebonised stand under a glass shade. £900

Louis XVI style marble and ormolu mantel clock, France, 19th century, lyre form frame on stepped oval base (key missing), 48cm. high.
(Skinner Inc.) £1,226

MAHOGANY

A mahogany mantel clock, by Breguet, 11¼in. high. £6,000

A Victorian mahogany eight-bell chiming mantel clock, the drum-shaped case flanked by carved scrolls, on rectangular base, 28in. wide x 18in. high. (Christie's S. Ken) £880

A fine Georgian inlaid mahogany striking mantel clock, the enamel dial signed Arnold, London, 13in. high. £3,000

A mahogany striking mantel clock with engraved silvered dial now signed *Brockbank & Atkins London*, the four pillar twin chain fusée movement with anchor escapement and strike on gong, 10¼in. high. (Christie's) £550

A 19th century Austrian quarter striking mantel clock, the mahogany case flanked by gilt wood dolphins and applied with gilt mounts, signed *Johann Kralik in Wien*, 1ft. 11in. (Phillips) £380

A Eureka mantel timepiece, the 4½in. circular enamel dial signed *Eureka Clock Co. Ltd, London*, the large bimetallic balance wheel visible beneath, 1ft. 1in. high. (Bonhams) £650

A fine decorated mahogany chain and fusee movement mantel clock, the dial inscribed *L.N.E.R.*, 50cm. high. (Onslow's) £510

A Regency mahogany striking mantel clock, the dial signed Bateman, Great Tower Street, London, 13½in. diam. £2,250

Mid 20th century mahogany cased mantel clock with a German chiming and striking movement, 18in. tall. (G. A. Key) £200

MAHOGANY

A 19th century mahogany and brass inlaid mantel clock, the circular painted dial signed Condliff, Liverpool, 35cm.high. £1,000

A Regency mahogany mantel timepiece signed Weeks Museum, Coventry St., on the enamel dial, 12in. high. £1,500

A Regency mahogany and brass inlaid mantel timepiece with circular enamel dial (damaged), 9½in. high. £400

A Victorian mahogany mantel clock with stepped chamfered top, inscribed Yonge and Son, Strand, London, the twin fusee movement with shaped plates and engraved border, 18½in. high. (Christie's) £1,100

A George III mahogany striking clock, the case on gilt brass ball feet with fish-scale sound frets to sides and front door, chapter disc signed *Gravel & Son, London*, 16¾in. high. (Christie's) £880

A 19th century mahogany nightwatchman's timepiece, the silvered dial with outer recording ring and with plunger above, the fusee movement with anchor escapement. (Phillips) £350

An early 19th century mahogany mantel regulator, the 7¼in. silvered dial signed Reid & Auld Edinr., 17in. high. £3,500

A late 19th century mahogany night watchman's clock, 5in. engraved silvered dial inscribed *H. H. Plante*, 15in. high. (Bonhams) £380

A 19th century mahogany and brass inlaid clock, with anchor escapement chiming the quarters on two bells, 1ft.10in. high. (Phillips) £800

MARBLE

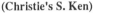

A Regency white marble and gilt bronze mantel timepiece, the gilt dial signed Viner, London, 8in. high. £650

A French ormolu and porcelain panelled mantel clock, signed on the dial *Le Roy & Fils, Palais Royal, a Paris, Rue Montpellier*, the eight-day movement with outside countwheel strike on a bell, 12in. high. (Christie's S. Ken) £550

Late 19th century red and black marble mantel clock with strike. (British Antique Exporters) £60

A late 18th century French white marble and ormolu mantel clock, the case surmounted by a twin handled urn flanked by columns wrapped with leaves, 15¹/₂in. high. (Phillips) £500

A fin-de-siècle pink marble and ormolu small mantel timepiece, signed *Le Roy & Fils 57 New Bond Strt. Made in France Palais Royal Paris* with pierced gilt hands, the going barrel movement with lever escapement, 6¹/₄in. high. (Christie's) £770

A Regency ormolu and marble mantel timepiece, the case on milled bun feet supporting the rectangular white marble base applied with a ribbon-tied fruiting swag, signed *Webster London*, 8in. high. (Christie's) £1,375

Louis XVI bronze and white marble mantel clock, early 19th century, urn finials and circular dial, 25in. high. (Skinner Inc.) £1,236

A good black marble and bronze mounted mantel timepiece in Egyptian style, single fusee movement signed on the backplate *Vulliamy, London*, 9in. high. (Christie's S. Ken) £26,400

A 19th century French gilt brass and white marble mantel timepiece, the rectangular case surmounted by a rooster, 7½in. high. (Phillips) £450

MARBLE

Victorian pink and black
marble mantel clock, 1860.
£100

Victorian black marble
mantel clock, 1880. £200

Black Faux marble curfew
clock by W. Gilbert Clock
Co., Conn., circa 1880,
17.1/8in. high. £300

An English ormolu and black
marble mantel timepiece, single
train fusée movement signed
Lamb, 86 Newman St., 7½in.
high.
(Bonhams) £400

An impressive 19th century
French ormolu and white
marble mantel clock, the
circular enamel dial with
pierced gilt hands, 2ft 3½in.
high. (Phillips) £1,050

Victorian rouge marble mantel
clock with eight-day French
movement and brass dial.
(British Antique Exporters)
£175

A Louis XVI white marble
and ormolu mounted mantel
clock, the dial signed Hardy
A Paris, 1ft.2in. high. £1,250

An English Regency black and
white marble mantel timepiece,
flanked by bronze recumbent
lions, on a rectangular black
marble base, signed Vulliamy,
11½in. wide. (Christie's) £2,420

An Empire white marble
clock, signed Robin, H. de
l'Empereur, circa 1810,
17¾in. high. £1,750

METAL CASED

Mid 19th century
Empire style ormolu
mantel clock, 22in.
high.   £600

A Charles X ormolu mantel
clock with glazed circular
dial, 19in. high.   £1,500

An Empire period ormolu
mounted mantel clock, the
dial signed Gaston Jolly a
Paris, 16in. high.   £1,000

**A French ormolu mantel clock,
inscribed on the dial *J.B. Baillon,
a Paris*, eight-day movement
with platform escapement,
striking on a bell, 8½in. high.
(Christie's S. Ken)   £1,540**

A rare mixed metal mantel
clock by Tiffany & Company,
New York, 1880-1885, the
front with mokume panels of
silver mixed with niello, brass
and red metal, 9in. high.
(Christie's)   £11,046

A French ormolu mantel
clock in the style of Louis XV,
inscribed Julien Leroy a Paris,
the eight-day movement with
outside count-wheel strike on
a bell, 21in. high. (Christie's)
£528

An Empire ormolu mantel
clock with glazed dial in
tapering plinth case surmounted by an oil lamp, 15in. high.
£2,500

An ormolu mantel clock with
enamel dial and drum-shaped
case, 12in. wide.   £500

An Empire ormolu mantel
clock in the form of a plinth
shaped bookcase with dial
in the upper half, 13in. high.
(Christie's)   £1,540

METAL CASED

An Empire gilt metal and bronze mantel clock, the base shaped as an orange tub, 17in. high. £4,250

A French Gothic style mantel clock, circa 1890, 11¾in. high. £525

Early 17th century South German gilt metal tabernacle clock or Turmuhr, 19¼in. high. £12,500

Louis XV style gilt-bronze mantel clock, retailed by Tiffany & Co., New York, circa 1900, the circular white enamelled clock face with Arabic hours and minutes with floral garlands, 24in. high. (Butterfield & Butterfield) £1,891

A Japanese gilt brass spring clock engraved with stylised flowering peony with going barrel for the outside Japanese countwheel strike on bell above the spring balance of the verge escapement to the chain fusee going, 4½in. high. (Christie's) £1,210

A Germanic early giltmetal timepiece, the case surmounted by a floral pierced and chased galleried dome surmounted by an urn finial, case and frame basically c. 1650, movement 18th century, 6¼in. high. (Christie's) £2,640

An ormolu mantel timepiece, round silvered Roman dial and anchor movement stamped *Silvani*, 11in. (Bonhams) £400

A good French mantel clock, the movement by Vincenti & Cie, enamelled to three sides, 12¾in. high. (David Lay) £580

A brass Eureka mantel timepiece, the enamel dial inscribed S. Fisher Ltd., 1ft.1in. high, under a damaged glass shade. £625

METAL CASED

A 19th century gilt brass
mantel timepiece, the enamel
dial signed Ecole Horlogerie
de Paris, 1ft.6½in. high. £900

An ormolu mantel clock of
rococo style, 29in. high,
19½in. wide.   £1,750

A 19th century ormolu
mantel clock, marketed by
Bigelow Kennard & Co.,
Boston, 24in. high. £1,000

An unusual George III gilt brass
watch lantern in the gothic
manner, the upper part with
pagoda pediment and pierced
square cover, originally hung
with bells, on paw feet, 16½in.
high.
(Canterbury)   £680

An ormolu and painted musical
pagoda clock, the tiered case on
stepped base with oriental
fretwork to the plinth, the
balustraded pagoda top
supported on dragons at each
angle, 18½in. high.
(Christie's)   £1,650

A 19th century French brass
and enamel mantel clock, the
arched case surmounted by a
pierced spire finial and with
turned corner columns decorated with three winged cherubs,
1ft.9in. high. (Phillips)   £520

E. F. Caldwell brass and
champlevé enamel mantel
timepiece, New York, 8¹/₁₆in.
high.
(Skinner)   £1,362

A Charles X ormolu mantel
clock with circular dial and
striking movement in a
foliate drum case, 19in. high.
                      £1,200

A Japanese gilt brass striking
spring clock, the case engraved
with stylised flowers and with
turned angle columns, 6in.
high.   £1,850

METAL CASED

A George III gilt-metal mantel clock with a 3¼in. dial by Ellicott, 11¾in. high. £1,750

Unusual brass drum-shaped night watchman's clock by T. Burk, Malta, 10.5cm. diam. £100

Late 19th century silver plated mantel clock, by Leroy & Fils, Paris, 14½in. high. £300

Late 18th century gilt metal and stone-set musical mantel clock for the Chinese market, signed Brockbanks, 19in. high. £35,000

Late 19th century French classical Revival brass and glass mantel clock, 14½in. high. £450

A small Restoration ormolu mantel clock in Louis XV style, the enamel dial signed S. Devaulx Palais Royal 124, 11in. high. £800

A 19th century French ormolu mantel clock, the circular chased dial signed Hy. Marc a Paris, 41cm. high. £1,250

An unusual gilt bronze nautical mantel clock in drum-shaped case, the silvered dial with Roman numerals, inscribed *J.W. Benson, London*, 19¼in. high. (Christie's S. Ken) £990

A George III ormolu mantel clock for the Oriental market, the dial signed W. Mahr, 19in. high. £6,000

Gilt bronze mantel clock, stamped Wm. Roskell, Paris, circa 1870, 43cm. high.
£850

Early 18th century chased and gilt brass night clock, signed B. Blaser in Bern, 335mm. high. £4,500

A Continental 'Zappler' time-piece, the movement mounted behind a chased gilt frame de-corated with two griffins, 2in. high. (Phillips) £320

A 19th century French ormolu mantel clock, the circular enamel dial signed Henry Voisin A Paris, the movement with silk suspension, 1ft. 1in. high. (Phillips) £480

A French ormolu mantel clock in the form of the front facade of Notre Dame Cathed-ral, 22in. high. (Christie's) £3,300

A gilt metal boudoir timepiece and thermometer of cheval form attributed to Thos. Cole London, the case of typical cast layered construction, 7in. high. (Christie's) £2,640

An electric mantel timepiece, the movement with enamel dial signed Dollond, London, 44cm. high. £1,000

A 19th century gilt bronze mantel timepiece, the silvered dial signed for Hunt & Roskell, London, 1ft.7¼in. high. £4,000

A Regency ormolu mantel clock, the dial in drum-shaped case, 9½in. wide. £1,500

METAL CASED

An ormolu mantel clock, the glazed dial signed Gosselin a Paris, 16¾in. high. £1,000

A Victorian lacquered brass mantel clock with French movement by F. Martie, 16in. high, 22in. wide. £650

A 19th century Austrian gilt metal repeating mantel clock, in shaped rococo case, 20cm. high. (Phillips) £220

An unusual gilt metal mariner's mantel timepiece, the circular white enamel dial with black Roman numerals, 20in. high overall.
(Spencer's) £280

A French 'Rheims' cathedral clock, the movement with Brocot type suspension, 21½in. high. £2,000

A 19th century French ormolu mantel clock, the case surmounted by a twin-handled urn decorated with fruit and swags, the circular enamel dial signed *Denigre Paris*, 1ft. 5³/₄in. high.
(Phillips) £520

A French gilt and silvered bronze gothic cathedral clock, the movement with silk suspension, signed *Vieyres*, 52cm. (Lawrence Fine Arts) £880

A miniature 19th century French ormolu mantel clock, with enamel dial signed *L. Leroy & Cie Paris*, 11.5cm. high. (Phillips) £620

A 19th century French ormolu and champleve enamel mantel clock, the gilt dial signed for Howell & James, 43cm. high. £900

METAL CASED

A gilt metal mantel clock with a 3¾in. enamel dial signed Grimalde & Johnson, Strand London, 10in. high. £1,000

A Swiss iron weight driven clock in the manner of Erhard Liechti, the wrought iron frame surmounted by a decorated strap and bell, 1ft. 3in. high. (Phillips) £6,000

A 19th century cartouche-shaped cast gilt brass case eight-day mantel clock, 12in. £300

A Rhenish chamber clock with iron posted frame to trains of brass wheels, vertical verge and balance escapement, countwheel strike/alarm on bell above, 17th-18th century, 15¹/₂in. high. (Christie's) £4,400

An attractive 19th century gilt brass and champlevé enamel mantel clock, the circular gilt dial with black Roman numerals, the movement striking the hours and half hours on a gong, 35cm. high. (Spencer's) £400

19th century brass framed and cloisonné panelled striking mantel clock, the French movement of drum case design, 11in. tall. (G. A. Key) £490

A 19th century ormolu mantel timepiece, the rectangular case with brickwork corners on ball feet, the circular silvered dial, signed *Wildenham*, 9in. high. (Phillips) £600

French brass mantel clock, 19th century, decorated with butterflies and flowers, Japy Frères gong striking movement, 13¹/₂in. high. (G. A. Key) £360

A Continental gilt metal candle alarm with florally engraved plinth case, 5in. high. £1,000

METAL CASED

A gilt metal timepiece, The Plato Clock, circa 1903, 6in. high.   £85

A small gilt brass mantel clock, the French carriage clock type movement with lever escapement and gong striking, 18cm. (Lawrence Fine Arts)   £176

Orrery clock under glass dome, Limited Edition numbered 259.   £375

A black japanned pendule Neuchateloise and wall bracket en suite, the twin going barrel movement with spring suspended verge escapement, signed *Henri Ducommun à la Chaux de fonds*, 36in. high. (Christie's)   £1,320

A 19th century Continental gilt brass and enamelled mantel timepiece, the case in the form of a ship's wheel, signed on a shaped cartouche for *Tiffany & Co.*, 8in. high. (Phillips)   £200

A 19th century French ormolu mantel clock, the case surmounted by a twin-handled urn with floral swags, flanked by two fluted Doric columns, 12^1/$_2$in. high. (Phillips)   £1,150

A late 19th century brass cased mantel clock in the French taste, striking the hours and half hours on a coiled gong, 28cm. (Phillips)   £230

A French ormolu 8-day mantel clock with porcelain dial, circa 1870, 17in. high, on serpentine shaped base with glass dome.   £500

A 19th century French ormolu and enamel mantel clock, the case decorated with polychrome champleve enamel, 24cm. high.   £400

OAK CASED

A late Victorian three-train oak mantel clock, the fusée anchor movement with silvered dial, the case with break-arch top, circa 1880, 20in. high.
(Tennants) £500

Victorian pollard oak cased mantel clock with eight day Continental movement.
(British Antique Exporters) £125

A Hiller talking clock, with single-train timepiece movement connected to the speaking movement, in oak case with full-height dial, 16¹/₂in. high, circa 1911.
(Christie's) £3,080

A Gustav Stickley oak mantel clock, early 20th century, the door with faceted cut-out framing brass dial, Seth Thomas movement, 13¾in. high.
(Skinner Inc.) £1,714

An oak cased railway station clock, the white 14in. dial with black Roman numerals, initialled B.R.W, 23in. high.
(Bonhams) £250

Carved oak cased chiming mantel clock, German movement, square dial with brass spandrels, 17¹/₂in. high.
(G. A. Key) £250

Gustav Stickley mantel clock, circa 1902, overhanging top above single door with copper hardware, Seth Thomas works, 21in. high
(Skinner) £4,224

A Westminster chime Admiral's hat mantel clock in an oak case, circa 1930. £30

L. & J. G. Stickley mantel clock, Fayetteville, New York, circa 1910, designed by Peter Heinrich Hansen, signed with Handcraft decal, 22in. high.
(Skinner Inc.) £4,630

ORMOLU & PORCELAIN

A 19th century French ormolu and porcelain mounted mantel clock, 41cm. high. £800

A gilt bronze and porcelain mantel clock, signed Leroy Freres a Paris, circa 1879, 10½in. high. £675

A Louis XVI ormolu mounted Sevres porcelain and biscuitware mantel clock, 16½in. high. £2,250

A 19th century French ormolu and porcelain mantel clock, the square dial signed Klaftenburger, London, together with a giltwood base, 46cm. high. £750

A Napoléon III ormolu and porcelain mounted striking mantel clock, the oval case draped with ribbon-tied oak leaves, the porcelain panels below painted with cherubs, 18¹/₂in. high. (Christie's) £1,540

A Louis Philippe ormolu and porcelain-mounted striking mantel clock, the foliate-cast case with Sèvres-style panels, stamped *Lagarde á Paris*, 18¹/₂in. high. (Christie's) £2,300

A 19th century French ormolu and porcelain mantel clock, the decorated dial signed for Miller & Co., Bristol, 43cm. high. £750

A 19th century French ormolu and porcelain mantel clock, the enamel dial signed Vieyres & Repignon a Paris, 11in. high. £900

A 19th century French ormolu and porcelain mantel clock, the enamel dial signed Grohe A Paris, 28cm. high. £675

ORMOLU & PORCELAIN

French porcelain mounted gilt bronze mantel clock by W. H. Tooke, Paris, 17in. high. £1,000

A 19th century French ormolu and porcelain mantel clock, 1ft.3in. high. £1,000

A French ormolu and Sevres style panel clock, signed on the dial Lagarde A Paris, 49cm. high. £3,750

An ormolu and porcelain French mantel clock, the shaped case decorated with swags and foliage and surmounted by two doves, 11in. high.
(Phillips) £440

An ormolu and dark blue ground Sevres pattern porcelain mantel clock, the circular dial with a dark blue border enclosing putti and trophies, late 19th century, 21¼in. high.
(Christie's) £2,420

A French 19th century porcelain and ormolu clock, dial signed *Chancellor & Son*, bell striking movement signed *Japy Freres*, 18in.
(Bonhams) £800

A 19th century French ormolu and porcelain mounted mantel clock, the case surmounted by an urn on a shaped base, 16in. high.
(Phillips) £950

19th century French ormolu and gilt metal mantel clock with Sèvres porcelain plaques at face, striking movement.
(G. A. Key) £450

A late 19th century gilt metal French mantel clock in the Louis XV manner, inset with pink porcelain panels, 46cm.
(Phillips) £280

271

ORMOLU & PORCELAIN

Late 19th century Sevres pattern pink-ground porcelain gilt bronze mounted mantel clock, 34cm. high. £1,000

A French gilt brass and jewelled porcelain mounted mantel clock, with the trade stamp of Japy Freres, 16¾in. high. £675

A 19th century French ormolu and porcelain mantel clock, the dial signed for F. Armstrong & Bros., Paris, 1ft.6½in. high. £750

A Louis XVI style French mantel clock, the silvered rectangular dial with porcelain cartouches for the Roman numerals, 19th century, 39cm. high.
(Duran) £944

A Victorian gilt-metal mounted porcelain mantel clock with circular white enamel dial inscribed *Hewell and James & Co.*, the case surmounted by two birds resting on stylised cloud bands, 13in. high.
(Christie's) £770

A 19th century French ormolu and porcelain mantel clock, the case surmounted by an urn flanked by lion mask mounts, 17in. high, together with a gilt wood base.
(Phillips) £1,000

A 19th century French gilt brass mantel clock with blue porcelain panels, signed Miller & Sons, London.
(Greenslades) £680

A 19th century French brass and porcelain mantel clock, 36cm. high. £2,500

A French porcelain and ormolu mantel clock, two-train movement with white enamel dial, in a bow-ended case cast with acanthus, 1ft. 2in. high.
(Bonhams) £650

ORMOLU & PORCELAIN

A 19th century French ormolu and porcelain mounted mantel clock, the dial signed E. W. Streeter, 11in. high. £750

A 19th century French ormolu and porcelain mounted mantel clock, the case surmounted by a gilt urn with ram's head supports, 14½in. high. (Phillips) £580

A Paris (Jacob Petit) clock-case and stand of scroll outline, blue JP marks, circa 1835, 37cm. high overall. £1,250

An ormolu and dark blue ground Sevres pattern porcelain mantel clock, signed *Lister & Sons S F 20 Paris,* late 19th century, 20in. high. (Christie's) £2,200

A Second Empire porcelain mounted ormolu mantel clock, the Sèvres style dial with Roman chapters, backplate with the stamp of *Brocot,* set with a further porcelain panel of Cupid, 13in. high. (Christie's) £605

An ormolu and dark blue ground porcelain mantel clock, the shaped dial centred with a maritime scene above a cartouche painted with a harbour scene 17in. high. (Christie's) £825

Victorian gilded spelter mantel clock, with pink and white polychrome decorated reserve panels and face, early 19th century, 15in. high. (G.A. Key) £365

A Charles X ormolu and porcelain clock, the movement signed Leroy, Paris 1102, 16in. high. £1,000

A French 19th century ormolu and porcelain mounted clock, painted dial with Roman chapter, bell striking movement, signed *R. and C.,* 14½in. (Bonhams) £650

PORCELAIN

A Meissen (Teichert) clock-case, blue Meissen mark, the movement by Lenzkirch, circa 1900, 51cm. high.
£950

A George III ormolu, Derby biscuit porcelain and white marble mantel clock by Vulliamy, with later enamelled dial, London, 1785, the porcelain damaged and restored, 19½in. high. (Christie's) £35,200

A Meissen clockcase with a seated figure of Cupid, blue crossed swords and incised numeral marks, circa 1880, 30cm. high. £1,000

A 19th century French porcelain mantel clock, the shaped case applied with flowers, the circular enamel dial signed Hry Marc, a Paris, 1ft 1½in. high. (Phillips) £640

A Second Empire porcelain and brass elephant clock, for the Turkish market, the elephant with turquoise glaze and with royal blue and gilt decoration, 11½in. high. (Christie's) £1,100

A Royal Worcester clock case, coloured in ivory and gold and encrusted with flowers, containing a French circular eight-day striking movement, 29cm., date code for 1887. (Phillips) £700

A Meissen clockcase of shaped outline, the movement with circular dial, blue crossed swords mark, circa 1880, 31cm. high. £2,250

Meissen type floral encrusted porcelain mantel clock, 19th century, three figures seated among floral scrollwork, 13in. high. (Skinner Inc.) £529

A Paris (Jacob Petit) blue-ground clockcase and stand, the movement by Hry. Marc a Paris, circa 1835, 34cm. high. £750

PORCELAIN

Late 19th century Dresden clock group, 66.5cm. high. £1,000

A Louis XVI ormolu and terracotta mantel clock, the dial signed Sotiau A Paris, with figures of Minerva and attendants, 18in. wide. £3,500

Ansonia porcelain mantel clock with Roman numerals. £275

A 19th century Continental porcelain mantel clock, the Meissen case decorated with four putti representing the Seasons, the associated movement stamped *Hy Marc Paris*, 1ft. 6in. high. (Phillips) £3,200

An unusual 19th century Austrian miniature porcelain timepiece, the shaped case decorated with flowers on paw feet, signed *Doker, in Wien*, 55mm. high. (Phillips) £460

A Martin Brothers stoneware mantel clock, the base decorated to each corner with fierce griffin-like heads, the arched pediment raised off twin griffin supports with applied lizard above, 31.5cm. high. (Phillips) £1,100

A 19th century French porcelain mantel clock with eight-day striking movement, inscribed Raingo Freres, Paris, 15in. high. £350

Weller Dickensware art pottery mantel clock, housed in elaborated pottery frame decorated with yellow pansies, 10in. high. (Skinner Inc.) £249

A Meissen clock case of shaped outline, circa 1880, the eight-day striking movement with enamel dial, 41.5cm. high. £1,500

ROSEWOOD

A rosewood mantel
timepiece, signed Birch,
London, 8½in.   £900

Rosewood mantel clock
by E. Ingraham & Co.,
Connecticut, circa 1862.
£1,750

A brass inlaid rosewood
night timepiece, the 4¾in.
dial signed Robt. Groves,
London.   £300

A 19th century rosewood mantel
timepiece, the square painted
dial signed Webster & Son
London, the fusée movement
with anchor escapement and
passing strike, 23cm. high.
(Phillips)   £900

A 19th century rosewood
mantel timepiece, the square
silvered dial signed Frodsham
Gracechurch Street, London,
the fusee movement with
anchor escapement, 9in.
high. (Phillips)   £850

A 19th century rosewood mantel
timepiece, the square silvered
dial signed *Muston & Garth,
Bristol*, the fusée movement with
anchor escapement, 11¼in.
high.
(Phillips)   £550

A 19th century rosewood
four-glass mantel time-
piece, signed Vulliamy
London, 7½in. high.
£4,500

Early 19th century long cased
striking mantel clock by J. R.
Chapman, two train movement
with circular dial enamelled,
17½in. tall.
(G. A. Key)   £750

A Regency rosewood mantel
timepiece, the dial signed
Arnold & Dent, Strand,
London, 10¼in. high. £1,000

ROSEWOOD

A Victorian rosewood four-glass mantel clock, the back-plate signed French, Royal Exchange, London, 9½in. high. £2,500

A 19th century French rosewood floral inlaid classical shaped 8-day mantel clock, 10in. high. £170

A Regency rosewood mantel timepiece, the case of Gothic style, the fusee movement with anchor escapement, 12½in. high. (Phillips) £410

A 19th century rosewood and brass inlaid mantel timepiece, signed Thwaites & Reed, Clerkenwell, London, the fusee movement with anchor escapement, 8in. high. (Phillips) £1,600

An unusual rosewood quarter chiming small mantel clock signed *Gibbs, 38 Banner St. London*, the shaped arched dial with Roman chapters, blued-steel Breguet hands, purpose made for the late 18th century miniature triple fusée movement now fitted with chains, 11in. high. (Christie's) £2,552

A 19th century rosewood mantel timepiece, the silvered dial signed Frodsham & Son, Grace-church Street, London, the fusee movement with anchor escapement, 30cm. high. (Phillips) £1,650

A French rosewood and marquetry mantel clock in the Turkish market manner, inscribed *Meyer, 6 Rue de Grenelle, Ste. Honore*, 46.5cm. (Lawrence Fine Arts) £528

Mid 19th century rosewood mantel clock with carrying case, signed James Murray, Royal Exchange London, 12in. high. £4,250

An early Victorian mantel clock, the movement striking on a carillon of eight bells and a coiled gong, the cream enamel dial inscribed *Viner, Bond St., London*, 21½in. high. (Christie's) £550

SILVER

A 19th century Austrian silver and lapis lazuli decorative mantel timepiece, 22cm. high. £3,750

A miniature silver and enamel timepiece, the rectangular case decorated with blue guilloche enamel, the dial signed for Harrods Ltd, 1½in. high. (Phillips) £380

An Austrian 19th century silver and enamel timepiece, with polychrome champleve dial, 18cm. high. £1,500

A silver mounted and tortoiseshell pique desk timepiece, with a domed top, pique worked with foliage pendant from ribbon ties, 1908 by Harris Adelstein, 9.5cm. (Lawrence Fine Arts) £506

An enamelled silver Renaissance Revival clock in the form of a camel, the case by Hermann Bohm, Vienna, the oval base finely painted with mythological scenes with ground of leafy scrolls, circa 1880, 9³/₄in. high. (Christie's) £4,147

A silver plated striking carriage clock with split compensated balance to gilt lever platform, 6½in. high. £900

An Austrian silver plated quarter chiming mantel clock, signed Carl Wolfe in Wien, 9½in. high. £650

A 19th century Austrian silver and enamel mantel timepiece, the movement set within a Chinese pale celadon Bi disc, 6¹/₂in. high. (Phillips) £780

A South German silver fronted Telleruhr, the circular movement signed Matthias Geill, on ebonised stand, 14in. high. £10,000

SILVER

Late 19th century Viennese silver and enamel mantel clock on oval base, 9¾in. high. £5,000

A Continental silver gilt miniature timepiece, the shaped case decorated with repousse scrolls and flowers, 4in. high, in a fitted tooled leather travelling case. (Phillips) £780

A fin de siecle silvered and parcel gilt brass windmill clock, 18½in. high. £1,250

An enamelled silver Renaissance Revival figural clock, Viennese, surmounted by a caricature of a violinist in frock coat and wide brimmed hat, the plinth painted with a scene of peasants dancing in rustic landscape, circa 1880, 10½in. high.
(Christie's) £2,871

An enamelled silver Renaissance Revival jewel casket fitted with a watch, the case by Simon Grünwald, Vienna, on winged paw feet, the side panels and broken arch pediment set with panels painted with mythological scenes, circa 1880, 5in. high.
(Christie's) £2,424

A fine silver gilt and enamel timepiece, the rectangular case with chamfered angles, floral gilt decoration and swags in high relief, on mother-of-pearl base with bun feet, 2¾in. high.
(Christie's S. Ken) £1,980

An Edwardian silver cased mantel timepiece, in plain balloon case with tied reed borders upon ogee bracket feet by W. Comyns, London 1909, 8¾in.
(Tennants) £750

A fine silver/gilt and enamel minute repeating timepiece by European Watch & Clock Co., for Cartier, in red leather travelling case, 2¹³/₁₆in. high.
(Christie's S. Ken) £5,500

A George V silver and tortoiseshell-mounted dressing table clock, 14cm. high, William Comyns, London 1910.
(Bearne's) £1,800

SWINGING DOLL

Bobbing doll timepiece, by Ansonia Clock Co., circa 1890, the bisque figure suspended from a spring under movement. £800

Swinging doll timepiece, by Ansonia Clock Co., circa 1890, 8in. high. £600

Swinging doll timepiece, by Ansonia Clock Co., circa 1890, 12in. high. £650

TORTOISESHELL

A boulle mantel clock in the Louis XV taste, in waisted tortoiseshell and brass inlaid case, 42cm. (Phillips) £500

A French late 19th century red tortoiseshell and gilt metal mounted mantel clock, signed on a white enamel plaque *Thuret a Paris*, the eight-day movement striking on a gong, 13in. high. (Christie's S. Ken) £550

A French green tortoiseshell and boulle mantel clock in waisted case surmounted by a figure of a cherub, 17in. high. (Christie's S. Ken.) £550

A 19th century French tortoiseshell and cut-brass bracket clock, the shaped case surmounted by a galleried fret and four finials, 2ft. 2in. high. (Phillips) £850

A red tortoiseshell boulle mantel clock in waisted case, the eight-day movement striking on a bell, with sunburst pendulum, 14½in. high. (Christie's) £660

A 19th century French red tortoiseshell and cut-brass inlaid mantel clock, the shaped case with gilt mounts, signed *Rollin à Paris*, 1ft. 4in. high. (Phillips) £380

TORTOISESHELL

A 19th century French red tortoiseshell and ormolu mounted mantel clock, signed *Balthazar a Paris,* 33cm. high.
(Phillips) £600

A boulle mantel clock in the Louis XV taste, the gilt metal face in waisted tortoiseshell and brass inlaid case, 30cm.
(Phillips) £300

A French boulle mantel clock, two-train movement and white enamel dial signed *Leroy à Paris,* in a waisted brass and tortoiseshell case, 12in. high.
(Bonhams) £520

A 19th century French boulle and polychrome enamel striking bracket clock in Louis XVI style, the waisted case applied with giltmetal foliate mounts on scroll feet surmounted by the winged figure of Peace, 35¼in. high overall.
(Christie's) £880

A Louis XIV tortoiseshell and ormolu striking pendule religieuse with flambeau urn finials, signed *Rabby à Paris,* the five-baluster pillar twin going barrel movement now with tic-tac escapement, 20¼in. high.
(Christie's) £1,540

A Regency tortoiseshell, and boulle and ormolu mounted bracket clock, signed on an enamel cartouche below the six, *Le Boeuf, Paris,* the two-train movement with outside countwheel strike on a bell, 34in. high.
(Christie's S. Ken) £1,540

A French torchere ormolu mounted mantel clock in the style of Louis XIV, the eight day movement striking on a gong, 11¼in. high.
(Christie's) £550

A miniature tortoiseshell silver-gilt carriage timepiece, the backplate stamped *French made,* Roman and Arabic enamel dial signed *Drew & Sons Picc. Circus London. W.,* 3⅛in. high.
(Christie's) £440

A French 19th century boulle clock, gilt dial with white enamel chapter and blue Roman numerals, bell striking movement marked *Vincente Cie,* 16in.
(Bonhams) £500

TWO PILLAR

A 19th century French white marble and ormolu mantel clock, 51cm. high.   £750

A Eureka electric clock with large vertical balance wheel, the movement supported on two brass pillars, on circular brass base with glass dome, 9½in. high.
(Christie's S. Ken)   £605

A small Louis XVI ormolu-mounted marble temple clock, 16in. high.   £3,750

A small French vari-coloured marble and gilt mantel timepiece, in drum-shaped case surmounted by a marble stylised urn finial, with timepiece movement, 8in. high.
(Christie's S. Ken)   £308

A lythalin and gilt metal mantel timepiece, the case supported by two columns with gilt capitals, on rectangular base, ivorine dial with Arabic numerals, 5½in. high.
(Christie's S. Ken)   £330

Charles X mahogany and ormolu mantel clock, circa 1830, with enamelled numbers suspended between columnar supports on a stepped base, 22in. high.
(Skinner Inc.)   £4,050

A French white marble and ormolu mounted mantel clock in drum-shaped case surmounted by a stylized urn finial, 18½ in. high.
(Christie's S. Ken.)   £715

A green lacquer mantel timepiece, the later single fusee movement with anchor escapement, 24¾in. high. (Lawrence Fine Arts)   £418

A French 19th century gilt ormolu portico clock, engine-turned gilt dial, putto on a swing pendulum, 18in.
(Bonhams)   £750

TWO PILLAR

Late 19th century French Empire crystal and ormolu mantel clock on ebonised base, 20¼in. high.   £900

A French Louis XVI style black marble and ormolu mounted mantel clock, 1ft. 9in. high.   £1,500

A 19th century French ebonised pillar clock, on gilt metal applied block base, with glass dome, 41cm. (Phillips)   £220

An unusual Continental musical portico clock, the circular white enamel dial with black Roman numerals indistinctly inscribed with maker's name, 20in. high overall.
(Spencer's)   £1,250

A Louis XVI grey marble and ormolu striking mantel clock, the white enamel Roman dial signed *Durand* with pierced gilt hands, twin going barrel movement with anchor escapement and sunburst pendulum, 21³/₄in. high.
(Christie's)   £1,980

A Louis Philippe ormolu and Baccarat portico mantel clock, the enamel dial signed *Hry Marc a Paris,* with foliate bezel drum shaped case, 16¾in. high.
(Christie's London)   £2,090

An Italian ormolu and cut glass portico mantel clock with chased dial, signed Lacroix a Turin, 16½in. high.
£1,500

An Empire ormolu mantel clock surmounted with a winged putto striking metal on an anvil at a forge, 12½in. wide.   £1,250

Louis Philippe ebonised mantel clock, mid 19th century, ormolu framed enamel dial, raised on spiral turned supports, striking the half-hour, case 26in. high.
(Skinner Inc)   £454

TWO PILLAR

A French Empire striking clock, the movement with outside count wheel, 21 in. high. £800

An early 19th century French mantel clock, by Piolaine, Paris, 17in. high. £750

A mid 19th century gilt metal striking mantel clock, 20½in. high. £1,000

Empire ormolu mantel clock, early 19th century, rectangular cornice on four columns above a circular dial, 21in. high. (Skinner Inc.) £1,051

An Empire ormolu mounted black and white marble mantel clock, the enamel dial signed 'a Paris', 21in. high. £6,000

A Charles X ormolu and mahogany mantel clock, the silvered dial with scrolling floral bezel, 19½in. high. (Christie's) £440

A George III gilt metal, alabaster and white marble clock, the backplate signed J. Burrows, Goodge Street, London, 19in. high. £500

French Empire ormolu and black lacquer mantel clock, early 19th century, under a glass dome, 19¹/₂in. high. (Eldred's) £257

A French 19th century ormolu mantel clock, on an oval rosewood plinth under a glass shade, 1ft.3in. high. £1,000

VASE SHAPED

An Empire ormolu man-
tel clock in the form of a
flattened urn with enamel
dial, 42cm. high.   £1,000

A Ginori pottery clockcase,
moulded as a two-handled
pilgrim flask with mask-
moulded neck, 16in. high.
(Christie's S. Ken.)   £121

An ormolu mounted por-
phyry tripod vase clock of
Athenienne form, 20in. high.
                        £8,500

Louis XVI style gilt-bronze-
mounted porphyry pendule à
cercles rolant, mid-19th century,
of urn-form richly embellished
with applied swags of berried
foliage and flowers, 16in. high.
(Butterfield & Butterfield) £4,724

A 19th century Austrian silver
and enamel timepiece, the case
in the form of a twin handled
urn, surmounted by a floral
spray and decorated with
classical scenes, 9in. high.
(Phillips)   £2,000

A fine and rare Louis XV
celadon craquelure glazed and
ormolu mounted mantel clock of
urn form with horizontal
chapter ring, signed on the
backplate *Masson à Paris*, 1ft.
11¹/₂in. high, circa 1765.
(Bonhams)   £21,000

A 19th century French porcelain
and gilt metal mantel timepiece,
the shaped case flanked by lion
masks on a shaped base, 11in.
high.
(Phillips)   £350

An impressive French 19th
century ormolu mantel
clock, the case in the form
of an urn flanked by gro-
tesque masks, 1ft 9½in.
high. (Phillips)   £720

A French blue-john and
ormolu mantel clock, the case
in the form of an urn flanked
by rams' head masks, 55cm.
high.
(Phillips)   £15,000

VASE SHAPED

A Charles X vase-shaped mantel clock with enamel dial and swan-neck handles, 13in. high £1,250

A miniature enamel and gilt clock, Austria, the urn shape vase houses a Swiss movement, eight-day clock. £2,000

A mid 19th century French mantel clock with eight-day movement, 21in. high. £3,250

An ormolu mantel clock of Louis XVI style, the dial signed Antide-Janvier a Paris in oval vase-shaped case, 20in. high. £1,250

Unusual Renaissance design gilt-brass mantel clock, late 19th century, the domed case surmounted by an urn with lotus bud finial supported by four winged snarling animal mask monopodia, 26½in. high. (Butterfield & Butterfield) £809

A Meissen porcelain clockcase, the circular gilt metal dial with blue Roman numerals, blue crossed swords and incised numeral marks, circa 1880, 60cm. high. (Christie's) £3,300

A George III ormolu mounted timepiece clock, by James Tregent, London, in the style of M. Boulton, 12½in. high. £10,000

An ormolu mounted malachite mantel clock and urn, supported by foliate capped paw feet, inset with a circular clock, 19th century, 19¼in. high. (Christie's) £2,420

A lady's boudoir timepiece in the form of an ormolu mounted cut glass scent bottle, signed Jas. Watts, London, 6½in. high. £1,000

WALNUT CASED

Walnut cased mantel clock by J. J. & W. Beals, Mass., circa 1840, 13in. high. £450

Mid 19th century Black Forest carved walnut figural clock, 28¾in. high. £3,000

An American walnut framed mantel clock, circa 1890. £150

A late 19th century walnut mantel clock, the dial signed Chas. Frodsham, Clockmaker to the Queen, No. 2057, 30cm. high. £1,000

A burr-walnut and bronze mounted mantel clock in rectangular case with decorative bronze frieze, signed below the six *Frodsham, Gracechurch Street, London,* twin chain fusée movement striking on a gong, 15¼in. high. (Christie's S. Ken) £880

A 19th century gilt brass and malachite mantel timepiece by Thomas Cole, the case in the form of a miniature chiffonier, the lever movement now converted to eight day duration, 5½in. high. (Phillips) £6,500

An Odd Fellows carved box with clock, America, early 20th century, shaped upper section crested with carved eagle, 13½in. high. (Skinner Inc.) £227

A Victorian burr walnut mantel clock, 6in. foliate engraved gilt dial, trefoil hands, two-train chain fusée movement with anchor escapement, 12in. high. (Bonhams) £1,500

A Black Forest 'cuckoo' mantel clock, the two train fusee movement with anchor escapement and skeletonised back plate. (Lawrence Fine Arts) £308

WALNUT CASED

A Black Forest trumpeter clock in walnut case, 39in. high. £3,000

A walnut cased combined timepiece, barograph, aneroid barometer and thermometer, signed Chadburn & Son, 26¾ x 14in. £600

A large Victorian chiming mantel clock with brass and silver dial, 28in. high. £1,250

A walnut musical alarm clock, the movement signed *Made in Wurttemberg*, circa 1920, 21cm. high.
(Auction Team Köln)   £211

Late 19th century walnut cased work's timepiece with punch mechanism.   £200

A 19th century walnut mantel timepiece, the rectangular case, with engraved silvered dial, signed *Fredᵏ Bryant, London*, the fusée movement with anchor escapement, 10½in. high.
(Phillips)   £650

A highly elaborate walnut fretwork architectural clock by Japy Freres & Cie, with visible Brocot escapement, 37½in. high. (Tennants) £800

A Heller musical chalet clock, Swiss, circa 1880, the carved wood case with stairs, balconies, beehives, doghouse and two train clock striking on bell, 18in. wide.
(Sotheby's)   £748

A Regency variegated wood mantel timepiece, signed Davd. Magson, 12¾in. high. £900

MIRROR CLOCKS

This was a wall clock with a mirror usually positioned under the dial. It was pioneered by Chauncey Jerome (1793–1868) in Connecticut, to compete, it is said, with the pillar and scroll clock. He began mass producing these, and though they looked quite expensive, made them so cheaply that when he sent a shipload to Britain Customs officers thought his valuation so low that he was just trying to avoid paying the proper tax. They therefore bought the entire cargo for HM government, calling his bluff, as they thought!

A mirror clock with polychrome stencilled eglomise tablet framing the painted iron dial, circa 1825, 31in. long. **£1,000**

A Federal mahogany mirror clock, by Asa Munger, Auburn, New York, circa 1830, 39in. high. £1,500

An Empire carved mahogany and veneer mirror clock, by Hotchkiss & Benedict, N.Y., circa 1825, 39in. high. **£650**

Empire carved mahogany mirror clock by Munger & Benedict, New York, circa 1830, 39½in. high. **£1,500**

New Hampshire mirror timepiece by James Collins, circa 1825, 8-day brass weight driven movement. £1,250

Classical Revival mahogany mirror clock by Marsh, Gilbert & Co., Connecticut, circa 1830, 36½in. high. **£500**

Giltwood mirror wall timepiece, A. Chandler, Concord, New Hampshire, circa 1830, 30in. high. (Skinner) **£1,154**

An Empire mahogany and mahogany veneer shelf clock, by Hotchkiss & Benedict, N.Y., circa 1830, 38in. high. **£1,250**

A late 17th century brass eight-day striking longcase clock movement by George Graham, London.   £4,500

A multi-dial longcase laboratory timepiece, by T. Wright. £1,500

A fine eight-day longcase clock movement with four and eight bell chime, inscribed J. Hallifax, London.
£1,200

An early 18th century longcase clock movement, the 10in. square brass dial with silvered chapter ring, subsidiary seconds, date aperture and engraved centre. (Phillips)   £1,000

A Comtoise longcase clock movement, the white enamel dial with Roman numerals and quarters in Arabic numerals, signed *Lafabrie Hger a Nogaro*, the cast brass face with sun and putti, 1810–20.
(Auction Team Köln)   £1,358

An unusual astronomical clock movement by Matthias Ernst, Lindau, the gilt dial with 60-minute ring enclosing seconds and anti-clockwise hour rings, circa 1700, 10in. wide.
(Christie's New York)
£3,927

A George I bracket timepiece movement, backplate signed L. Bradley, London, dial 6in. x 8¼in.   £1,250

An early 18th century longcase clock movement, the 11in. square brass dial with silvered chapter ring signed Chr Gould, Londini Fecit. (Phillips)   £2,000

An eight-day striking and chiming longcase clock movement inscribed John Fletcher.
£350

MYSTERY CLOCKS

A Belle Epoque mystery time-piece, 25in. high. (Christie's) £3,080

A Continental spelter mystery timepiece on a rectangular base, 32cm. high. £500

A South German giltwood calendar mystery clock, signed Joseph Holtzel, 18th century, 32in. high. (Christie's) £6,380

PENDULE D'OFFICIER

An Empire ormolu grande sonnerie striking pendule d'officier, the foliate cast case on chased paw feet, signed *Auguste Droz*, 8¹/₂in. high. (Christie's) £2,530

An early 19th century Austrian quarter chiming pendule d'officier, the gilt dial with machined centre, 6¹/₂in. high. (Phillips) £900

An ormolu quarter striking pendule d'officier with Turkish chaptered enamel dial signed Courvoisier et Compe., 8½in. high. £2,400

An 18th/19th century quarter striking pendule d'officier with verge movement, 225mm. high. £3,750

An Empire ormolu grande sonnerie striking pendule d'officier, signed *Louis Duchène*, with pierced blued hands, the circular movement with chain fusée, 8¹/₄in. high. (Christie's) £2,970

An ormolu pendule d'officier with grande sonnerie and alarm, 8¼in. high. £3,750

A Viennese picture clock, depicting an inland river scene, the Roman enamel dial set into the clock tower, the going barrel movement with pierced-out plates and lever escapement, 29 x 24¹/₂in.
(Christie's) £935

A Viennese quarter striking picture clock depicting carousing cavaliers at a tavern with lakeland views and castle, with silk suspended pendulum in carved giltwood frame, circa 1850, 39¹/₂ x 29in.
(Christie's) £3,740

A musical picture clock with figures on a river bank with the clock face in church tower, in a carved gilded frame, 29¹/₂ x 34¹/₂in. overall, circa 1850. £1,500

A Big Ben musical picture clock in black wooden case, the melody playing every quarter, or on pulling the cord, 70cm. high.
(Auction Team Köln) £304

A Viennese picture clock depicting sportsmen and their dogs, twin going barrel movement stamped *Villenense* with recoil escapement and strike on gong, 28¹/₄ x 23in.
(Christie's) £1,650

A German framed automaton windmill novelty timepiece, the printed landscape depicting a windmill with automaton sails, dated *1892* above the doorway, 20¹/₄in. high.
(Christie's) £1,210

A musical clock set into the frame of a Bavarian landscape picture, with Roman numerals and playing two melodies.
(Herholdt Jensen) £421

A rare French automaton clock picture, Napoléon III, Paris, circa 1851, depicting the Crystal Palace, Hyde Park, with two rows of automated figures, 122cm. wide.
(Sotheby's) £7,260

A Viennese quarter striking picture clock, the painting on copper depicting a harvest scene with the sea and mountains in the background, circa 1860, 35¹/₄ x 36¹/₂in.
(Christie's) £2,200

This name is given to one of the most attractive of American shelf clocks, having delicate feet, slender pillars, one at each side and one in the centre, with a broken arch or double scroll at the top. They are sometimes also called Terry clocks, as Eli Terry, a Connecticut clockmaker and businessman, was the first to produce them in large numbers around 1816. They continued in production until the 1830s, and other notable manufacturers were Seth Thomas and Silas Hoadley, also of Connecticut.

Federal mahogany pillar and scroll clock, by Ephraim Downes, Conn., circa 1825, 31in. high.   **£800**

A Federal mahogany pillar and scroll clock, by E. Terry & Sons, circa 1835, 31in. high.   **£1,000**

A late Federal mahogany pillar and scroll shelf clock, Seth Thomas, Plymouth, Connecticut, circa 1820, with a glazed cupboard door flanked by colonettes and enclosing a white dial with Arabic chapter ring, 31in. high.
(Christie's)   **£893**

A Federal mahogany shelf clock, labelled Seth Thomas, Plymouth, Connecticut, first quarter 19th century, the swan neck pediment above a rectangular case with double glazed door, 29in. high.
(Christie's)   **£866**

A Federal pillar and scroll shelf clock by Seth Thomas, Plymouth, Connecticut, circa 1805, the swan's-neck pediment centering three brass urn finials, 31in. high.
(Christie's)   **£2,290**

A Federal mahogany pillar and scroll clock, by E. Terry & Sons, Conn., circa 1820, 29in high.   **£1,500**

Federal mahogany pillar and scroll clock, by Ephraim Downs for G. Mitchell, Conn., circa 1820, 31in. high.   **£900**

Federal mahogany pillar and scroll clock, E. Terry & Sons, Conn., circa 1825, 31in. high.   **£675**

Federal mahogany pillar and scroll clock, by Eli & Samuel Terry, Conn., circa 1825, 28½in. high. £750

Federal mahogany pillar and scroll clock, Riley Whiting, Winchester, Connecticut, circa 1820, 30in. high. (Skinner Inc.) £413

Federal mahogany pillar and scroll clock, Bishop and Bradley, Waterbury, Connecticut, circa 1825. (Skinner Inc.) £988

Federal mahogany pillar and scroll clock, Eli Terry and Sons, Plymouth, Connecticut, circa 1820, 30-hour wooden movement, 32in. high. (Skinner Inc.) £578

A Federal mahogany pillar-and-scroll shelf clock, by Eli Terry & Sons, Plymouth, Connecticut, 1815–1825, on bracket feet, 31in. high. (Christie's) £943

Antique American pillar and scroll shelf clock in mahogany with brass finials, painted dial, 31in. high. (Eldred's) £315

A Federal mahogany eglomise shelf clock, by Eli Terry and Sons, Plymouth, Connecticut, circa 1820, with swan neck pediment, 30½in. high. (Christie's New York) £2,075

Federal mahogany pillar and scroll clock, Riley Whiting, Winchester, Connecticut, circa 1825, thirty-hour wooden movement, 30in. high. (Skinner Inc.) £497

A Federal mahogany pillar-and-scroll shelf clock, by Eli Terry & Sons, Plymouth, Connecticut, 1815–1825, on bracket feet, 31in. high. (Christie's) £1,245

ROLLING BALL CLOCKS

Also known as the ball clock or Congreve clock, this is a design in which a ball, instead of a balance or pendulum, is used to unlock the escapement or train. It was first invented by Nicolas Grollier de Servière (1593–1686) of Lyon, in the 17th century, but is best known in the form developed by William Congreve, the Comptroller of the Woolwich laboratory from 1808–23. In 1808 he produced an example with pediment shaped top containing three dials, supported above the escapement, which is a pivoted table with grooves, along which the ball rolls alternately from side to side, reversing the angle of the table as each 'journey' is completed.

A fine 19th century brass rolling ball clock in the form of a Greek temple, the dials on the tympanum indicate the hour, the minute and the quarters of a minute, on brass ball feet, 19in. x 15in. £4,200

A modern brass Congreve clock, on four column supports, surmounted by five ball and spike finials, on ball feet, minute dial flanked by two subsidiary dials for hours and seconds, 16in. high.
(Christie's S. Ken)   £990

SEDAN CLOCKS

This is a large dialled watch clock, some 4–6in. in diameter, which usually had a bow for hanging in a conveyance. Dating from the second half of the 18th century, it was often circular, though square or octagonal examples are known, with a wooden or metal case and a 30 hour verge watch movement behind the much larger dial.

A gilt quarter repeating sedan clock, dial signed Lepine, 5¼in. diam.
£450

19th century red japanned wall clock of sedan clock form, with gilt decoration, 16in. diam.   £650

An early 19th century French brass octagonal cased portable or hanging clock, the movement signed **Du Louier a Rouen.**   £375

Gilt-metal verge chaise clock, 19th century 104mm. diam. £1,250

American giltwood hanging sedan clock, 1820-40, 20½in. high.
£900

The shelf clock, either weight or spring powered, was designed, as its name suggests, to stand on a shelf, and is the first truly indigenous American clock. It became the best known and most typical American clock because it was adopted and developed by the infant manufacturing industry in Connecticut. Eli Terry's first production model was in a box case with a plain glass door, on the inside of which were painted the hour numerals and simple corner spandrel decorations. The wooden movement could be seen through the glass, with an hour bell below, a pendulum in front, and a weight on each side.

Victorian 'ginger bread' framed shelf clock with an Ansonia Clock Co. striking movement. £135

Round Gothic shelf clock, probably by Brewster & Ingraham, circa 1845, 20in. high. £625

An Empire carved mahogany shelf clock, by M. Leavenworth & Son, Conn., 30in. high. £1,500

A hammered copper shelf clock, by Tiffany & Co., New York, early 20th century, on rectangular brass platform base, 11in. high. (Skinner Inc.) £628

Empire mahogany carved shelf clock, by Eli Terry & Son, Conn., circa 1825, 31in. high. £900

Federal mahogany shelf clock, by Aaron Willard, Mass., circa 1825, 34in. high. £7,500

An Empire carved mahogany shelf clock, by Riley Whiting, Conn., circa 1825, 29½in. high. £375

A Federal mahogany shelf clock, by Reuben Tower, Massa., 1836, 34½in. high. £8,500

A Federal inlaid mahogany
shelf clock, by David Wood,
Mass., circa 1800, 33¾in.
high.   £50,000

Double steeple mahogany
wagon spring shelf clock,
by Birge & Fuller, Conn.,
circa 1846, 26in. high.
                    £1,750

Empire mahogany hollow
column clock, Connecti-
cut, circa 1835, 31in.
high.   £375

A rosewood shelf clock, attributed to Atkins Clock Mfg.
Co., Conn., circa 1855, 18¾in.
high.   £1,500

Round gothic mahogany
veneer shelf clock, Brewster
and Ingrahams, circa 1845,
with eight day brass spring
movement, 19¾in. high.
(Skinner Inc.)   £296

Empire mantel clock by Samuel
Terry of Bristol, reverse painted
upper tablet flanked by
stencilled columns, carved eagle
cornice, carved paw feet, 29½in.
high.
(Eldred's)   £240

Federal mahogany and
tiger maple shelf time-
piece, by Aaron Willard,
Boston, circa 1815,
35½in. high.   £12,500

An Empire mahogany shelf
clock, bearing partial label of
Forestville Mfg. Co., circa
1830, 32in. high.   £350

A Federal mahogany inlaid
shelf timepiece, by A. Whit-
combe, Massa., circa 1790,
13½in. high.   £15,000

A Federal walnut shelf time-piece, possibly rural Massachusetts, circa 1820, the hood with moulded cornice above a glazed kidney door, 32in. high. (Skinner Inc.) £2,414

Rare Federal mahogany inlaid shelf timepiece, John Gains, Portsmouth, New Hampshire, circa 1800, eight-day weight driven brass movement, 41in. high. (Skinner) £13,580

Massachusetts mahogany shelf timepiece, John Bailey, Lynn, Massachusetts, circa 1808, flaring French feet, 36in. high. (Skinner Inc.) £2,638

A carved mahogany shelf clock, by Marsh, Gilbert & Co., Conn., circa 1825, 37in. high. £900

Rosewood shelf timepiece, probably Atkins Clock Mfg. Co., Bristol, Connecticut, circa 1855, 30-day wagon spring movement, 17½in. high. (Skinner Inc.) £651

Empire triple decker shelf clock, by Birge, Mallory & Co., circa 1840, 36in. high. £500

An early 19th century American mahogany shelf timepiece, signed Aaron Willard, Boston, the whole surmounted by scroll crestings. (Lawrence Fine Arts) £3,960

A Victorian carved walnut shelf-clock by Seth Thomas Company, Thomaston, Connecticut, circa 1890, of violin form carved with foliage centring a glazed cupboard door painted in gilding with musical motifs, 29in. high. (Christie's) £2,450

A Federal stained maple shelf-clock, O. Brackett, Vassalboro, Maine, 1815-1825, with moulded cornice above a square glazed door with floral painted corners, 29¼in. high. (Christie's) £14,852

SKELETON CLOCKS

The skeleton clock first became popular in France in the second half of the eighteenth century, not finding favour with the English for almost a hundred years. The wheels of the movement pivoted not in a solid plate but in an open, usually brass, framework, which would be mounted on a wooden or marble base and covered by a glass dome. The dial was often a plain silvered ring fixed to the front frame. The later Victorian examples show clear Gothic influence, being often in the shape of a cathedral, say Westminster Abbey, or even the Brighton pavilion. These are elaborate works of art and sell for correspondingly high prices.

A skeleton clock of Lichfield Cathedral type, dated 1851, 17½in. high. £1,000

A Victorian helical-geared small skeleton timepiece, the silvered frame with double-screwed pillars, single chain fusée with helical gearing to the anchor escapement, 10in. high. (Christie's) £1,760

A rare early 19th century floor standing skeleton timepiece, signed *Inventum a Jocobo Wright, Quondam Coll: Hert et Nuper Aul: Mag: Oxon: 1826 Jepson Fecit*. (Phillips) £2,400

A 19th century brass striking skeleton clock, the pierced shaped and waisted plates with six turned screwed pillars, on oval ebonised base, with glass dome, 13in. high. (Christie's S. Ken.) £1,430

A Victorian brass skeleton clock, 12½in. high, with glass dome. £3,250

An unusual English skeleton clock, the movement placed between two C-scrolls, anchor escapement, based on the famous model by William Strutt, 29cm. high. (Duran) £528

A 19th century French brass skeleton alarm timepiece, with engraved A plates, 10¼in. (Phillips) £420

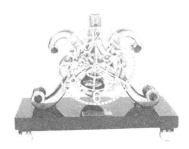

A Great Exhibition alarum skeleton timepiece, annular white enamel chapter ring with concentric alarum setting disc, 9¾in. overall.
(Bonhams) £450

A Victorian brass 'Strutt' epicyclic skeleton clock, slate base with plaque signed W. Wigston, Derby, No. 51, W. Strutt Esq. Inv., 10¼in. high. £4,250

An unusual brass skeleton timepiece, the pierced plates with shaped silvered chapter, signed on an oval plate Brown & Co., London, 6¼in. high. (Phillips) £500

A 19th century skeleton timepiece, pierced silvered chapter ring, single fusée movement with passing bell strike and dead beat escapement, 14in. high.
(Bonhams) £400

A Victorian skeleton timepiece, 5in. pierced silvered dial and Roman numerals, the movement with shaped polished scroll plates, single fusée with chain and half dead beat escapement, 16in. high.
(Bonhams) £480

A Victorian brass skeleton timepiece, the single fusée movement with four-armed wheels and anchor escapement, on oval white marble and ebonised wood base, 16in. high.
(Christie's) £418

A 19th century brass skeleton clock, the pierced shaped plates in the gothic style with pierced and engraved silvered chapter ring, 1ft. 8in. high.
(Phillips) £2,300

A skeleton clock with an annular silvered chapter ring and pierced hands, the plaque signed Litherland Davies & Co., 17½in. high. £3,750

A Victorian brass striking skeleton clock, the six pillar twin chain fusée movement with anchor escapement, the wheels with five crossings, 21in. high.
(Christie's) £1,870

A 19th century French brass skeleton timepiece with alarm, the A-frame movement with enamel chapter ring, 9½in. high. (Phillips) £520

An interesting brass skeleton timepiece with detent escapement in scroll frame, on ball feet, by Brotherston & Son, Dalkeith, 8½in. high. (Christie's S. Ken) £1,650

A Victorian skeleton clock with passing strike, the 7in. elaborately pierced silvered dial with Roman numerals, 17in. high. (Bonhams) £550

A Victorian skeleton timepiece, the unusual scroll frame surmounted by two crosses, the arcaded Roman chapter ring signed *J. Burton. Bradford*, 16½in. over dome. (Christie's) £747

A 19th century brass skeleton timepiece, the pierced scroll plates with silvered chapter ring, the fusee movement with six spoked wheels, 1ft 3in. high. (Phillips) £600

A brass skeleton timepiece, with stylised gothic plates, turned feet on white marble base, the single chain fusée movement with six-spoke wheelwork, with pendulum, 11¼in. high. (Christie's S. Ken) £528

A brass two-train Westminster Abbey skeleton clock on veined white marble base, the chapter-ring with gothic numerals, 23in. high. (Christie's S. Ken) £2,420

A 19th century brass skeleton timepiece, the shaped plates with silvered chapter ring, the fusée movement with five spoked wheels and anchor escapement, 10¾in. high. (Phillips) £520

A brass framed skeleton clock, the pierced chapter ring with black Roman numerals, contained in a glass dome (cracked), 51cm. high overall. (Henry Spencer) £720

A 19th century brass 'Cathedral' skeleton clock, 64cm. high overall.
(Henry Spencer) £1,400

Single train brass striking skeleton clock by Thwaites, eight day warranted movement, under brass dome, 18in. tall.
(G. A. Key) £620

Chiming skeleton clock of York Minster type, by Riddels Ltd., Belfast, 25in. high. £4,500

A brass two-train cathedral skeleton clock with gothic numerals, eight-day fusee movement with six-spoke wheel work striking the half-hours on a bell and the hours on a gong, 19¹/₂in. high.
(Christie's S. Ken) £1,650

An unusual gilt great wheel skeleton clock within wirework case, the arched openwork case flanked on either side by half column surmounted by urn linked with chain to central urn finial, French, circa 1825, 15¹/₂in. high.
(Christie's New York) £3,927

A French brass small skeleton timepiece, the going-barrel movement with four-armed wheels, anchor escapement and silk suspended foliate engraved pendulum, on oval ebonized wood base, 8³/₄in. high.
(Christie's) £495

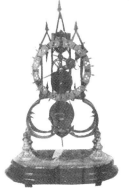

English skeleton clock, with pierced and silvered dial and Graham escapement, 19th century, 40cm. high.
(Duran, Madrid) £718

An attractive Victorian brass skeleton timepiece, signed *J. Blackhurst, Crewe*, of scrolling balloon design, 20in. high overall. (Tennants) £900

A 19th century brass skeleton timepiece, the scroll plates with silvered chapter ring signed *Thos Bunyan*, on a marble base, 42cm. high. (Phillips) £500

An early Victorian brass striking skeleton clock of Lichfield Cathedral type, 16½in. high. £900

A 19th century skeleton timepiece, the glass dial with visible motion work, 7½in. high. £750

Early 19th century French skeleton timepiece in foliate gilt surround, 14in. high. £1,850

A small brass skeleton timepiece in rafter frame, the brass chapter-ring with Roman numerals, signed on a brass strip *Salmon, Pimlico, 1841*, the single chain fusée movement with four-spoke wheel work, 7½in. high. (Christie's S. Ken) £550

A quarter chiming skeleton clock and vitrine, W.F. Evans & Sons, Handsworth, retailed by Bell Bros., Doncaster, the brass quadruple frame pierced to represent Westminster Abbey, third quarter 19th century, 21½in. high. (Christie's New York) £3,927

A 19th century fusée skeleton clock by Louis B Twells of Ashbourne, the circular framework supporting a bell with hammer on shaped supporting brackets, 17½in. high. £550

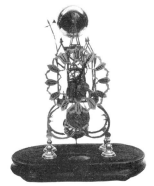

Victorian skeleton clock signed by John Neal, on wooden pedestal base, lacking glass casing, late 19th century. (Duran, Madrid) £442

Brass skeleton clock, spring-driven pendulum striking movement, probably English, 20th century, 16in. high. (Eldred's) £273

A 19th century brass skeleton clock, the pierced screwed plates with six baluster pillar movement, 13¾in. high. (Christie's S. Ken.) £825

A small skeleton timepiece, on mahogany base with glass dome, 11in. high. £1,000

15in. brass skeleton timepiece with strike and chain drive, under dome. £400

A Victorian brass skeleton chiming clock of York Minster type, 27½in. high overall. £4,250

A 19th century skeleton timepiece, with skeletonized dial and Roman numerals, the scroll plates surmounted by a bell with eight-day fuseé movement, 14in. high. (Christie's S. Ken) £605

A Victorian striking skeleton clock by *Jas. Condliff Liverpool* signed to the front of the block base with going barrel, six-arm greatwheel of large diameter, five-arm wheels thereafter to anchor escapement, 15in. high. (Christie's) £3,850

A 19th century brass skeleton timepiece, the shaped plates with silvered chapter, the fuseé movement with five spoked wheels and anchor escapement, 1ft. 1in. high. (Phillips) £700

A brass skeleton timepiece, the chain fusee movement with anchor escapement, probably by Haycock of Ashbourne, 17in. (Lawrence Fine Arts) £418

A 19th century brass skeleton timepiece, the substantial seven spoked great wheel with going barrel, Robt. Roskell, 1ft. 4½in. high. (Phillips) £1,800

A French alarm skeleton timepiece with A-shaped plates, and five screwed pillar movement, with glass dome, 9in. high. (Christie's S. Ken.) £528

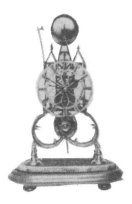

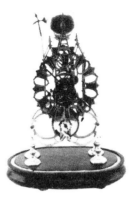

Mid 19th century brass
skeleton timepiece with
fretted silvered dial,
16in. high. £425

A brass skeleton timepiece
with coup perdu escapement,
on oval base with two
plinths, 14in. high. £1,500

Late 19th century brass
skeleton clock with fusee
movement, England, 16in.
high. £750

A 19th century brass skeleton
timepiece, the fusée movement
with five spoke wheels and
anchor escapement with passing
strike, signed on an applied swag
W. Gibbs, 18½in. high.
(Phillips) £450

A Victorian brass skeleton clock
with a single fusée movement
and painted chapter and second
ring inscribed *Widenham
London*, under glass dome, 17in.
high.
(G.A. Sworder) £600

A 19th century brass skeleton
clock, the pierced plates of
'Brighton Pavilion' design,
signed on an applied swag W &
M. Dodge Manchester, 1ft.
9½in. high.
(Phillips) £3,200

An unusual miniature brass
skeleton clock, the circular
silvered dial with black Roman
numerals, maker's name *Whaley,
Lambeth*, 13cm. high.
(Henry Spencer) £580

A fine skeletonized mantel
regulator with calendar, signed
Edward François, H'Ger, 14
Boulevard ds Filles du Calvaire,
circa 1900, 15½in. high.
(Christie's) £7,713

A 19th century brass skeleton
timepiece, the fusée movement
with five spoked wheels and
anchor escapement, 10¾in.
high.
(Phillips) £380

A skeleton clock, the silvered dial signed John Carr Swaffham, 9½in. high.
£1,000

A Eureka electric striking clock, signed Eureka Clock Co. Ltd., London, 11in. high overall.
£2,500

A 19th century brass skeleton clock, on an oval rosewood base, under a glass shade, 1ft. 11in. high.
£2,500

An early Victorian brass striking skeleton clock, signed Harrison Darlington, 12¼in. high, excluding dome.
£2,000

A brass skeleton timepiece, the chain fusee movement with anchor escapement, the pierced silvered chapter with Roman numerals, 13in. high. (Lawrence Fine Arts)
£308

A brass chiming skeleton clock, on oval oak base with glass dome, English, circa 1900, 24in. high including dome.
£5,500

A 19th century English brass skeleton clock with steel chapter ring, on white marble oval base and under a glass dome, 18in. high.
£700

An unusual 19th century brass skeleton timepiece, the fusee movement with maintaining power and lever platform escapement, 1ft.1¾in. high. (Phillips)
£1,000

A brass skeleton timepiece with spring detent escapement on oval white marble base, 17in. high excluding dome.
£2,250

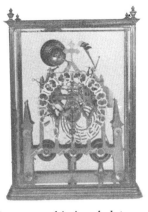

A 19th century brass skeleton clock of Gothic design, 12in. high. £500

A quarter chiming skeleton clock, the pierced plates of open and angular design, 21in. high. £3,000

A Brighton Pavilion skeleton clock with pierced silvered chapter ring, 16½in. high. £3,500

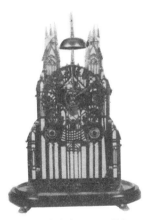

An English brass striking skeleton clock of York Minster type, on wood base with glass dome, 59cm. high. £2,000

A gilt-brass rolling ball clock of standard form, the posted fusée movement with silvered annular dials, signed *Dent*, 17³/₄in. high. (Christie's) £2,300

A brass three-train 'Westminster Abbey' skeleton clock, striking on gong and nest of eight bells having mercury pendulum, 24in. high. £6,000

A Victorian brass chiming skeleton clock on rosewood base with replacement perspex gabled cover, 24in. high. £3,500

A 19th century French skeleton timepiece, the plates of inverted Y form, the three pillars terminating in floral cast nuts, 37cm. high. (Phillips) £3,700

A 19th century brass skeleton timepiece, the fusee movement with six spoked wheels and anchor escapement, 1ft. 2¾in. high. (Phillips) £450

STRUT CLOCKS

The strut clock is a small, shallow-cased clock which was made from about 1850 onwards. It stands on a table, and is supported by a strut in the same manner as a photograph frame. Notable manufacturers of the strut clock were the Cole brothers who were noted for the high quality and precision of their products. Strut clocks were also popular in the Art Nouveau and Deco periods, with many being produced by Liberty and WMF.

A Victorian strut clock with enamel dial signed Baudin Freres, Geneve, 8in. high. £750

A gilt-metal strut clock, the silvered dial signed Hunt & Roskell London, 5½in. high, with a velvet lined travelling case. £1,250

A Victorian gilt metal strut timepiece, the easel with pierced foliate decoration, the rear inscribed *HOWELL & JAMES REGENT ST. LONDON.*, 12½in. high.
(Christie's) £308

An attractive strut timepiece with square agate surround, the frosted gilt movement with bimetallic balance and lever escapement, engraved to the dust cover *Cartier*, $3^3/_4$in. square. (Christie's S. Ken) £1,100

A 19th century gilt brass strut timepiece in the manner of Thomas Cole, the shaped rectangular case with engraved decoration, 6in. high. (Phillips) £1,300

An ormolu strut clock, in the manner of Thos. Cole, the silvered dial signed Hunt & Roskell, London, 5½in. high. £1,250

A 19th century gilt metal strut clock, after Thomas Cole, in scrolling oval case, 13cm. (Phillips) £240

A gilt metal calendar strut clock, the backplate stamped Thos. Cole, London, 5½in. high. £2,750

The table clock is a small metal cased clock with a horizontal dial, designed to be placed on a table and viewed from above. They were mostly made in Germany and date from the late 16th to early 18th centuries. The earliest are also known as drum clocks in which the iron movement is typically of skeleton form with balance, in a gilt brass case with silver chapter ring.

Table clock is also a more accurate description of many particularly English clocks dating from 1675–1800 termed mantel or bracket clocks.

An early Anglo-Flemish weight driven clock, circa 1600, 19cm. high. £1,000

An enamelled silver grande sonnerie world time table clock, signed Patek Philippe & Co., Geneve, 7½in. diam. £27,500

A French 19th century white marble and bronze table clock, trumpet playing winged putto carrying a drum incorporating an eight day cylinder movement, signed *Falconnet*, 9in. (Bonhams) £480

An early electric Eureka table clock in glazed mahogany case, the signed white enamel dial with Roman numerals and subsidiary seconds, dated 1906, 13¼in. high. (Christie's) £715

An ormolu and bronze table clock of Louis XVI design, the terrestrial globe case supported by three putti on shaped base edged with scrolls, 30in. high. (Christie's) £3,520

An important silver mounted gilt table clock, the movement signed *D. Buschman [Augsburg]*, raised on four paw feet each chased with winged mask, circa 1660, 6in. high. (Christie's) £5,423

A 19th century Japanese table clock in glazed shitan wood case, with chain fusee going and spring barrel striking train with outside countwheel, 7½in. (Christie's) £3,520

A Germanic late Renaissance quarter-striking hexagonal table clock signed Michael Fabian Thorn, the movement with baluster pillars, steel great wheels, chain fusee for the going, 6in. diam. (Christie's) £4,620

A 17th century German quarter striking table clock, decorated with the figure of a hound with automated eyes and tail, the dial to the side with silvered chapter and centre alarm set, 8in. high. (Phillips) £5,400

A 16th century gilt metal drum clock, 6cm. diam., together with an alarm mechanism of drum form. £2,250

A gilt quarter striking table clock with alarm by *Johann Gottlieb Thÿm à Thorn*, on four silvered lion feet, the sides with conforming glazed panels, early 18th century, $5^{1}/2$in. wide. (Christie's) £4,488

A mahogany Steeple table clock, the American 8 day movement by the Gilbert Clock Co. Winsted CT, striking on a gong, the painted metal dial with Roman numerals, 43cm. high, circa 1850. (Auction Team Köln) £126

A Biedermeier ormolu mounted walnut and parquetry automaton table clock with organ, the front with an automaton representing a garden grotto with rotating glass rods simulating water jets spouting into the mouths of dolphins, $22^{1}/4$in. high. (Christie's) £14,300

An interesting 19th century Japanese table clock in pierced cast gilt brass drum case glazed to the top, the white enamel chapter-ring with Japanese numerals, $4^{3}/4$in. high. (Christie's S. Ken) £2,420

A 17th century gilt brass table clock, the rectangular case surmounted by a bell, 17cm. high. £3,250

An early 18th century gilt brass Continental table clock, the square case with glazed apertures to the sides and winged paw feet, 13cm. square. (Phillips) £2,000

A mid 17th century French gilt brass table clock with minute hand, calendar and alarm, signed G. Estienne A Caen, 12in. high. £175,000

A German gilt brass octagonal quarter striking table clock, the verge movement signed Christoph Forcker, Breslau, 3¾in. high. £3,000

An incomplete gilt-metal 16th century clock case, with later chapter ring and later glazed circular aperture, length of base 200mm. £2,250

A mid 16th century South German gilt brass drum clock case, 2¾in. diam. £1,350

A good 18th century ormolu mounted ebony table clock, made for the Turkish market, the case of typical domed form, rococo scroll feet, engraved *Geo. Prior London,* 20in. high. (Phillips Sevenoaks) £6,200

A German brass hexagonal stack-freed table clock, stamped M.L. on the backplate of the brass movement, with walnut parquetry veneered hexagonal case with glazed dial aperture, 14.8cm. diam. (Christie's) £4,180

A Germanic Renaissance gilt metal table clock case, the backplate signed Johannes Benner Aug., the case partly 16th/17th century, the movement 17th century, 17in. high. £4,500

A 16th century gilt metal table clock, by Hans Gruber, the whole case well engraved, 23cm. high. £6,000

A 17th century South German gilt metal quarter striking table clock, the movement signed J. O. H., for Johann Ott. Halaicher, 13.5cm. sq. £3,250

A French rosewood regulateur de table, signed Breguet et Fils on the silvered dial, 25¼in. high. £8,500

311

Smith's alarm clock in chromium plated case. £5

'Looping' Swiss travel alarm clock in red leatherette case. £8

Switana alarm clock with paper dial. £10

A late 18th century French brass alarm travelling clock, the rectangular case with shaped and engraved dial plate and circular enamel dial, 6in. high. (Phillips) £1,600

Early 60's Equity made alarm clock with luminous hands and central optical moving design. £10

A modern Swiss singing bird box in engine-turned lacquered brass case, surmounted by a French 8-day alarm clock, 6in. high, with travelling case. £1,750

'Ebosa' Swiss travel alarm clock, circa 1960. £10

Veglia travelling alarm clock, made in Italy, 1950's. £5

'Darling' Swiss travel alarm clock, circa 1960. £10

This term is used to describe a wide range of portable timepieces. In the 16th and 17th centuries they tended to be made in watch form, while being too large to be worn. Notable English makers of these included Edward East (c.1610–c.1693). They came usually with a protective outer case and some had a striking mechanism. In the 18th century they developed into a kind of carriage clock often with an elaborate chiming and striking, and later repeating, mechanism. France was the most prolific source of travelling clocks, and their production continued into the 20th century.

A Galle carved and acid-etched clock, 13cm. high.
£3,800

A small satinwood mantel timepiece, the dial signed Donaldson, 6¾in. high.
£1,000

Late 19th century Faberge gold mounted and jewelled nephrite miniature timepiece, 5.5cm.   £4,500

Sterling silver 8-day travelling clock, Swiss movement 'Black Starr & Frost, New York', 4 x 2in.   £225

An enamel and hardstone quarter repeating travelling clock, signed E. Mathey, Nocturne, 70mm. high.   £1,500

A Swiss travelling clock, the enamel face inscribed 'Goldsmiths and Silversmiths Co. Ltd.', London import marks for 1913, 2½ x 1¼in. wide.
£900

A rosewood mantel or travelling clock, the 3½in. dial signed Frodsham, 10in. high.
£3,500

9ct. yellow gold cased boudoir clock, London, 1912, 5.6cm. high.   £450

An Empire musical Staart-
klok with painted dial,
179cm. high.   £12,500

Early 19th century alarm
clock with silvered square
dial, inscribed Samuel
Taylor.   £275

George III mahogany
wall timepiece, dial sig-
ned W. Thomas Lincoln,
4ft.11in. high.   £1,850

A French Art Deco wall
regulator in walnut casing with
octagonal silvered metal dial
signed *MF Manufacture
Francaise d'armes et cycles,
Saint Etienne*, circa 1920, 74cm.
high.
(Auction Team Köln)   £253

A Dutch oak alarm Staartklok
arched hood surmounted by
three giltwood figures, in typical
case, painted dial with typical
Dutch scene in the arch, gilt
repoussé spandrels, 48in. high.
(Christie's S. Ken)   £715

A unique wall clock, designed
and executed by Margaret
Gilmour, the square tin body
decorated in repoussé with Celtic
entrelac designs on a hammered
ground, 45.7cm. square.
(Christie's)   £12,100

A Regency mahogany wall
regulator, the movement of
two week duration, 65in.
high.   £4,250

An 18th century travelling wall
timepiece with alarm, the
engraved brass dial with
silvered chapter ring, signed in
the arch, *Willm. Allam, London*,
5in. high. (Phillips)   £2,400

A Georgian mahogany wall
timepiece, the 1ft.7in. diam.
painted wood dial signed
Field, Bath, 3ft.7in. high.
                     £900

A wall clock in carved mahogany case.   £200

A George III brass wall clock, the dial signed Edwd. Pashier, London, 1ft.6½in. high.
£2,250

An unusual Regency wall timepiece, the 14-inch brass dial inscribed *Greenwood, York*, the anchor movement with tapering plates, circa 1820, 32in. high.
(Tennants)   £1,250

English station clock, in mahogany casing, striking on the hour, the white metal dial with large black Roman numerals, signed *T Barton & Sons*, 64cm. high, first half 19th century.
(Auction Team Köln)   £234

A 19th century oak Dutch 'Staartklok', the arched hood surmounted by three gilt wood figures, 4ft. 7in. high.
(Phillips)   £680

An interesting mid 18th century alarm verge travelling wall clock, the weight-driven rectangular verge movement with alarm train to the side and short bob pendulum, 8¼in. high. (Christie's S. Ken) £1,430

A George III mahogany wall clock, 11in. round brass dial inscribed John Newman, Piccadilly, 47in. high overall.
(Dreweatt Neate)   £1,850

A fine R.A.F. operations room sector clock with painted dial divided into coloured triangles of red, yellow and blue for 2½ minute periods, made by W. Elliott Ltd., 1941.
(Christie's)   £1,320

A late 18th century oak striking wall clock, in the gothic taste, the engraved centre with subsidiary rings for seconds and date signed Rollison, Sheffield, 72in. high.
(Christie's S. Ken.)   £1,540

An early 19th century thirty-hour wall alarm timepiece, the 6in. brass dial signed *Whitehurst Derby*.
(Bonhams) £400

Highland Railway, a mahogany eight-day wall clock, dial inscribed H. Ry. Ferguson, Inverness, 58in. high. £800

A 19th century mahogany wall timepiece, the brass dial signed Mattw. & Thos. Dutton, London, 2ft.2½in. high. £3,500

An 18th century Japanese mahogany pillar clock, the brass front plate shaped and engraved as a basket of flowers flanked by two baluster turned brass pillars, 39.5cm. high.
(Henry Spencer) £300

French 'Ox-eye' musical clock in walnut case inlaid with brass and mother of pearl, the marble dial with enamel cartouches, signed *Larroumets à St Palais*, the 43 tooth comb musical movement sounding just before the hour, circa 1860.
(Auction Team Köln) £1,967

Oak observatory wall regulator, dial signed T. Cooke & Sons, London, in glazed case, 4ft. 7in. high. £3,000

An 18th century alarm wall timepiece, signed Cartwright, London, with single steel hand and alarm set disc to the centre, 8in. high.
(Phillips) £800

A fine Caledonian Railway signal box wall regulator clock, in truncated mahogany wall case with circular sliding hood, 62in. high.
(Christie's) £1,650

A Glasgow style wall clock, pewter covered curved triangular form with chased Arabic numerals, the hands set with abalone, 27.4cm. high.
(Christie's) £1,760

A good mahogany striking drop-dial wall clock, with hexagonal bezel, the white painted dial indistinctly signed, 29½in. high. (Christie's)   £550

A 19th century wall clock contained in an oak case, with brass dial, 43in. high.   £850

A 19th century 8-day rose-wood and oak cased wall clock with painted metal dial.   £200

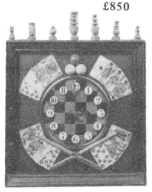

A Victorian Gothick quarter chiming wall clock, the case with soundfrets to the pedimented top, doors to sides, the front applied with carved wood trefoil spandrels, signed *W. Potts & Sons Leeds*, 35in. high. (Christie's)   £1,870

A fin-de-siècle mahogany and boxwood gaming wall clock, the framed and glazed baize lined dial with chequerboard chapter disc with raised Arabic chapters, the frame 20 x 20in. square. (Christie's)   £770

An imposing late 19th century shop interior wall clock and bracket, the 17½in. cream painted dial with black Roman numerals inscribed *Fredjohns Ltd, Jewellers, Wimbledon*, total height 62in. (Bearne's)   £920

An unusual chiming oak hooded wall clock with verge movement, signed on a silvered plaque in the arch George Prior, London, 26in. high. (Christie's)   £880

Hen. Mowtlow Londini Fecit, a rare Charles II ebonised wall timepiece with alarm, the 5½in. square dial signed on the brass chapter ring, alarm disc to the matted centre, 17½in. overall. (Christie's)   £3,300

A mahogany wall timepiece, the chain fusee movement with anchor escapement, the eight inch painted dial with Roman numerals. (Lawrence Fine Art)   £660

Victorian oak wall clock
with pendulum, 1890.

£680

A figured mahogany trunk
dial wall timepiece, the 15in.
silvered dial signed Charles
Fox, 57½in. long   £1,000

A mahogany wall clock,
the 12¼in. dial signed
Vulliamy London, 24in.
high.   £1,850

A small tower clock movement,
cast iron with brass wheels,
anchor escapement, with large
black copper dial with gold
Roman numerals and hands,
dial 105cm. diameter.
(Auction Team Köln)   £1,405

A 19th century Dutch oak
Staartklok, the painted dial
with automaton figures,
4ft.1in. high.(Phillips)
                       £850

A 19th century Japanese
hardwood stick wall timepiece,
the movement with verge bob
pendulum escapement, the trunk
with adjustable register, 2ft.
3½in. high.
(Phillips)   £1,000

A George III eight-day wall
clock, the dial inscribed
Gray and Reynolds, Wim-
borne, 16in. high.   £2,000

An Edwardian mahogany wall
clock, inscribed Evans & Sons,
Birmingham, over panelled
pendulum cover, 162cm.
(Phillips)   £550

A Georgian brass pantry clock,
30-hour movement, the dial
signed Wm. Brice, Sandwich
on a silvered disc, 4½in. high.
(Christie's)   £2,420

WALL CLOCKS

A late 17th century walnut wall clock, dial signed John Knibb, 24½in. high. £7,500

19th century Tiffany bronze banjo-shaped wall clock, 38in. high. £5,000

Georgian inlaid mahogany wall clock, designer Moore, London. (H.P.S) £675

An 18th century mahogany hooded wall clock by Ellicott, London, the shallow arched case decorated with three finials, the five pillared twin fusée movement with verge escapement, 2ft. 7in. high. (Phillips) £5,500

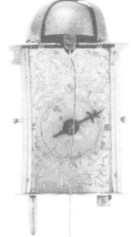

A small engraved gilt brass weight driven chamber clock, German, dated 1625, with maker's punch 'LP', the iron posted frame movement with pillars of square section, 97mm. high. (Christie's) £2,342

A Junghans wall regulator in carved walnut casing with half columns, the dial with brass chapter ring and Roman numerals, 70cm. high, circa 1890. (Auction Team Köln) £211

A mahogany wall timepiece, the chain fusee movement with anchor escapement, mottled plates signed Dent, London. (Lawrence Fine Arts) £297

An R.A.F. 2nd World War period sector clock, the dial sectors in colours with R.A.F. crest, 17¼in. diameter overall. (Christie's) £1,760

An adapted George III brass mounted mahogany wall clock, the dial signed Mattw. & Willm. Dutton, London, 38in. high. £1,850

WALL CLOCKS
AMERICAN

An early 19th century American mahogany cased wall clock, 30in. high. £900

Handpainted opal glass hanging clock, Wavecrest-type circular frame housing, Welch Company, Forestville, Connecticut, 6in. high. (Skinner Inc.) £155

American rosewood banjo timepiece, circa 1870, 29in. long. £1,100

Howard banjo clock in rosewood veneers, black, dark red and gilt reverse-painted tablet with throat glass, 28½in. high. (Eldred's) £876

A classical carved mahogany and eglomisé eight-day wall clock, labelled *Eli Terry, Jr.*, Connecticut, circa 1835, height 36in. (Sotheby's) £1,286

A Federal gilt and eglomisé lyre-shaped wall clock, dial signed Aaron Willard, Boston, early 19th century, 40½in. high. (Christie's) £1,790

A cherry wall regulator timepiece, by Seth Thomas Clock Co., Conn., circa 1880, 36in. long. £750

Waterbury oak long drop regulator school house clock with hexagonal face, 32¼in. high. £450

Late 19th century walnut regulator timepiece, by the Chelsea Clock Co., Mass., 35in. high. £900

AMERICAN

A mahogany wall timepiece,
Elnathan Taber, Massa.,
circa 1825, 34.7/8in. long.
£7,500

Rosewood veneer wall
regulator, by Seth Thomas,
Conn., circa 1860, 31¼in.
long.   £625

A Federal mahogany lyre
timepiece, Henry Allen
Hinckley, Massa., circa
1825, 38in. high. £2,250

An unusual mid 19th century
American rosewood hanging
wall timepiece, the 7in. circular
white painted dial signed *E.
Howard & Co. BOSTON*, 28½in.
high.
(Christie's S. Ken)   £286

A mahogany and eglomise
gallery clock, Crosby &
Vosburgh, New York, circa
1850, the octagonal surround
centring a glazed door,
25ft. ½in high.
(Sotheby's)   £926

A Federal gilt and eglomise
girandole clock, by Lemuel
Curtis, Concord, Mass., circa
1816, 46in. high.   £10,000

Late 19th century walnut
regulator timepiece, by
The E. Howard Watch &
Clock Co., Boston, 40in.
high.   £900

A walnut calendar time-
piece, by New Haven Clock
Co., circa 1900, 32in. long.
£500

A walnut regulator wall
clock, by E. Howard &
Co., Boston, circa 1875,
43in. high.   £3,750

CONTINENTAL

A French Louis XVI 3-month duration console clock, signed on a porcelain plaque Nicolas Texier a Philippeville, 23½in. high. £5,500

An 18th century South German verge 'Telleruhr' timepiece, signed below the six *Martin Heigl*, the circular brass movement with four turned brass baluster pillars, 15in. high. (Christie's S. Ken) £990

German 17th century gilt-metal clock, back-plate signed Johann Michael Brugel, 15in. high. £7,500

A German ISGUS time-clock in oak case with brass mountings, the metal dial with Arabic numerals, with two-colour stamping mechanism, 108cm. high, circa 1930–5. (Auction Team Köln) £515

A late 17th century Italian day and night clock, signed Jean Baptiste Gonnon a Milan, 20 x 23½in. £3,500

Louis XV style gilt-bronze-mounted ebony clock and thermometer, signed *J. Molteni et Cie, Paris*, the ebony case applied with pierced foliate-and-scroll cast gilt-bronze edges, 45in. high. (Butterfield & Butterfield) £1,576

A French bracket wall clock, the white enamelled dial signed Causard Horloger Du Roy, Paris, the back plate stamped Vincenti, Paris. £3,250

A small Black Forest wall clock, circa 1850, the 6cm. enamel dial mounted on a repousse brass surround, 4¾in. high. £900

A mid 18th century Amsterdam oak hooded Friesland clock, the repeat alarm movement with an anchor escapement. (Woolley & Wallis) £2,700

CONTINENTAL

Early 19th century Fries-
land wall clock, Holland,
45in. high.   £750

A South German wall timepiece,
with a repoussé brass surround
and silvered Roman chapter
ring, 13½in. high.
(Bonhams)   £380

Late 19th century softwood
German wall clock, the white
enamel dial with 8-day movement, 13in. high.   £675

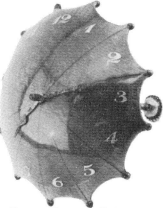

An 18th century Continental
thirty-hour wall clock, the
shaped pierced painted dial with
single hand, the posted frame
movement with verge
escapement.
(Phillips)   £1,050

Bassetaille enamelled clock,
open blue umbrella incor-
porating 24ct. gold leaf
numerals on dome, 3½in.
diam., France, circa 1900.
                        £450

Late 17th century Swiss
clock with shaped rectangular iron dial, 40cm. high.
                      £2,250

A Black Forest wall clock,
circa 1840, the 11in. moulded wood dial with alarm
disc, 15½in. high.   £475

An Austrian Biedermeier
mahogany quarter striking
wall clock, 41½in. high.
                      £2,250

A French electrical wall regulator signed Systeme Campiche
de Metz and Mees Nancy on
the dial.   £1,350

CONTINENTAL

A German weight-driven wall clock, circa 1600, 18in. high.   £6,000

A Dutch marquetry 'Koort-staartklok' with automaton, 19th century, 39in. high.
£2,000

An 18th century Dutch 'Stoelklok', 71cm. high.
£900

An ebonised 'Zaanseklok', the brass 30-hour straight line movement with vertical verge escapement, signed *Claus Van Rossen op de Koog*, basically circa 1700, 28¹/₂in. high. (Christie's)   £3,080

A wall clock by André Dubreuil, the green-tinted domed glass clock with copper face of repoussé decoration, mounted in a black iron scrolling frame, 77.5cm. long.
(Christie's)   £2,420

A fine inlaid walnut grande-sonnerie Lanterndluhr with calendar, Fertbauer in Wien, the waisted glazed case with ebony mouldings, striking grande sonnerie on two bells, circa 1800, 57in. high.
(Christie's)   £43,384

An ormolu and bronze clock with glazed enamel dial, indistinctly signed . . . Armentieres, 32½in. high.   £2,000

French 18th century wall clock with dual striking, by Basnard.   £350

A musical 19th century German carved wood wall clock, 6ft.11in. high.   £8,500

ROUND FACE

A Georgian giltwood wall dial clock, the 14in. enamel dial signed Geo. Yonge, London, 24in. diam.
£2,250

A fine 18th century English dial timepiece with verge escapement, signed William Ward, Bloomsbury. £2,250

A Georgian mahogany wall dial clock, the dial signed Robt. Mawley London, 13½in. diam. £1,350

A mahogany wall timepiece, the repainted white enamel convex dial with Roman numerals, moon hands and signed Middleton, London. (Lawrence Fine Arts) £352

Mid 19th century wall clock in circular mahogany case, the enamel dial inscribed Ed. Russell, Foulsham. £400

A Regency mahogany wall timepiece, the silvered engraved dial signed *Edw. Tutet London*, Roman and Arabic chapters, 15³/4in. diameter. (Christie's) £825

Early 19th century inlaid mahogany clock with brass bezel and convex 10in. dial. £650

An 8-day fusee wall clock in mahogany case, the cream painted dial inscribed 'Ganthony'. £1,000

A George III mahogany wall timepiece, the 12in. silvered dial signed Jefferys, London, 1ft.4½in. high. £1,800

VIENNA REGULATORS

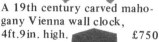

Mid 19th century walnut and ebonised Vienna wall timepiece.   £600

A 19th century carved mahogany Vienna wall clock, 4ft.9in. high.   £750

A Continental eight-day mahogany weight driven two-train Vienna regulator, 58in. high.   £475

A mid 19th century Biedermeier mahogany Vienna regulator, 40½in. high.   £7,500

An ebonized and rosewood Vienna regulator by Lechner M., Pesten, mid 19th century, the case with moulded chamfered corners, 44½in. high. (Christie's New York)   £741

A 19th century grande sonnerie Vienna wall clock, 4ft. 1in. high. (Phillips)   £3,000

Viennese regulator clock, attributed to Gustav Becker, early 20th century, with weight driven time and strike movement, 44½in. high. (Skinner Inc.)   £244

Victorian Vienna wall clock, with a striking movement to an enamelled and brass dial, glazed door and side panels to a walnut case. (G. A. Key)   £340

A walnut veneered and ebonised Vienna regulator, the movement with dead beat escapement, maker's mark *H.E. & Co.,* 131cm. (Lawrence Fine Arts)   £748

WALL CLOCKS

VIENNA REGULATORS

A late Biedermeier rosewood Vienna regulator stamped Crot Berlin 302 on the back-plate of the weight driven movement, 39½in. high.
£1,250

Victorian Vienna wall clock with pendulum, 1880.
£300

A walnut veneered striking Vienna regulator, the movement with dead beat escapement, 52¾in. high. (Lawrence Fine Arts)
£935

A 19th century walnut and ebonised Vienna style wall timepiece, 5ft.7¾in. high. (Phillips)
£1,750

A 19th century Austrian rosewood Vienna wall timepiece, the circular enamel dial with subsidiary seconds signed *Franz Möhslinger in Wien*, the weight driven movement with dead beat escapement, 3ft. 3½in. high. (Phillips)
£1,100

A mahogany Vienna regulator with satin birch line inlay to the glazed case, 19th century, 36½in. high.
£2,500

Victorian Vienna wall clock with striking movement, the mahogany case with fluted detail, glazed door and side panels.
(G. A. Key)
£400

A giltwood Vienna regulator, 6½in. circular white enamel dial (cracked), with subsidiary seconds, brass bezel and deadbeat escapement, 3ft. 2in. high.
(Bonhams)
£900

A XIX century walnut Vienna wall clock, the circular cream enamelled dial with black Roman numerals enclosing a subsidiary seconds dial, 59in. high. (Spencer's)
£600

ZAPPLER CLOCKS

A Schwartzwald wooden zappler wall clock, the dial bearing the date 1740, 36cm. high. £2,500

18th century German zappler wall clock with brass and iron thirty-hour movement. £1,000

A German zappler wall clock, dial signed Johan Bohm, 30.5cm. high. £2,000

A Germanic iron chamber clock, the posted frame 30-hour movement with fabricated wheels, 22in. high. £4,000

Unusual late 18th century Black Forest wall clock of wood construction. 13in. high. £2,250

An 18th century German wooden wall clock, the shaped painted dial with giltwood hands and centre alarm set, 1ft.2¾in. high. (Phillips) £3,200

A German zappler wall clock, containing a bird-cage iron movement, dated 1743, 44cm. high. £3,000

A German zappler wall clock with thirty-hour movement, 29cm. high. £900

A German zappler wall clock with thirty-hour movement, 30cm. high. £2,500

Victorian gilded metal watch stand designed as a mother-of-pearl bird-bath. £100

Late 19th century nickel plated paperweight time-piece, by New Haven Clock Co., 7½in. high. £175

A mahogany and rosewood watch stand on inverted bun feet, 6½in. high. £150

German porcelain watch holder entitled 'Gravelotte'. £300

A French Napoleonic prisoner-of-war carved bone watchstand, in the form of a classical arch supported by two Roman soldiers, height 8¾in., width 6in. £450

German porcelain watch-holder 'Unser Fritz'. £300

A gilt metal clock, by Thos. Cole, London, simulating a watchstand in the form of a miniature chiffonier set, 5¼in. high. £5,500

German porcelain watch-holder 'Sedan' £300

20th century American ebony and ivory watch-stand, 6¼in. high. £350

A nickel cased railway watch, cracked white enamel dial with Roman numerals, inscribed *G.W.R.*
(Bonhams) £130

A gold hunter-cased physician's chronograph, the keyless nickel finished lever movement with chronograph train, 51mm. diam.
(Christie's) £739

An 18ct. gold lever watch, the gold dial inscribed with twenty-four hour divisions, the case marked London 1860, 50mm. diam. £800

A fine and rare late 18th century gold, enamel and seed pearl quarter repeating and musical open-face pocket watch, the reverse with an enamelled scene of Belisarius receiving alms, 59mm. diameter.
(Christie's) £44,000

A Continental silver gilt and translucent red enamel form watch in the shape of an umbrella, with painted gilt Arabic numerals and outer twenty-four hour ring, 4in. diameter.
(Christie's S. Ken) £715

A gold enamel and stone-set minute repeating keyless hunter pocketwatch for the Eastern market, the covers decorated with translucent green enamel on guilloche background, 55mm. diameter.
(Christie's) £4,620

A late George V gentleman's 18 carat gold cased pocket watch with engine turned gilt metal dial, London 1933.
(Henry Spencer) £230

A French gold quarter repeating pocket watch, the face with Roman numerals and guilloché border.
(Finarte) £1,844

A Swiss gun metal keyless lever watch, the movement with tourbillion visible through the back, 53mm. diam.
(Phillips) £880

(A)

A fine gold openface centre seconds world time dress watch, retailed by Cartier, the movement by Agassiz. (Christie's)
£4,315

A Blois enamel early verge watch, signed Jehan Augier A Paris on the movement top-plate, with vase pillars, fusee and gut to four-wheel train, 61mm. diam. (Christie's)
£46,200

A gold openface free sprung fusee lever watch with winding indicator, signed Aldred & Son, Yarmouth, the 18ct. gold case, London, 1891, 53mm. diam.
£1,250

An unusual gold keyless openface double sided full calendar and moonphase pocket watch, inscribed *Avertisseur Electrique et Calendrier*, 48mm. diameter. (Christie's S. Ken)
£1,540

An 18ct. gold slim half hunting cased keyless lever watch, the Swiss gilt movement with compressed balance, inscribed *Asprey, Bond St., London,* 1908. (Lawrence Fine Arts)
£1,100

A silvered Arnex pocket watch with the profiles of John and Robert Kennedy in relief on the back, the white enamel dial with the American eagle and Stars and Stripes in the centre, circa 1970.
(Auction Team Köln)
£80

A gold repousse pair cased verge watch signed Wm. Addis London 1812, 48mm. diam.
£1,800

A gold and enamel cylinder watch, enamelled on the machined cuvette *Ami Sandoz & Fils, Geneve*, silvered dial, case back with multi-coloured enamelled flowers, 44mm. (Bonhams)
£280

A Swiss gold and enamel bridge-cock verge watch signed Alliez Bachelard & Terond Fils N. 61141, 45mm. diam.
£1,000

(B)

A gold hunting cased keyless pocket chronometer by J. Bennett, hallmarked 1876, 52mm. diam. £2,000

An 18th century silver pair cased verge watch, signed G. Bryan, London, 399, 50mm. diam. £650

Mid 19th century lady's 18ct. gold open face pocket watch, Berthoud, Paris. £750

A gilt-metal and enamel watch, signed Bouvier A Geneve, the reverse enamelled with an Arcadian couple by an altar of love, 54mm. diam. (Christie's) £660

An early 18th century gold pair cased verge watch, the movement with pierced Egyptian pillars and pierced engraved cock, signed *Brounker Watts, London.* (Phillips) £4,200

An enamelled gold convertible cased cylinder watch, signed J. FS. Bautte & Co., Geneve, with gilt cylinder movement jewelled to the third wheel, 36mm. diam. £2,500

An openface floral enamel silver gilt centre seconds watch for the Chinese Market, signed Bovet, Fleurier, 55mm. diam. £3,000

A Swiss gold, enamel and gem set verge watch, the bridgecock movement signed Fres. Bordier, Geneve No. 35751, 44mm. diam. £950

A silver repousse pair cased striking coach clock watch, signed Johan Georg Brodt, circa 1725, 126mm. diam. £12,500

332

(B)

An 18ct. gold half-hunter
cased quarter repeating
pocket watch, inscribed
A. Bach, London £1,000

Swiss gold cased open-
faced half-repeating
pocket watch, signed
Leon Boillat, Geneva
£900

A triple colour gold and
enamel verge watch by
Pierre Bry of Paris,
circa 1790, 46mm. diam.
£1,500

A Swiss gold hunter cased keyless lever watch, signed Borel
Fils & Cie, the case enamelled
with scene of the Nile and on
the reverse Cleopatra, 49mm.
diam. (Phillips)   £2,300

A Continental silver hunter
case Chinese duplex watch,
signed *Euge Bournand & Cie
A Ste Croix*, 56mm. diam.
(Phillips London)   £500

A Continental silver pair
cased verge watch, signed
Blanc Pere & Fils, Geneve,
the silver champleve dial
signed P. B., London, 50mm.
diam.   £700

An early 18th century gold, gilt
metal and tortoiseshell pair
cased verge watch, the
movement with Egyptian pillars,
signed *Paul Beauvais*, 59mm.
diameter.
(Phillips)   £500

A platinum dress watch with
integral stand, retailed by
Bucherer, Lucerne, 42mm.
wide.   £900

An American 14ct. vari-
coloured gold box-hinged
hunter-cased watch,
movement signed P. S.
Bartlett, 53mm. diam.
£2,250

(C)

A French gold quarter-repeating cylinder watch, gilt cuvette signed Robert O. Courvoisier, 60mm. diam. £2,500

A gold pair-cased repousse verge watch, signed Crayton, London, circa 1780, with gilt full plate movement, fusee chain, verge escapement, 40mm. diameter. (Christie's) £2,250

A Swiss gold centre seconds quarter-repeating cylinder watch, gold cuvette signed La Croix et Fils a Geneve, 55mm. diam. £2,250

An unusual silver lever watch, the fusee movement signed Clerke, London, the enamel dial with blue guilloche centre, 1866, 48mm. diam. (Phillips) £420

A silver pocket watch by the Cortebert Watch Mfg Co, with Swiss anchor escapement, the two coloured enamel dial with windows for hours and minutes and seconds dial below, 5.5cm. diameter, circa 1900. (Auction Team Köln) £328

An engraved gold hunter-cased pocket chronometer, signed on the cuvette Constantaras Freres, Constantinople, 55mm. diam. £1,250

A gold openface chronograph with minute recorder mounted on centre arbour, signed Henry Capt, Geneva, 55mm. diam. £900

A French gold and enamel verge watch, the bridgecock movement signed Chevalier et Comp^e 1829, 50mm. diam. £1,250

An 18ct. gold open faced keywind watch, signed Cooper, Colchester, hall-marked 1866, 45mm. diam. £375

(C)

A gold pair cased half quarter-repeating cylinder watch, by John Cowell, London, 54mm. diam. £2,750

Gold pair-cased cylinder watch by Alexander Cumming, London, 1781, 53mm. diam. £1,850

A gilt-metal and enamel verge watch, signed Cabrier, 50mm. diam. £900

An 18th century Swiss gold repeating pocket watch, the white porcelain dial signed *Jn Chaponniere à Genève*, the case enamelled with figures and musical symbols, 50mm. diameter. (Duran) £5,000

An enamelled gold verge watch, the bridge pierced with scrolls spelling *Chevalier*, white enamel dial with Arabic chapters, gold beetle-and-poker hands, the back enamelled with scene of children playing in the woods, circa 1790, 53mm. diameter. (Christie's) £2,552

A white metal keyless pocket watch by Cyma, the white enamel dial with Hebrew characters, the signed movement with monometallic balance and lever escapement, 50mm. diameter. (Christie's S. Ken) £220

A gold and enamel dumb quarter-repeating verge watch by Champion of Paris, hallmarked 1777, 40mm. diam. £2,500

A silver and tortoiseshell triple case Turkish market verge watch, the movement signed *Geo Charle London*, 63mm. diam. (Phillips) £340

A gold and enamel pair-cased verge watch by J. Cowan of Edinburgh, hallmarked 1778 and casemaker's initials IL, 55mm. diam. £2,750

(D)

A verge watch, the movement signed Daniel Delander, London, 334, 55mm. diam. £950

Early 18th century silver verge oignon by Etienne Dominice, 58mm. diam. £2,250

An enamelled gold cylinder watch, signed F. Delynne a Paris, no. 206, 40mm.diam. £15,000

An 18th century silver and horn pair cased verge watch, signed Conrs. Dunlop, London 3451, the inner case marked London 1762, 52mm. diam. £2,000

An important Swiss silver keyless lever deck watch, the frosted gilt ³/₄-plate movement signed *Paul Ditisheim. La Chaux de Fonds*, jewelled to the centre in screwed châtons, 65mm. diameter. (Christie's) £14,300

An Austrian silver and horn pair-cased coach clockwatch with alarm, signed Joseph Derchinger Wienn, with chain fusee, basically circa 1700, 106mm. diam. (Christie's) £3,080

An engraved gold openface lever watch, signed Lucien Dubois, Locle, 48mm. diam. £1,000

A gold half-hunter minute repeating keyless lever watch, the half-plate movement signed Donne & Son, London, repeating on two gongs, 58mm. diam. (Christie's) £3,300

A gold openface lever watch, signed Paul Ditisheim, La Chaux-De-Fonds, 56mm. diam. £2,200

(D)

A silver pair cased verge watch No. 656 by Andrew Dunlop of London, 56mm. diam., circa 1700. £1,600

Dent 18ct. yellow gold cased open-faced pocket watch, London, 1898, signed. £900

A French gold and enamel verge watch, signed Dutertre₁ a Paris, 43mm. diam. £1,000

(E)

An 18th century gold pair-cased verge watch, with square baluster pillars and pierced cock signed Jas Evans, Shrewsbury, 48mm. diam. (Phillips) £500

A rare late 18th century gilt metal lever watch, signed on backplate *Josiah Emery Charing Cross London 1094,* the later consular case with case maker's mark *TG,* 58mm. diam. (Phillips) £14,500

An 18ct. gold open-face Duplex pocket watch in engine-turned case with ribbed band, inscribed Thos. Earnshaw, London, (staff broken), 51mm. diam. (Christie's) £825

Cartier platinum and diamond set keyless lever watch by the European Watch Co., 46mm. £3,250

An early 19th century silver pair cased verge watch, signed John Ebsworth, London, the silver champleve dial with semi-circular day and night aperture, 55mm. diam. (Phillips) £1,600

A gold keyless lever watch, signed Geo. Edward & Sons on ½-plate gilt movement jewelled to the third, 53mm. diam. £1,000

(F)

A small gold openface five-minute repeating watch, signed Fayette S. Giles, 36mm. diam. £1,600

A gold hunter-cased chrono-meter, the enamel dial signed French, Royal Exchange, London 1867, 51mm. diam. £1,500

A small gold half-hunter cased minute repeating free-sprung lever watch, movement signed Joseph Fleming & Co., 40mm. diam. £3,000

A silver, part-gilt watch with white enamel dial, the movement signed *Le Fleuron, Beaucort*, the back with floral relief decoration, circa 1900, 4cm. diameter.
(Auction Team Köln) £131

A rare quarter repeating watch incorporating an automaton of Moses, Fleury l'Aîné, signed in the watchmaker's hand *Fait par A. Fleury à la Chaux de Fonds en Suisse, Vendu à Berbiee 1807*, within a plain 18ct. gold case, 64.5mm. diameter.
(Christie's New York) £84,150

Fontac London No. 227, an unusual gilt, silver and enamel verge pocket watch in consular case, the silver back cover with blue enamel scene depicting Aesop's fable The Fox and the Crow, 57mm. diameter.
(Christie's) £770

A French gold and enamel verge watch, the bridge-cock movement signed Le Febure A Paris No. 792, 36mm. diam. £750

A gold hunter-cased quarter repeating calendar watch, signed L. A. Favre Brandt, Geneve, 53mm. diam. £1,850

A French gold skeletonised cylinder calendar watch, the dial plate signed Fleury A Nantes, 33mm. diam. £1,500

(G)

A gold floral enamel dress watch, signed L. Gallopin & Co., Suc'rs to Henry Capt, Geneva, 44mm. diam. £1,850

A gold pair cased verge watch by Daniel Grignion of London, hallmarked 1726, 54mm. diam. £2,000

An enamelled gilt metal verge watch, signed Gregson A Paris, with white enamel dial, 53mm. diam. £750

A silver pair cased verge stop watch, the movement with pierced cock signed Wm. Graham, London, No. 11437, the cases marked London, 1797. £325

A Continental enamel verge pocket watch in consular case, the reverse with painted scene of a Satyr and two nude figures in a landscape, signed *Les Freres Goyffon a Paris*, 46mm. diameter. (Christie's S. Ken) £1,320

A late 18th century gold and enamel verge watch, the movement signed Gregson A Paris 13123, 50mm. diam. £800

A silver pair-cased verge watch, signed W. Graham London, with pierced carved mask cock and foot, outer case plain, 51mm. diam. (Christie's) £1,540

An 18th century French gilt metal verge watch, inscribed Gribelin A Paris, the gilt dial with enamel numerals and chapter, 60mm. diam. (Phillips) £1,400

A gold, enamel and split pearl-set verge watch by Thos. Gray of Sackville Street, circa 1780, 47mm. diam. £4,000

(H)

A gold repousse pair-cased quarter repeating watch, signed Horman Klein Kotz, circa 1725, 45mm. diameter overall.
(Christie's) £3,600

A Swiss gold hunter cased keyless lever watch, the steel bar movement signed Henry Hoffman, Locle, 54mm. diam.
(Phillips) £633

A gold and agate verge watch, movement signed Hen. Hurt London, 45mm. diam. £2,500

A silver pair cased verge watch, signed *Alfred Heald Wisbech*, white enamel dial with painted centre of a rural scene of a man ploughing the land, London 1860, 55mm.
(Bonhams) £190

A Hamilton American gold watch, the Swiss anchor movement with Breguet escapement and compensation balance, the silvered dial with Arabic numerals, 4.5cm. diameter, circa 1920.
(Auction Team Köln) £202

A silver keyless open-face eight-day calendar pocket watch by Hebdomas in engine-turned case, the white enamel dial with eccentric chapter-ring, 47mm. diameter.
(Christie's S. Ken) £660

A gold and enamel reversible hunter or openface lever watch, the three-quarter plate move-ment signed Hamilton & Co., London, No. 35103, 41mm. diam. £1,000

A fine enamelled gold verge watch, the case signed *Huaud le Puisne fecit*, the purpose made movement signed *Hoendshker, Dresden*, finely painted with "Roman Charity" after Simon Vouet, 40mm. diameter.
(Christie's) £22,330

An 18 carat gold watch, the movement with 'Savage' two pin lever escapement, signed *Hampson & Shelwell*, 1817, 54mm. diameter.
(Phillips) £650

(H)

A French gold and enamel verge watch, the bridge-cock movement signed Hessen a Paris, 38mm. diam. £800

A gold half hunting cased lever watch by W. G. Hallett of Hastings, hallmarked 1867, 43mm. diam. £750

A gold verge watch by Andre Hessen of Paris, 52mm. diam., circa 1790. £1,500

A 10 carat gold plated railwayman's pocket watch, the bar movement signed *Made in USA*, with white enamel dial signed *Hamilton* and black Arabic numerals, 5cm. diameter, circa 1905. (Auction Team Köln) £206

A child's construction kit for a pocket-watch with original box and instructions, bearing the stamp *Hamley's, 612 Oxford Street.* (Christie's S. Ken) £550

A gold and Huaud enamel verge watch, the case signed *Fratres Huaud Pinxerunt,* the reverse painted with a polychrome enamel of the Virgin Mary and St. Elizabeth holding Christ and St. John the Baptist, circa 1750, 37mm. diameter. (Christie's) £6,600

A Swiss gold and enamel keyless lever watch, the dial signed Hartog, 48mm. diam. £2,000

A gold pair cased verge watch, signed Jams. Hagger, London 200, 54mm. diam. £3,500

An 18th century verge pocket watch with silver dial and case, by J. Hocker, Reading. £325

(I)

A white metal keyless open-face
Mickey Mouse pocket watch by
Ingersoll in plain case, the white
dial with Arabic numerals,
49mm. diameter.
(Christie's S. Ken)   £440

A finely enamelled gold centre
seconds watch by Ilbery,
London, the engraved gilt partly
skeletonised duplex movement
with going barrel, Geneva, circa
1820, 57.5mm. diameter.
(Christie's)   £19,140

A multi-colour gold filled
hunter cased pocket watch,
signed Illinois Watch Co.,
fifteen jewel movement,
53mm. diam.   £375

(J)

Fine gold keyless free
sprung lever dress
watch, signed Jump,
London, 53mm. diam.
          £2,000

An 18 carat gold, emerald and
diamond-set lady's back-wind
bracelet watch, signed Jaeger Le
Coultre, Swiss, 1950s, 17mm.
diameter. (Christie's)   £1,035

Jules Jurgensen, Copenhagen,
an 18ct. gold open faced watch,
signed white enamel dial, Roman
numerals and subsidiary seconds,
signed damascened nickel movement, 50mm. (Bonhams) £1,300

(K)

An enamelled gold pendant
watch and chain, signed Ed.
Koehn, Geneva, retailed by
J. E. Caldwell & Co., Phila.,
29mm. diam.   £900

A gold Karrusel lever watch,
the movement signed John
Dyson & Sons Leeds, 55mm.
diam.   £5,000

A gold keyless free-sprung
lever Karrusel watch,
movement signed Grant &
Son, plain case, London
1909, 55mm. diam.
          £5,000

(L)

Late 19th century gold open faced eight-day lever watch, engraved London and Ryder, 17 New Bond Street, 55mm. diam.   £750

A 19th century Austrian silver, enamel and rock crystal verge watch, the circular movement signed F.S. Lompejo in Wien, 60mm. diam. (Phillips)   £880

Mid 19th century gold open-face pivoted detent chronometer for the American market, Swiss, the dial signed William F. Ladd, 46mm. diam.   £475

A keyless pink gold open-face pocket watch by A. Langer & Sohne, Glashutte b/Dresden in plain case with engraved monogram to the reverse, the white enamel dial with Arabic numerals, 49mm. diameter. (Christie's S. Ken)   £660

A rare silver openface self-winding watch, the dial signed *Loehr Patent*, the square gilt lever movement with compensation balance and flat blued hairspring, 1880s, 48mm. wide.
(Christie's)   £1,276

A heavy 18ct. gold open-face Duplex pocket watch in plain case with small cartouche to the rear and foliate scroll decoration to the band, signed James Lytle, Sligo, 52mm. diameter. (Christie's)   £605

An unusual nickel cased early waterproof keyless open-face pocket watch in plain case, signed *Lund & Blockley, to the Queen, London*, 58mm. diameter.
(Christie's S. Ken)   £605

A keyless gold openface minute-repeating watch with perpetual retrograde calendar, signed on the case Eugene Lecoultre, 54mm. diam.   £7,500

An 18ct. gold hunter cased quarter repeating Duplex watch, the movement with extra jewelling to the repeat train signed J.R.Losada, London 1855, 42mm. diam. (Phillips)   £1,900

A Swiss gold and enamel
cylinder watch, the move-
ment signed Mottu, Geneve,
34mm. diam.   £1,000

A silver-gilt pocket chronometer, movement sig-
ned Septimus Miles, plain
case, London 1819, 57mm.
diam.   £1,850

A gold openface split second
chronograph, signed C. H.
Meylan, Brassus, 48mm.
diam.   £750

An enamelled gold openface
dress watch of Napoleonic
interest, signed Movado, the
18ct. gold case with London
import mark 1910, 47mm.
diam.   £2,750

A chased gold hunter cased
minute repeating lever
watch with automaton,
signed Paul Matthey-Doret,
Locle, 58mm. diam.
                    £7,500

A gold repousse pair-cased quar-
ter repeating verge watch, signed
Jon. Magson, embossed with a
Trojan War scene within asym-
metrical scroll border, 48mm. diam.
(Christie's)   £1,430

An 18ct. gold minute repeating keyless lever watch, the
movement signed James
Murray, London, 1882,
51mm. diam.   £1,500

A Swiss gold and enamel open-
faced keywind watch, signed
Milleret & Tissot a Geneve,
34mm.   £675

A French gold, enamel and
pearl verge watch, the bridge-
cock movement signed Martin
A Paris 11750, 37mm. diam.
                      £2,250

Early 19th century quarter repeating gold pocket watch, by Moulinie Bautte & Moynier, Geneve. £900

A silver gilt and enamel hermetic bag watch, champagne dial signed *Movado Ermeto*, the slide winding movement in case with black enamel bands, 47mm., circa 1933.
(Bonhams) £190

Silver open-faced full plate keyless tourbillon watch by Mobilis, 53mm. diam. £2,500

A silver repoussé pair cased verge watch, signed *T. May*, pierced bridge balance cock, plain pillars, white enamel dial border with black Roman numerals, London 1796, 52mm.
(Bonhams) £380

An early 18th century gold quarter-repeating pair-case verge pocket watch by Hr. Massy, London, in gilt shagreen covered outer case, 55mm. diameter.
(Christie's S. Ken) £2,420

A silver verge pocket watch, the white enamel face signed *Gabriel Mansion a Huy* and with Arabic numerals, 5.5cm. diameter, 1800–50.
(Auction Team Köln) £140

A repousse gold pair-cased verge watch, signed J. Markham, London, no. 6828, 51mm. diam. £1,850

Late 18th century gilt-metal pair cased striking cylinder chaise watch No. 213 by Marriott of London, 132mm. diam. £3,500

A silver pair cased verge stop watch, the movement with pierced cock signed Thos. Munro, London 1146, 57mm. diam. £475

A gold duplex watch, the full plate movement signed John Newton, London, No. 604, 54mm. diam.   £800

An 18ct. gold keyless lever chronograph, the movement signed Nicole & Capt., London, Patent No. 7255, 48mm. diam.   £750

A gold openface medical chronograph, signed Ulysse Nardin, Locle & Geneve, 55mm. diam.   £2,000

An open faced silver verge watch, signed *Robt. Neill Belfast*, silver dial with applied gilt Roman numbers with subsidiary second dial and foliage border, hallmark, London 1820, 55mm. (Bonhams)   £140

A unique gold hunter cased chronograph, cast and chased in the form of a buffalo, the case and movement by Nicole, Nielsen & Co., London, for Edward and Sons, London and Glasgow, 60mm. diameter. (Christie's)   £15,312

An English silver pocket watch, the porcelain dial with a shield flanked by two females and marked *Amicitia Amor et Veritas* beneath the letter *G*, by P. R. J. Ness, marks for Birmingham 1838, 55mm. diameter. (Duran)   £267

(O)

A silver verge alarm watch by Charles Oudin, circa 1820, 57mm. diam.   £600

A mid 18th century silver pair-case verge pocket watch in plain outer case, illustrated with a pair of fighting cocks and signed *Henry Owen*, the inner and outer case hallmarked *London 1759*, 47mm. diameter. (Christie's S. Ken)   £418

A three colour gold quarter repeating verge watch signed Del Orme, a Paris, with gilt full plate movement, pierced cock, repeating on bell, 42mm diameter. (Christie's)   £1,750

(P)

A repousse gold pair cased verge watch by Harry Potter of London, hallmarked 1780, 53mm. diam. £2,000

An 18ct. gold hunter-cased minute-repeating chronograph, signed Albert H. Potter & Co., Geneva, 52mm. diam. £8,500

A gentleman's 18ct. gold half hunter cased keyless pocket watch, inscribed C. R. Pleasance, Sheffield. £275

A gilt metal and tortoiseshell pair cased quarter repeating verge watch made for the Turkish market, signed Geo. Prior, London, 62mm. diam. £1,250

JS. Patron, Geneve, a late 18th century gold, enamel and seed pearl verge pair-cased pocket watch, the decorative outer case with enamelled scene of a couple in a garden to the reverse, 49mm. diameter. (Christie's) £2,970

An 18th century gold pair-cased verge watch, signed Wm Plumley, Ludgate Hill, the outer case of repousse work depicting a classical scene, 50mm. diam. (Phillips) £950

An 18 carat gold and enamel keyless lever watch, the movement signed *Phillip & Phillip, London,* 1868, 36mm. diam. (Phillips) £460

An 18ct. gold pair-cased pocket watch with repoussé decoration by Porthouse, Penrith 1766. (Christie's) £1,430

A gold pocket chronometer, the fusee movement signed Wm. Pickman, with enamel dial and gold hands, 54mm. diam. £1,250

(R)

A gold duplex watch, the movement signed Radford, Leeds, No. 2588, 53mm. diam.   £1,400

A nielloed silver sector watch, signed Record Watch Co., Tramelan, 60mm. wide. £1,400

Early 19th century Rentzsch duplex movement watch, 96mm. diam.   £1,000

An 18ct. gold open faced watch, the reverse with the enamel portrait of a Maharajah, inscribed Rotherhams, London, the three-quarter plate movement with pointed lever escapement, 49mm. diam. (Christie's)   £935

Russells Ltd., Liverpool, an 18ct. gold minute repeating keyless hunter pocketwatch in plain case with engraved monogram to the front cover and armorial crest to the reverse, hallmarked *London 1920,* **53mm. diameter.** (Christie's)   £2,970

Robert & Courvoisier:fine and rare gold bras en l'air verge pocket watch in engine-turned case, a gilt automaton indicating the time with its arms by depressing the pendant, 56mm. diameter. (Christie's)   £12,650

A Continental gilt enamel and paste set open-face verge pocket watch, the white enamel dial with paste set bezel, Arabic numerals and signed *Reimirol & Cie,* 55mm. diameter. (Christie's S. Ken)   £770

A silver fan-form sector watch, signed *Record Watch Co., Tramelan, Sector Watch* circa 1910, the white enamel dial with sector scale calibrated for 0 to 12, 60mm. wide. (Christie's)   £1,316

A rare verge automata pocket watch, with aperture above the twelve revealing painted figures revolving past a landscape, signed *Roux Roman Bordier & Compe,* 52mm. diameter. (Christie's S. Ken)   £1,100

(S)

A verge watch, quarter-repeating on two visible bells, the gilt movement signed Georg Schmit, Neustadt, 56mm. diam. £2,000

A silver sector watch, signed Sector Watch, Tramelan, with shaped lever movement jewelled to the third wheel, 60mm. diam. (Christie's) £924

An 18th century gold and enamel pair cased watch, signed Geo. Phi. Strigel, London, 1770, 48mm. diam. £2,750

A 'Dutch import' silver and tortoiseshell triple case verge watch, signed Samson, London, decorated at the centre with a river scene, 57mm. diam. (Phillips) £620

An extraordinary silver verge watch in the form of a dolphin by J. Sermand [Geneva], the hinged mouth opening to reveal the dial, circa 1640, 40mm. long. (Christie's New York) £67,320

A silver oignon with alarm, Sourdeval a Paris, the movement with Egyptian pillars, pierced bridge chased with scrolls, strapwork and birds, the barrel of the alarm train chased with leafy scrolls on matted ground, 18th century, 60mm. diameter. (Christie's) £1,276

A 19th century Continental gold and enamel pair cased verge watch, the movement with pierced cock signed *Jean Robert Soret 29020*, 49mm. diameter. (Phillips) £1,000

An 18ct. gold open faced key wind watch, signed *Swinden & Sons, Temple St., Birmingham*, hallmarked 1824, 47mm. (Lawrence Fine Arts) £308

An open faced keyless cylinder fob watch, the movement stamped Savoye Freres & Cie, signed on the cuvette Faucard a Dinard, 30mm. diam. £325

(T)

A slim gold and champ-
leve enamel cylinder
watch by Edward R.
Theurer, circa 1850,
45mm. diam.   £3,000

An 18ct. yellow gold hunting cased duplex pocket
watch, by Tolkien &
Gravell, hallmarked London,
1813.   £650

A Swiss gold and enamel
verge watch, the bridge-
cock movement signed
Ph^e. Terrot, 57mm.
diam.   £1,500

A Swiss repousse gold quarter
repeating bridge-cock verge
watch signed Terrot &
Thuillier Geneve 5889,
49mm. diam.   £2,000

An 18th century Swiss silver
pair cased verge watch,
signed Philippe Terrot, with
signed silver champleve dial,
the outer case decorated with
a repousse design, 50mm.
diam. (Phillips)   £400

A gold openface minute
repeating chronograph with
register, signed Touchon &
Co., Geneva, 18ct. gold case,
52mm. diam.   £2,000

(V)

A Swiss nickel keyless lever
watch of very large size, the
enamel dial with subsidiary
seconds signed for J.C. Vickery,
13.5cm. diam. (Phillips)   £350

A small oval gilt metal
verge watch, signed N.
Vallin, length including
pendant 53mm. £4,250

Vulcain: a 1920s white gold and
sapphire keyless dress watch in
square case with cabochon
winder and sapphires set to the
band, the brushed silvered dial
with raised Arabic numerals
and subsidiary seconds, 40mm.
square. (Christie's)   £748

(W)

A gold quarter repeating duplex watch, the movement signed Rd. Webster, Cornhill, London, 5248, 53mm. diam. £1,000

A gold openface watch by the American Waltham Watch Co., within a plain 18ct. gold cuvette, 48mm. diam. £1,250

An 18th century gold pair cased pocket watch, the fusee movement inscribed John Walker, Newcastle upon Tyne 736. £850

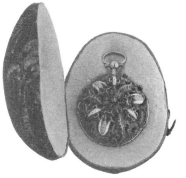

An 8 day pocket watch by Wyss Freres, Switzerland, in nickel steel case, the white enamel decentralised dial with black Arabic numerals and engraved, 5cm. diameter, circa 1910. (Auction Team Köln) £140

An Austrian gold and enamel verge pendant watch of small size, the frosted gilt fusée movement with bridge cock inscribed with the initials *J.S. Wien*, 29mm. diameter. (Christie's S. Ken) £2,640

An 18 carat gold half hunter case keyless pocket chronometer with one minute tourbillion, signed *Joseph White & Son*, 55mm. diam., together with the original presentation case. (Phillips London) £13,500

A gold pair cased watch, the full plate movement signed David Whitelaw, No. 120, and inscribed Edw Henderson, Edinburgh 1815, 55mm. diam. £500

An 18th century silver pair cased quarter repeating verge watch, the movement with pierced tulip pillars, signed *Windmyller, London*, 57mm. diameter. (Phillips) £800

A gold box hinge huntercased watch, by American Waltham Watch Co., within an engraved 14ct. gold box hinged case, 55mm. diam. £1,000

ARNOLD

A gold openface fusee lever watch, signed J. R. Arnold, Chas. Frodsham, London, 1853, 55mm. diam. £1,000

A gold pocket chronometer, the movement signed John Arnold & Son, 53mm. diam. £7,500

A silver cased pocket chronometer by John Arnold, London, 50mm. diam. £12,000

John Roger Arnold No. 1956, a rare 18ct. gold pocket chronometer in plain consular case, the white enamel dial with Roman numerals and large subsidiary seconds, gold hands, *London 1805*, 57mm. diameter. (Christie's) £14,300

A pocket chronometer movement by John Arnold & Son, London, the frosted gilt fusée movement with pierced and engraved cock, with enamel dial and silver case, diameter of top-plate 40mm. (Christie's S. Ken) £1,320

A pocket chronometer movement by John Roger Arnold, the signed and numbered enamel dial with subsidiary seconds and gold hands, 49mm. diam., circa 1820. (Phillips) £1,300

AUDEMARS PIGUET

Audemars Piguet No. 154003, gold hexagonal cased skeleton keyless lever watch, 50mm. diam. £2,750

An openface platinum dress watch with 19-jewel movement with gold train, signed Audemars Piguet & Co., no. 36541, 43mm. diam. £1,000

A skeleton keyless lever watch by Audemars Piguet & Cie, the movement with gold train, 45mm. diam. £2,500

A gold keyless openface split-second chronograph pocketwatch in plain case, the nickel plated movement with bi-metallic balance and swanneck regulation, 46mm. diameter.
(Christie's)   £920

A Swiss 18ct. gold and enamel quarter repeating keyless lever Jaquemart watch, circa 1900, bi-metallic compensation balance, repeating on two gongs, 53.5mm. diameter.
(Christie's)   £2,175

Breguet, Paris, No. 6216, a gold open-face minute repeating keyless pocket watch in drum shaped case, bimetallic balance and micrometer regulation, 52mm. diameter.
(Christie's)   £5,280

A rare Swiss 18ct. gold automaton cheeping bird watch in the manner of Ph. Du Bois, Le Locle, circa 1790, applied with three-coloured gilt monkey jacks clashing cymbals to mark the quarters, the cheeping bird in a gold cage, 65.5mm. diameter.
(Christie's)   £62,700

Patek Philippe & Co., Geneve, No. 24139, a fine and rare gold two-train two time-zone independent jumping seconds and minute repeating keyless hunter pocketwatch in plain case with five-piece hinges engraved *Aleksei Aleksandrovich Sapozhnikov*, 1864, 55mm. diameter.
(Christie's)   £29,900

S. Smith & Sons, No. 1900–5, a rare and impressive 18ct. gold keyless openface minute repeating, split-second chronograph with one minute tourbillon pocketwatch made by Nicole Nielsen, signed by *Smiths & Son*, hallmarked *London 1899*, 63mm. diameter.
(Christie's)   £76,300

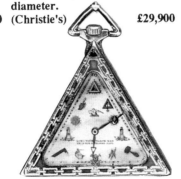

A 1920's gold and enamel keyless open-face dresswatch, the unsigned movement jewelled to the third, 46mm. diameter.
(Christie's)   £550

A silver triangular Masonic keyless open-face pocket watch, the movement signed *Tempor W. Co.*, 55mm.
(Christie's)   £1,210

A French enamelled gold watch case base, circa 1700, the outside painted with Neptune calming the waves, 45mm. diameter.
(Christie's)   £1,265

BARRAUD & LUNDS

A gold keyless openface free sprung fusee lever watch with winding indicator, signed Barraud & Lunds, London, 1893, 51mm. diam.   £1,500

A gold hunter-cased lever watch, signed Barraud & Lunds, London, 1882, 50mm. diam.
£650

A gold open faced lever watch by Barraud & Lunds, hallmarked 1871, 47mm. diam.   £650

BENSON

An 18ct. gold keyless lever chronograph, the movement with compensated balance, signed J. W. Benson, London, the case marked London 1882, 53mm. diam. (Phillips)
£600

An 18ct. gold hunter-cased keyless chronograph, the movement signed J. W. Benson, No. 2516, London, 54mm. diam.   £1,850

A fine and rare 18ct. gold keyless open-face split-second chronograph carousel by J.W. Benson, in plain case, the white enamel dial with Willis to the back, with chain fusée, London 1906, 59mm. diameter. (Christie's S. Ken)   £26,400

BREGUET

A gold quarter repeating jump hour ruby cylinder watch, inscribed Breguet No. 2097, 48mm. diam.   £4,250

A gold minute repeating keyless lever chronograph, signed Breguet No. 1310, 56mm. diam.   £7,500

Breguet No. 58: a gold quarter repeating duplex watch, gilt Lepine calibre, 44mm. diam.
£3,000

BREGUET

19th century gold and enamel quarter repeating cylinder watch, inscribed Breguet, 47mm. diam.
£3,000

Gold cased five minute repeating keyless lever chronograph 'Paris' watch by Breguet, 55mm. diam. £7,500

A gold jump seconds dual time cylinder watch, gold cuvette signed Breguet a Paris No 4275, 55mm. diam. £3,000

An 18ct. gold openface quarter repeating verge watch with jacquemarts, Swiss, signed on the cuvette Breguet & Fils, no. 23592, 55mm. diam.
£2,750

A gold openface quarter repeating pocketwatch in engine turned drum case, the white enamel dial with Arabic numerals signed at VI *Breguet et Fils*, 54mm. diameter. (Christie's) £7,700

Early 19th century silver openface clock watch, Swiss, the cuvette signed Breguet & Fils, the top plate signed Japy, 58mm. diam. £1,500

A French gold and enamel cylinder watch, the movement signed Breguet A Paris, 51mm. diam.
£2,500

A French gold jump hour cylinder watch with plain balance and gold cuvette inscribed Breguet A Paris No. 8416, 50mm. diam.
£2,250

A Swiss gold minute repeating grande sonnerie keyless lever clock watch, the cuvette signed for Breguet No. 4722, 57mm. diam. £25,000

A Continental gold quarter repeating automata and erotic pocket watch in engine turned case, with skeletonised dial, 56mm. diameter.
(Christie's) £3,740

A Swiss gold and enamel pendant watch in the shape of a fan, the frosted gilt movement with cylinder escapement jewelled to the third, 43 x 40mm.
(Christie's) £1,100

Vacheron & Constantin, an unusual gold and black enamel keyless open-face pocket watch, the American case stamped *A.W.C. Co.*, 34mm. diameter.
(Christie's) £385

John Arnold, London No. 339, a silver openface chronometer pocketwatch, in plain consular case, Arnold's spring detent escapement set into the top plate, the case hallmarked *London 1783*, the casemaker's stamp *WW*, 52mm. diameter.
(Christie's) £3,680

Patek Philippe & Cie, a rare 18ct. gold keyless two-train independent jumping seconds hunter pocketwatch in plain case, the front cover with a mounted emblem of a crossed sword and arrow, 52mm. diameter.
(Christie's) £11,500

Chas. Frodsham, a good 18ct. gold and enamel minute repeating keyless half hunter pocketwatch in plain case with blue enamel chapter ring, the signed white enamel Willis dial with Roman numerals, 53mm. diameter.
(Christie's) £5,500

Badollet, Genève, a gold enamel and stone-set cylinder hunter pocket watch, the signed frosted gilt bar movement with cylinder escapement, 35mm. diameter.
(Christie's) £1,430

Blois, a gold and enamel watch cover, circa 1660, the recto painted with a mother and three children clasping an apple, 58mm. diameter.
(Christie's) £2,125

A gold and enamel hunter cased pendant watch, the frosted gilt movement with cylinder escapement under cuvette, 29mm. diameter.
(Christie's) £462

A gold, enamel and pearl-set quarter repeating calendar watch, signed *Des Arts & Compe, No. 5467*, with gilt verge movement, 51mm. diameter. (Christie's) £4,130

Morisset R & C Lukins, a gold enamel and pearl-set cylinder clock watch, signed *Morisset R & C Lukins London No. 1893*, 60mm. diameter. (Christie's) £4,048

Grandjean & Co., a gold and enamel keyless hunter pocket watch, bimetallic balance and lever escapement under signed cuvette, 40mm. diameter. (Christie's) £825

An 18ct. gold diamond and ruby-set lady's pendant watch, signed on the movement *Le Coultre & Cie*, circa 1890, the back chased with floral decoration and set with diamonds and rubies as flower heads, 24mm. diameter. (Christie's) £658

Parkinson & Frodsham, London, an 18ct. gold minute repeating keyless hunter pocketwatch, the frosted gilt three-quarter plate movement signed *Parkinson & Frodsham, No. 1963, 16 Queen Victoria Street, London*, 54mm. diameter. (Christie's) £2,300

Robert, Genève, a gold, enamel, pearl and stone-set keyless hunter pendant watch in decorative case, the nickel bar movement under signed cuvette with bimetallic balance and lever escapement, 37mm. diameter. (Christie's) £825

Patek Philippe, an unusual late 1920's deck watch in plated brass drum shaped case, counterpoised lever escapement, 90mm. diameter. (Christie's) £4,950

Blois, a gold and enamel watch case base, circa 1650, the outside depicting Diana the Huntress with two attendants, 58mm. diameter. (Christie's) £3,188

A nineteenth century quarter repeating verge openface pocket watch, the white enamel chapter ring with Arabic numerals, 55mm. diameter. (Christie's) £990

CARTIER

A slender gold stem wind open faced lever pocket watch, signed Cartier, Paris, 45mm. diam. £1,000

Cartier, a King George VI £5 coin containing a watch, with concealed catch in the rim, the matt silvered dial with Roman numerals and blued steel moon hands, 36mm. diameter. (Christie's) £2,640

An 18ct. gold dress watch, silvered dial, signed *Cartier*, damascened nickel keyless lever movement signed *European Watch and Clock Co., 1929*. (Bonhams) £700

COURVOISIER

A small engraved gold pocket chronometer, signed Courvoisier & Comp'e, Chaux-De-Fonds, 46mm. diam. £600

A gold hunter cased quarter repeating duplex watch, signed Courvoisier Freres, 18ct. gold case, 50mm. diam. £1,000

A gold quarter repeating cylinder watch, the enamel dial signed Courvoisier & Compe, 54mm. diam. (Phillips) £600

ELGIN

14ct. gold hunting case pocket watch, 'Elgin', jewelled gilt movement and white porcelain dial. £375

An Elgin watch in very narrow 14ct gold case, Swiss anchor movement, the dial with gilt Arab numerals, 17 jewels, 4.5cm. diameter, circa 1920. (Auction Team Köln) £80

14ct. gold hunting case pocket watch, 'Elgin', lever set jewelled nickel movement and white porcelain dial. £600

EROTIC

A gold hunter cased quarter repeating watch with concealed erotic automaton, Swiss, circa 1890, 50mm. diam. £4,500

A gold keyless automata quarter-repeating hunter pocket watch with modern conversion to 'peeping Tom' erotic scene, in plain case with engraved initials to the front cover, 54mm. diameter.
(Christie's S. Ken) £4,400

An unusual gold duplex hunter pocket watch in plain case, the white enamel dial with eccentric chapter-ring with Roman numerals, 47mm. diameter.
(Christie's S. Ken) £550

A gilt verge watch with concealed erotic scene of a monk and courtesan by Mauris a Geneve, circa 1790, 53mm. diameter. £4,500

An English silver verge pocket watch, the movement signed *London Nr 525*, the enamel face painted with a castle motif, the centralised dial with Arabic numerals and gilt hands, 5.5cm. diameter, circa 1850.
(Auction Team Köln) £1,171

An 18th century French ladies' watch hanging from a brooch, the gold case with a double secret back opening to reveal an erotic scene.
(Duran) £4,444

A Swiss gold and enamel bridgecock verge watch with secret erotic panel depicting a priest and a country girl, the gilt movement signed Fournier A Geneve, 55mm. diameter. £4,000

A Swiss gold openface skeletonised quarter repeating verge watch with erotic automaton, circa 1820, 56mm. diam. £6,000

Swiss watch decorated in neo classical manner with enamelled decoration and pearls inset in gold, the back opens to reveal a scene of love-making, circa 1800. £5,000

An 18 carat gold openface split-second chronograph watch, signed Patek Philippe & Co., Geneve, circa 1910. (Christie's) £5,060

An 18 carat white gold oval dress watch, signed Patek Philippe & Co., Geneve, with circular nickel-finished jewelled lever movement, 46mm long. (Christie's) £1,770

An 18 carat gold openface keyless lever watch, signed Vacheron & Constantin, Geneve, circa 1925, 44mm diameter. (Christie's) £961

An 18 carat gold openface keyless lever watch with 24 hour dial signed Patek Philippe & Co., Geneve, Chronometro Gondolo, circa 1913. (Christie's) £5,060

German School, an enamelled gold watch panel, unsigned, circa 1650, the recto depicting a battle scene, the verso representing a boar's hunt, 35mm diameter. (Christie's) £1,110

An 18 carat gold keyless lever minute repeating, perpetual calendar and chronograph hunter-cased watch, signed Charles Humbert Fils, circa 1910. (Christie's) £20,240

An 18 carat gold coin watch, signed Audemars Piguet, Geneve, circa 1948, with nickel-finished lever movement, 34mm. diameter. (Christie's) £1,012

An 18 carat gold openface keyless lever minute repeating watch, signed E. Thomas, circa 1930, 48mm diameter. (Christie's) £1,922

Blois, a gold and enamel watch cover, unsigned, circa 1650, the obverse with the abduction of Helen of Troy, the reverse with lakeside landscape, 46mm diam. (Christie's) £2,024

A rare 18 carat gold and enamel openface keyless lever watch, signed Vacheron & Constantin, Geneve, circa 1930. (Christie's) £13,156

An 18 carat gold one minute lever tourbillon watch signed Ch. He. Grosclaude & Fils, Fleurier Suisse, circa 1870. (Christie's) £25,300

A 14 carat gold Swiss diamond and sapphire-set hunter-cased fob watch, unsigned, circa 1910, 27mm diameter. (Christie's) £506

An 18 carat gold openface keyless lever minute repeating, perpetual calendar and moon-phase watch, signed Audemars Piguet, Geneve, circa 1920. (Christie's) £16,192

Blois, a gold and enamel watch cover, unsigned, circa 1650, the front depicting Rebecca at the Well, the reverse with Italianate landscape, 48mm diam. (Christie's) £4,048

An 18 carat gold openface keyless lever chronograph watch, signed Ulysse Nardin, Lode & Geneve, Chronografo Medical, circa 1925. (Christie's) £1,518

An 18 carat gold openface keyless lever watch signed Vacheron & Constantin, Geneve, circa 1910, 55mm diameter. (Christie's) £2,277

An 18 carat gold hunter-cased keyless lever minute repeating chronograph watch, unsigned circa 1890, 46mm diameter. (Christie's) £2,428

An 18 carat pink gold open-face keyless lever watch with black dial, signed Vacheron & Constantin, Geneve, circa 1920. (Christie's) £1,416

FRODSHAM

An 18ct. gold cased key-wind pocket watch by Charles Frodsham, dated 1884, in green morocco case. £1,000

A gold hunter-cased tourbillon watch, the movement signed Chas. Frodsham, 61mm. diam. £35,000

An eight-day fusee keyless pocket chronometer, by Chas Frodsham, hallmarked 1915, 72mm. diam. £25,000

An eighteen carat gold open faced keyless lever fly-back chronograph, signed *Charles Frodsham*, presentation inscription on cuvette dated 1893, 53mm.
(Lawrence Fine Art) £770

An 18 carat gold half hunter case minute repeating keyless lever chronograph, signed *Cha's Frodsham 84 Strand London*, 54mm. diam.
(Phillips) £3,600

An 18ct. yellow gold three-quarter plate English keyless lever pocket watch, by Parkinson & Frodsham. £375

GARON

An early 18th century gold, gilt metal and shagreen pair cased quarter repeating verge watch, signed *Pet' Garon, London*, with silver dust ring, 57mm. diameter.
(Phillips) £1,000

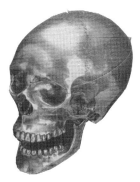

A finely modelled silver skull watch opening to reveal the engraved silver chapter ring with Roman numerals and Arabic five-minute divisions, signed *Pete. Garon, London*, 75mm. long.
(Christie's) £1,760

An engraved silver paircase verge watch by Peter Garon, London, the cock and back plate furniture pierced and engraved with leafy scrolls and mask, circa 1705, 53mm. diameter.
(Christie's) £829

JAQUEMART

A French gold quarter repeating erotic Jaquemart watch, with a panel below opening to reveal two lovers, 55mm. diam. (Phillips) £3,000

A Swiss gold hunter cased minute repeating keyless lever Jaquemart watch, the movement jewelled to the centre and with jewelled repeat train, 51mm. diameter. (Phillips) £3,400

A good 19th century French gold quarter repeating Jacquemart watch, the dial with enamel chapter and skeletonised centre, 64mm. diam. (Phillips) £7,200

JURGENSEN

A gold hunter cased minute repeating watch, signed J. Jurgensen, Copenhagen, 18ct. gold case, 53mm. diam. £6,000

A gold hunter cased lever watch, signed J. Jurgensen, Copenhagen, 18ct. gold case, 50mm. diam. £1,500

An 18ct. gold openface minute-repeating split-second chronograph with box and certificate, signed Jules Jurgensen, Copenhagen, 55mm. diam. £15,000

LE ROY

A gold French verge pocket watch, by Le Roy A Paris, white enamel dial with Roman numerals and outer Arabic minute ring, 40mm. (Bonhams) £320

A French gold open faced key wind calendar watch, the cylinder movement with bridge cock, signed *Le Roy a Paris*, 46mm. (Lawrence Fine Art) £1,210

A gilt metal and leather coach watch with alarm by *Jul'n le Roy à Paris*, the two-train verge movement with pierced backplate furniture, mid 18th century, 11.3cm. diameter. (Christie's New York) £3,366

A gold and enamel watch in the form of a mandolin, circa 1820, with unsigned Continental verge movement, 64mm. long.
(Christie's) £3,289

Ato, Paris, a fine 1930's pink and white gold openface keyless digital dresswatch in plain case, 45mm. diameter.
(Christie's) £2,860

A nineteenth century gold and enamel Mandolin form watch, the hinged movement with verge escapement, 63mm. length.
(Christie's) £1,980

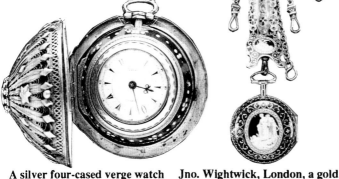

A silver four-cased verge watch for the Turkish market, signed *Edward Prior, London, No. 75513*, early 19th century, the outer case filigreed and set with a semi-precious stone, 65mm. diameter.
(Christie's) £1,250

Jno. Wightwick, London, a gold and enamel pair case pocketwatch with gilt and enamel chatelaine, the outer case with a painted enamel scene in a cartouche, hallmarked London 1775, 43mm. diameter.
(Christie's) £3,850

Hi. Grandjean & Cie, Locle No. 28498: a fine and rare 18ct. gold eight day twin train hunter pocket watch in chased and engraved case with floral decoration, 49mm. diameter.
(Christie's) £3,080

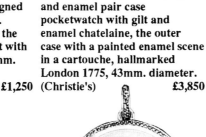

A rare gold perpetual calendar moonphase independent seconds and flying 1/5 second keyless chronograph hunter pocket watch in plain case, hallmarked *London 1879*, 52mm. diameter.
(Christie's) £10,450

A gold, enamel and stone-set openface keyless pendant watch, the case scratched *2896*, inscribed on the dial and movement *Cartier*, 31mm. diameter.
(Christie's) £1,100

Dent, 33 Cockspur Street, London No. 30585, an 18ct. gold minute repeating keyless hunter pocketwatch in plain case with engraved armorial crest to the front cover, 53mm. diameter.
(Christie's) £4,025

A vari-colour gold and enamel 'pie-crust' watch, signed *Courvoisier Freres*, 48mm. diameter.
(Christie's) £1,012

An early Dutch silver oval verge watch, the gilt movement signed *Reijnier Passchier A Amsterdam*, circa 1630, 38mm. over pendant.
(Christie's) £5,500

A nineteenth century gold and enamel form watch in the shape of a mandolin, the frosted gilt fusee verge movement with bridge cock signed *Chevalier & Cochet*, 59 x 27mm.
(Christie's) £3,080

Jelly Fish 1985, created by the artist Andrew Logan and produced in a limited edition of 30 pieces.
(Christie's) £1,650

Breguet, a fine and rare silver hour and quarter striking and repeating alarm duplex coachwatch with original leather covered and numbered outer case and supporting bracket, 1833, 82mm. diameter.
(Christie's) £16,500

Dunhill, a 9ct. gold petrol burning lighter, a watch mounted to the hinged front cover, signed *Scilla Watch Co.*, hallmarked *London 1926*, 54 x 44mm.
(Christie's) £935

Jno. Harris, London, a late eighteenth century gold pair cased verge pocket watch, the outer case chased and engraved with floral decoration, 50mm. diameter.
(Christie's) £660

An 18ct. gold keyless minute repeating hunter pocketwatch in engine-turned case, repeating on two gongs operated by a slide in the band, with wolf-tooth winding, 51mm. diameter.
(Christie's) £2,185

W. Thomas, London, an unusual 18ct. gold minute repeating chronograph keyless half-hunter pocket watch in plain case, hallmarked *London 1867*, 47mm. diameter.
(Christie's) £2,200

LE ROY

A French gold jump hour cylinder watch, the gold cuvette signed Leroy hger Du Roi Palais Royal No. 114 cof, No. 4780, 42mm. diam. £2,400

Julien Leroy, Paris, an 18th century silver pair-cased pull quarter repeat calendar and alarm coach-watch in pierced metal outer case, pierced, chased and engraved inner case with gimballed pendant, with white enamel dial. (Christie's) £4,950

A French quarter repeating cylinder watch, the gold cuvette signed Leroy et fils Horloger Du Roi A Paris No. 4001, 45mm. diam. £1,250

LEPINE

A gold and enamel verge watch, Lepine of Paris, circa 1790, 41mm. diam. £2,000

A Continental gold quarter repeating ruby cylinder watch, the gilt Lepine calibre movement jewelled to the second, enamel dial signed Fourcy 3954 on the reverse, 60mm. diam. (Christie's) £1,540

A slim gold and enamel open faced keywind watch with Lepine calibre movement. £1,000

LIGHTERS

An unusual cigarette lighter mounted with a watch, signed 'The Golden Wheel Lighter', fitted with adjusted 6-jewel lever movement, signed Cyma, 52mm. high. (Christie's) £234

Dunhill: an unusual 9ct gold petrol burning lighter with a watch mounted in the front wound automatically on operating the lighter, in engine turned case with wind guard, 47 x 42mm. (Christie's) £2,530

An 18ct. gold combined watch and lighter by Dunhill, engine-turned silvered Deco dial with Arabic numerals set in a hinged reeded octagonal frame, 1930, 49mm. high. (Christie's) £2,420

366

LIGHTERS

A 9ct. gold combined cigarette lighter and watch by Dunhill, the base stamped Made in Switzerland, 5.3cm. high. £900

A large white metal petrol-burning table lighter with clock mounted to the front, the matt gilt dial with stepped bezel, 10 x 8cm.(Christie's S. Ken) £165

Dunhill, an 18ct. white gold, diamond and emerald-set petrol burning lighter with watch inset to the hinged front cover, 43 x 38mm.
(Christie's) £3,520

LONGINES

A gold open faced keyless lever dress watch by Longines, with damascened nickel movement, 44mm. diam. £750

An Art Moderne 18ct. bi-colour gold open face pocketwatch, Swiss jewel movement by Longines. £800

An 18ct. chased gold hunter-cased lever watch, signed Longines, with damascened nickel movement jewelled to the third wheel, 52mm. diam. £1,400

MARTINEAU

A Dutch enamel and silver pair cased verge watch with false pendulum, signed Martineau, London, 52mm. diam. £1,500

A gold pair case verge watch set with rubies, signed Jos. Martineau Sen., London, 53mm. diam. £20,000

An 18th century silver pair cased quarter repeating verge watch, signed Martineau, London, the signed silver champleve dial with arcaded chapters, 50mm. diam. (Phillips) £1,200

A 19th century Continental gold duplex calendar pocketwatch, in engine-turned drum case with ribbed band, inscribed on a sector *Breguet*, 53mm. diameter. (Christie's) **£1,955**

A late nineteenth century gold, stone-set and enamel form watch in the shape of a beetle, with matching enamel and stone set pendant, 50mm. length. (Christie's) **£1,870**

Fureur, an unusual openface keyless Tourbillon pocket watch, the plain case with visible escapement to the reverse, 52mm. diameter. (Christie's) **£2,750**

A gold and enamel automaton watch, circa 1820, with verge movement, the eccentric white enamel dial with Arabic numerals, bearing the signature of *Breguet a Paris*, 54mm. diameter. (Christie's) **£10,626**

Charles Frodsham, an unusual silver fast oscillating 60 second timer, the brushed silvered dial inscribed *Char. Frodsham, 84, Strand London*, the case hallmarked *London 1884*, 75mm. diameter. (Christie's) **£1,430**

Brandt Jeanrenaud & Robert, an early nineteenth century gold quarter repeating openface pocket watch, verge movement with decorative bridge cock, repeating on two gongs, 56mm. diameter. (Christie's) **£880**

Longines, an early twentieth century gold and enamel Lyre keyless form watch, the covers decorated with black and red enamel set with stones and with chased and engraved decoration, 33 x 32mm. (Christie's) **£1,100**

An unusual gold openface two-train independent seconds split second function keyless pocketwatch, the two-train frosted gilt bar movement with bi-metallic balance, 50mm. diameter. (Christie's) **£1,495**

Chevalier et Compe, an early nineteenth century gold and enamel and seed-pearl openface verge pocket watch, signed frosted gilt fusee movement with pierced bridge cock, 50mm. diameter. (Christie's) **£3,850**

A gold minute repeating hunter pocket watch, in engine turned case, signed on the cuvette *Munoz Degrain, Valencia*, 52mm. diameter.
(Christie's) £1,870

An unusual gold musical and erotic seal in oval case, the movement wound by the pendant and operated by a slide in the band, 30 x 25mm.
(Christie's) £5,500

Cartier, a fine black enamel and gold minute repeating hunter pocketwatch, movement signed *European Watch and Clock Co. Inc.*, 49mm. diameter.
(Christie's) £17,600

Chas. Frodsham, No. 08805, an 18ct. gold keyless openface minute repeating pocketwatch, bi-metallic balance and English lever escapement, repeating on two gongs, hallmarked *London 1899*, 48mm. diameter.
(Christie's) £3,680

Du Chesne à Paris, a late seventeenth century gilt verge Oignon pocket watch, the signed frosted gilt fusee movement with decorative bridge cock showing mock pendulum, 57mm. diameter.
(Christie's) £990

A gold quarter repeating automata openface pocket watch, engine turned gilt dial with vari-coloured gilt Jacquemarts, verge movement repeating on two gongs, 53mm. diameter.
(Christie's) £2,200

Piguet & Meylan, Geneve, a gold quarter repeating musical cylinder pocketwatch, the reverse with sunburst engine-turning, stamped under the dial *P. & M. 79 D 661*, 56mm. diameter.
(Christie's) £4,370

Just & Son, London, 2842, a 19th century gold and enamel seed-pearl set pocketwatch for the Chinese market, the white enamel dial with Arabic numerals and typical gold spade hands, 54mm. diameter.
(Christie's) £6,325

Dent, London, a good 18ct. gold openface keyless split second chronograph pocketwatch in plain case, signed black dial with Arabic numerals and five minute divisions, hallmarked London 1889, 57mm. diameter.
(Christie's) £8,250

A gold open face Masonic watch, signed Dudley Watch Co., Lancaster Pa., no. 597. £2,500

A Swiss silver Masonic keyless lever watch, the triangular case with mother-of-pearl dial, 60mm. high. £1,200

A gold openface Masonic watch, with nickel 19-jewel movement, signed Dudley Watch Co., Lancaster, Pa., 45mm. diam. £1,500

A Swiss silver Masonic watch, the circular movement with triangular mother-o'-pearl dial inscribed *Love Your Fellow Man Lend Him A Helping Hand*, 58mm. high. (Phillips) £750

A silver Masonic dress watch by Solvil Watch Co., G. Schwab-Loeille, Geneve, with 15-jewel keyless lever movement, mother-of-pearl dial with chapters formed from the working tools of the various degrees of Freemasonry, 1930s, 55mm. long. (Christie's) £1,021

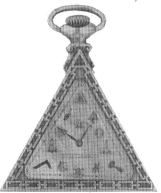

A silver keyless triangular Masonic pocket watch, the reverse and sides with Masonic symbols, the polished and plated movement signed Solvil *Watch Co.*, 54mm. along the side. (Christie's S. Ken) £3,850

An unusual eight-day alarm Masonic travelling clock with giltmetal bezel, the white enamel dial with coloured Masonic symbols, in triangular folding leather case, 81mm. (Christie's) £770

A Swiss silver Masonic watch, the circular movement signed Solvil, the enamel dial decorated with Masonic symbols, 68mm. high. (Phillips) £1,350

A silver pair cased verge pocket watch, square baluster pillar movement signed *Jm^s Robinson*, in an outer shagreen covered case, London 1745, 50mm. (Bonhams) £550

PATEK PHILIPPE

An 18ct. gold openface centre seconds watch, signed Patek Philippe & Co., Geneva, no. 185202, 46mm. diam. £2,250

A gold and rock crystal keyless lever dress watch, by Patek Philippe, 46mm diam. £2,000

An 18ct. gold openface dress watch, signed Patek Philippe & Co., with nickel 18-jewel movement and silvered dial, 45mm. diam. £750

A gold openface dress watch, signed Patek Philippe & Co., Geneve, within an 18ct. gold case, signed on movement and case, 48mm. diam. £1,300

Patek Philippe, a rare early 1920s keyless gold open-faced pocket watch with up-and-down indication in plain case, the white enamel dial with Arabic numerals, subsidiary seconds, power reserve indication at twelve, 49mm. diameter. (Christie's) £11,000

A platinum openface dress watch, signed Patek Philippe & Co., Geneva, on movement and case, with original box and guarantee certificate, 44mm. diam. £2,400

A chased and enamelled platinum openface watch, signed P. Philippe & Co., no. 200063, 43mm. diam. £1,500

An 18ct. gold openface watch minute repeating on three gongs, signed P. Philippe & Co., Geneve, 48mm. diam. £10,000

An 18ct. gold openface lever watch, signed Patek Philippe & Cie, Geneve, with nickel movement jewelled to the centre, 50mm. diam. £1,250

Cartier, a rare 1930's slim platinum, enamel, ruby and diamond-set dress watch, the movement signed *European Watch and Clock Co. Inc*, 50mm. diameter.
(Christie's) £4,620

Tho: Tompion London, an early giltmetal verge watch movement signed and numbered on the gilt top-plate with foliate pierced and engraved open-footed and eared cock, 59mm. diameter.
(Christie's) £1,540

Audemars Piguet, a fine and rare 1920's 18ct. white gold keyless digital calendar wristwatch in slim plain case, import mark *Glasgow 1929*, 46mm. diameter.
(Christie's) £7,150

Piguet & Co., Sentier, an unusual gold open-face keyless Masonic pocket watch in drum shaped case, the signed and frosted gilt bar movement with bimetallic balance and lever escapement, 48mm. diameter.
(Christie's) £2,750

A gold minute repeating calendar chronograph keyless hunter pocketwatch in plain case with engraved monogram to the front cover and presentation to the reverse, 56mm. diameter.
(Christie's) £2,200

Romilly, Paris, a late eighteenth century gold enamel and seed-pearl set openface verge pocket watch, the reverse with painted enamel scene of a girl and a putti in a garden scene, 40mm. diameter.
(Christie's) £1,760

Lam. B. Vrythoff, Hagae, an early 18th century gold triple case verge pocketwatch, the outer gilt and tortoiseshell case with pin work decoration, 55mm. diameter of outer case.
(Christie's) £1,650

Vaucher Fleurier, a fine gold and enamel open-face Duplex pocket watch for the Chinese market, the monometallic 'Bat's-wing' balance with Duplex escapement, 54mm. diameter.
(Christie's) £11,000

Henry Capt., Genève, a good gold and enamel open-face keyless quarter repeating pocket watch, the nickel-plated bar movement jewelled to the hammers, 48mm. diameter.
(Christie's) £990

A gold and enamel quarter repeating watch for the Chinese market, circa 1835, with gilt-finished cylinder movement, repeating on two gongs, 58mm. diameter.
(Christie's) £8,096

A gilt-metal pair cased watch, signed *In. Cranford, London*, with gilt verge movement, the silver champlevé dial with Roman numerals, 50mm. diameter.
(Christie's) £860

F. Vazquez, a gold, enamel and stone-set hunter pocket watch in decorative case, the bar movement with bimetallic balance and lever escapement under cuvette, 33mm. diameter.
(Christie's) £550

Ellicott, London No. 8422, a good late eighteenth century gold and enamel cylinder pair case pocket watch, the signed frosted gilt fusee movement with pierced cock and diamond endstone, 45mm. diameter.
(Christie's) £1,100

Russells Ltd, Manchester, a fine and rare 18ct. gold perpetual calendar minute repeating chronograph keyless hunter pocketwatch made by Nicole Nielsen, London, in plain case, 60mm. diameter.
(Christie's) £19,550

Vaucher Fleurier, a fine gold and enamel openface Duplex pocketwatch for the Chinese market, the reverse with a painted scene of a gentleman and lady in a landscape, 54mm. diameter.
(Christie's) £7,150

An unusual Swiss gold openface keyless quarter repeating chronograph pocketwatch, the hinged cuvette engraved *Fontana Freres*, 50mm. diameter.
(Christie's) £1,760

Longines, a gold and enamel keyless pendant watch in decorative case, the signed 3/4-plate movement under signed cuvette with lever escapement, 35mm. diameter.
(Christie's) £880

Ch. Ed. Lardet, Fleurier, an 18ct. gold keyless openface split second chronograph pocket watch in plain case with engraved monogram to the reverse, 52mm. diameter.
(Christie's) £1,100

PATEK PHILIPPE

An 18ct. gold openface minute-repeating watch, signed Patek Philippe & Cie, 47mm. diam. £6,000

A 14ct. gold openface lever watch, signed Patek Philippe & Co., Geneva, no. 89566, 50mm. diam. £1,000

An 18ct. gold openface split-second chronograph, signed Patek Philippe & Cie, 47mm. diam. £3,000

A platinum openface dress watch, signed Patek Philippe & Co., Geneva, no. 890237, 43mm. diam. £1,250

An 18ct. gold openface chronograph, signed Patek Philippe & Co., Geneve, with nickel 23-jewel movement, 48mm. diam. £3,000

An 18ct. gold openface watch with perpetual calendar, signed Patek Philippe & Co., 46mm. diam. £10,000

A platinum openface split-second chronograph, signed Patek Philippe & Co., 47mm. diam. £5,000

An enamelled gold openface watch, signed P. Philippe & Co., nickel eighteen-jewel cal. 17-170 movement, 44mm. diam. £1,500

An enamelled platinum open-face dress watch, signed Patek Philippe & Co., Geneva, no. 814228, 42mm. diam. £1,250

PATEK PHILIPPE

A large gold openface lever watch, signed Chronometro Gondolo, by Patek Philippe & Cie, 56mm. diam. £1,500

A gold openface lever watch, signed Patek Philippe & Cie, Geneva, retailed by Bailey, Banks & Biddle, Phila., 50mm. diam.   £1,250

An enamelled platinum open-face dress watch, signed Patek Philippe & Co., Geneva, no. 810822, 39mm. diam. £1,300

PRIOR

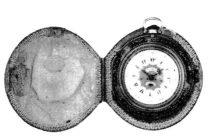

A silver triple cased Turkish Market verge watch by E. Prior of London, hallmarked 1882, 65mm. diam.   £900

A triple cased silver verge pocket watch for the Turkish market by Ge. Prior, London, with tortoiseshell covered outer case and shark skin covered carrying case, diameter of outer case 61mm.
(Christie's S. Ken)   £770

A quadruple case verge watch for the Turkish market, signed Edw. Prior, London, 70mm. diam.   £6,000

SMITH

An 18ct. gold keyless lever watch, the movement jewelled to the centre and signed S. Smith & Son, the case marked London, 1901, 52mm. diam.   £750

An 18ct. gold minute repeating perpetual calendar chronograph hunter pocket watch with moonphase, by S. Smith & Sons Ltd, in plain case, 50mm. diameter.
(Christie's)   £5,720

A silver fusee lever watch with winding indicator, signed Smith & Son, London, the case, London, 1899, 52mm. diam. £1,000

A nineteenth century gold and enamel musical erotic automata seal, the base hinged to reveal the painted enamel automated erotic scene, 30 x 25mm.
(Christie's) £5,500

Patek Philippe, an 1890's gold keyless hunter pocket watch, the bimetallic balance with counterpoised lever escapement, 49mm. diameter.
(Christie's) £1,430

An interesting Continental gold openface retrograde seconds cylinder pocketwatch in engine-turned drum case with milled band, 54mm. diameter.
(Christie's) £3,080

An early nineteenth century quarter repeating and musical cylinder pocket watch, in engine-turned drum case, the frosted gilt two-train movement with cylinder escapement, 54mm. diameter.
(Christie's) £2,310

Thomas Reid, Edinburgh No. 1100, an interesting 22ct. gold openface halfquarter repeating pocketwatch in plain consular case with presentation to the reverse, hallmarked *London 1799*, 50mm. diameter.
(Christie's) £1,495

Szervo Janos, Glashütte i/Sa, an unusual silver openface chronometer deckwatch in plain case, dial with Roman numerals, engraved *Glashütte*, the case with the stamp of *A. Lange & Söhne*, 70mm. diameter.
(Christie's) £5,750

A Continental gold, enamel and stone-set keyless hunter pendant watch in plain matt case, the frosted gilt bar movement under cuvette, with cylinder escapement, 30mm. diameter.
(Christie's) £550

Vacheron & Constantin, a gold and enamel keyless openface dress watch, the reverse with painted enamel scene of a courting couple, 43mm. diameter.
(Christie's) £2,750

Thos. Grignion, Covent Garden, London, No. 1784, a mid eighteenth century gold and enamel pair cased verge pocket watch, hallmarked *London 1762*, 46mm. diameter.
(Christie's) £2,310

A gold quarter repeating erotic automaton watch, circa 1810, cuvette with a spring loaded push piece revealing the couple in action, 55mm. diameter.
(Christie's) £4,048

A gold enamel and pearl-set form watch in the shape of a mandolin, the back hingeing to reveal the white enamel dial, 64 x 25mm.
(Christie's) £1,100

A charming gold, enamel and pearl-set form watch in the shape of a tulip, the frosted gilt fusee verge movement with bridgecock, 36 x 30mm.
(Christie's) £2,750

A rare gold, enamel and pearl-set 'Petit souscription a tact' watch, signed *Le Roy au Palais Royal N. 88, No. 2481*, suspending from a pearl-set pendant and a textured ring, 56mm. diameter.
(Christie's) £15,180

An 18ct. gold minute repeating keyless pocket watch in good quality plain case, the bimetallic balance with lever escapement and diamond endstone, hallmarked *London 1896*, 54mm. diameter.
(Christie's) £1,980

Francis Nawe at London, a late sixteenth century English giltmetal verge watch circa 1580, signed on the backplate with border engraved with fruit and foliage, 77mm. over pendant.
(Christie's) £12,100

A copper and enamel watch cover, signed *Les freres Huaut*, circa 1690, the front painted with Diana the Huntress with a dog in a landscape, 43mm. diameter.
(Christie's) £4,048

A good early nineteenth century gold and enamel cylinder openface pocket watch, the hinged cuvette inscribed *Breguet a Paris, No. 134*, 54mm. diameter.
(Christie's) £2,200

Lucas Decaux, Norwich, an early eighteenth century silver paircase verge pocket watch with mock pendulum, the silver champlevé dial with eccentric chapter ring, 55mm. diameter.
(Christie's) £3,080

TIFFANY

An 18ct. gold openface minute-repeating split-second chronograph, Swiss, retailed by Tiffany & Co., 54mm. diam. £6,000

A gold openface chronograph, Swiss, retailed by Tiffany & Co., New York, signed Tiffany, 53mm. diam. £900

A gold miniature keyless lever watch, the steel bar movement jewelled to the centre and signed for Tiffany & Co., N.Y., 27mm. diam. £500

An 18ct. gold openface five-minute repeating watch, signed P. Philippe & Co., no. 97353, dial signed Tiffany & Co., 45mm. diam. £3,250

A small 18ct. gold openface five-minute repeating split-second chronograph, signed Tiffany & Co., the movement by P. Philippe, no. 111758, 42mm. diam. £4,500

A Swiss gold openface split-second chronograph, retailed by Tiffany & Co., N.Y., 18ct. gold case, 51mm. diam. £1,500

TOMPION

A silver pair cased verge watch, the movement signed Tho. Tompion, London, 2631, 55mm. diam. £4,000

An early 18th century quarter repeating verge watch movement, signed *Tho Tompion, London, 136,* with pierced tulip pillars and engraved cock, 56mm. diameter. (Phillips) £2,000

A late 17th century silver pair cased verge watch, signed Tho. Tompion, London 0292, 57mm. diam. £2,500

VACHERON & CONSTANTIN

A finely enamelled gold open-face dress watch, signed Vacheron & Constantin, 47mm. diam.   £3,000

A gold openface lever watch, signed Vacheron & Constantin, Geneva, within an engine-turned 18ct. gold case, 58mm. diam.   £1,000

A gold openface chronograph, signed Vacheron & Constantin, Geneve, with an 18ct. gold fob, 51mm. diam.   £1,850

Vacheron Constantin, a German issue Luftwaffe watch, the silvered dial with Arabic numerals and subsidiary dials for seconds, 60mm. (Bonhams)   £1,500

A silver open-face chronograph pocket watch in plain case by Vacheron & Constantin, Geneve, the white enamel dial with luminous Arabic numerals, 51mm. diameter. (Christie's S. Ken)   £990

A 14ct. rose gold openface dress watch and chain, signed Vacheron & Constantin, Geneve, with 17-jewel nickel lever movement, 42mm. diam.   £941

VULLIAMY

A gold and enamel duplex watch by Vulliamy No. MXRC, signed and numbered on the movement, 41mm. diam.   £3,000

A late 18th century gold dumb quarter-repeating cylinder pocket watch by Just. Vulliamy, London, in engine-turned and engraved consular case, 54mm. diameter. (Christie's S. Ken)   £4,620

A gold openface quarter repeating duplex watch, signed Vulliamy, London, 18ct. gold case, 1835, 45mm. diam.   £1,500

Gerald Genta, 18ct. gold and crystal quartz wristwatch, signed by the makers and numbered *G 2984 7 41519*, 33mm. diameter.
(Christie's) £1,210

Tiffany, a gold US $20.00 coin wristwatch with milled band, the nickel plated bar movement under snap on back signed *M & W. Ullmann*, 34mm. diameter.
(Christie's) £935

Universal, a pink gold chronograph wristwatch, model Compax, in circular case, signed movement jewelled to the centre, 33mm. diameter.
(Christie's) £1,100

Movado, a 1930's steel single button chronograph wristwatch in cushion case, the matt silvered dial with Breguet numerals, outer pulsation ring, the movement with 17 jewels numbered *52296*, 29mm. square.
(Christie's) £1,760

A gold triple calendar and moonphase chronograph wristwatch, the brushed gilt dial with outer date ring and central date hand, the movement jewelled to the centre with 17 jewels, 35mm. diameter.
(Christie's) £2,200

Corum, an unusual 18ct. gold calendar and moonphase quartz wristwatch, model Meteorite Peary No. 36, the back inscribed *Dial made of meteorite found by Robert E. Peary*, 34mm. diameter.
(Christie's) £1,760

Universal, a gold triple calendar and chronograph wristwatch, model Tri-compax, the signed movement jewelled to the centre, 36mm. diameter.
(Christie's) £1,650

West End Watch Co., a 1910's gold octagonal wristwatch with domed bezel and glass, the frosted gilt movement jewelled to the third, 37 x 25mm.
(Christie's) £660

Chopard, an 18ct. gold calendar quartz wristwatch, model Gstaad, the recessed blue dial with diamond set numerals, 33 x 31mm.
(Christie's) £2,200

Eberhard & Co., a late 1930's gold chronograph wristwatch in circular case, the signed movement numbered *3422*, 39mm. diameter.
(Christie's) £3,080

Bulgari, a gold calendar quartz wristwatch in circular case, the matt black dial with baton numerals and Arabic numerals at XII and VI, 30mm. diameter.
(Christie's) £1,897

International Watch Co., an unusual pink gold wristwatch, the silvered dial with raised dot and baton numerals, subsidiary seconds, 35mm. diameter.
(Christie's) £1,650

Gubelin, a gold automatic triple calendar moonphase water resistant wristwatch in circular case with stepped lugs, monometallic balance and micrometer regulation under separate dust cover, 36mm. diameter.
(Christie's) £2,970

Ulysse Nardin, an 18ct. gold automatic calendar chronograph wristwatch, the polished bezel with tachymetric scale, the white dial with raised baton numerals, 36mm. diameter.
(Christie's) £2,200

Longines, a rare and early gold single button chronograph wristwatch in circular case, the white enamel dial with red telemetric and tachymetric scales, black Arabic numerals, 38mm. diameter.
(Christie's) £1,870

Corum, a platinum and diamond quartz wristwatch, model Romulus, the matt silvered dial with maker's mark, 30mm. diameter.
(Christie's) £1,650

Corum, an unusual 18ct. gold rectangular wristwatch, model Buckingham, the snap on back with maker's mark numbered *5979 47*, 39 x 35mm.
(Christie's) £770

Chopard, a ladies gold Happy Diamond wristwatch in circular case, glazed ring surround to movement containing five loose diamonds, 21mm. diameter.
(Christie's) £1,210

Gold calendar wrist-
watch by Baume &
Mercier, circa 1945,
37mm. diam. £2,250

A circular steel gent's wristwatch, by Pierce, the silvered
dial with centre seconds, date,
and Arabic numerals, 32mm.
diam. (Phillips) £160

A Swiss 18 carat gold
gentleman's dress wristwatch by
Baume & Mercier, with signed
circular movement, 34 x 25mm.
(Phillips) £550

A 19th century gold and enamel
ladies bracelet watch in circular
case with seed pearl-set bezel,
the white enamel dial with
Roman numerals, 30mm.
diameter.
(Christie's) £2,200

A World War II German pilot's
wristwatch in base metal circular case, the frosted gilt movement signed Laco, jewelled to
the centre with 22 jewels,
55mm. diam. (Christie's)
£418

Tavannes, an early gold
wristwatch in elliptical case, the
white enamel dial with Arabic
numerals, the nickel-plated bar
movement jewelled to the third
under snap-on back, 45 x 27mm.
(Christie's) £935

A circular Swiss silver Service
wristwatch, the enamelled
dial with subsidiary seconds,
the front cover pierced to
reveal the numerals, 35mm.
diam. (Phillips) £200

An 18ct gold wristwatch in
circular case, the black dial
signed Van Cleef & Arpels,
the movement signed Piaget,
33mm. (Christie's) £550

A gent's steel and gilt metal
circular wristwatch, by Baume
& Mercier, the quartz movement
with signed dial and date aperture, 33mm. diam. (Phillips)
£380

A gold coin watch, 'Le Jour' Swiss movement, in a twenty dollar United States gold piece dated 1904.' £1,500

An 18 carat tri-colour gold wristwatch by Montre Royale, 27mm. wide, London 1976. £1,500

An early self-winding wristwatch, signed Harwood Self Winding Watch Co. Ltd. £200

A steel automatic Voyager calendar wristwatch in typical case, the rotating bezel inscribed with various capital cities, the white dial with outer 24 hour ring, 37mm. diameter.
(Christie's) £1,100

An 18ct. gold automatic wristwatch in oval case, the white enamel dial signed Baume & Mercier, Geneve, with very slim automatic movement.
(Christie's) £770

Glycine, a 1930s white and pink gold digital wristwatch in rectangular case, the pink gold top cover with apertures for hours, minutes and seconds, the case with hinged back, 37 x 23mm.
(Christie's) £3,520

An 18ct. gold circular gent's wristwatch, by J.W.Benson, the enamel dial with Roman numerals, the case marked London 1916, 34mm. diam.
(Phillips) £420

An unusual gold wristwatch, signed Hamilton Electric, the battery-powered nickel movement with electro-magnetic balance. (Christie's) £616

A gent's circular steel automatic wristwatch, by Blancpain, with perpetual calendar, the white dial with subsidiaries for day, date and month, 34mm. diam.
(Phillips) £2,200

Piaget, a gentleman's gold automatic wristwatch, the signed movement with microrotor, 34mm. diameter.
(Christie's) £1,100

LeCoultre, a 1930's gold rectangular Duoplan wristwatch in stepped case with back wind, 35 x 19mm.
(Christie's) £1,430

Piaget, a ladies 18ct. gold quartz wristwatch model Polo, gold dial with dot minute ring, 23mm. diameter.
(Christie's) £2,090

An 18ct. gold and enamel roulette wristwatch, signed *Corum Casino Royal*, recent, the silvered matt dial with Arabic numerals in the pattern of a Roulette table, 34mm. diameter.
(Christie's) £2,100

Corum, an 18ct. gold rectangular wristwatch in the shape of a gold ingot, the back secured by four screws with maker's mark no. 322823, the signed movement with 18 jewels, 40 x 23mm.
(Christie's) £990

Dunhill, a fine and rare 1920's 18ct. gold octagonal wristwatch, the snap on back with integral dust cover with maker's mark *G. Ferrero, Geneve*, hallmarked *London 1925*, 30 x 26mm.
(Christie's) £2,200

Longines, a rare silver Lindbergh hour-angle wristwatch for long distance aviation, the white enamel chapter ring with Arabic numerals, 46mm. diameter.
(Christie's) £3,850

International Watch Co., a pink gold rectangular wristwatch, the signed movement jewelled to the centre, 32 x 25mm.
(Christie's) £1,210

Universal, a pink gold Tri-Compax triple calendar and moonphase wristwatch, engraved with the monogram of the King of Jordan, 36mm. diameter.
(Christie's) £1,980

Omega, a 1920's gold tonneau wristwatch, the silvered dial with Arabic numerals, 32 x 30mm.
(Christie's)   £880

Ebel, a steel automatic chronograph wristwatch, the black dial with raised Roman numerals, 37mm. diameter.
(Christie's)   £1,210

Three colour gold and diamond set quartz wristwatch in square case, with integral three colour gold woven bracelet, 24 x 24mm.
(Christie's)   £1,430

Omega, a gold World War II pilot's wristwatch in circular case, the signed movement jewelled to the third with bimetallic balance, 46mm. diameter.
(Christie's)   £1,430

Universal, an early small gold Compur chronograph wristwatch, the silvered dial with outer telemetric and tachymetric scales, dot and Arabic numerals, 30mm. diameter.
(Christie's)   £1,210

International Watch Co., an 18ct. gold perpetual calendar and moonphase automatic wristwatch, model Da Vinci, in circular case, with spares and accessories, 37mm. diameter.
(Christie's)   £6,380

Universal, a steel and yellow metal water-resistant triple calendar and moonphase chronograph wristwatch, in circular case with faceted lugs, 34mm. diameter.
(Christie's)   £2,070

An asymmetrical 18ct. gold wristwatch, signed *Churchill Watch Co., London, No. 14*, 52mm. long.
(Christie's)   £2,000

Omega, a gold triple calendar and moonphase wristwatch in circular case with down turned lugs, the silvered dial with raised dagger numerals, 34mm. diameter.
(Christie's)   £1,782

A white gold wristwatch, the lapis lazuli dial signed Piaget with milled band, 24mm. wide. £1,350

A gold self-winding wrist-watch with calendar, signed Universal, Geneva, within an 18ct. gold case. £600

A gold wristwatch with nickel 21-jewel movement, signed Lord Elgin, with 14ct. gold bracelet. £425

Uhrenfabrik Glashütte, a World War II military chronograph wristwatch with rotating bezel, the black dial with luminous Arabic numerals, 38mm. diameter.
(Christie's) £605

A gold chronograph wristwatch in circular case, the silvered dial with outer tachymetric scale, Arabic numerals, subsidiary dials for running seconds, elapsed minutes, hours and date, 31mm. diameter.
(Christie's) £1,100

A battery-operated advertising display in the form of a wristwatch in gilt case with milled bezel, with leather strap and gilt buckle, 115mm. diameter.
(Christie's S. Ken) £110

A gold self-winding wrist-watch, signed Piaget, no. 7311215, the leather strap with 18ct. gold buckle. £800

A gold self-winding wrist-watch with calendar, signed Lucien Picard, Seashark, with textured 14ct. gold bracelet. £500

A circular Swiss gold gentle-man's wristwatch, inscribed *Mendys, La Chaux de Fonds,* 38mm. diam. (Phillips London) £190

A 14ct. gold, ruby and diamond watch, covered Swiss jewelled movement, circa 1940. £2,000

An 18ct. gold wristwatch with 21-jewel movement, signed Corum. £400

A silver gentleman's quartz wristwatch, the black dial inscribed *Gucci*, 43mm. long. (Phillips London) £180

A gentleman's large gold full calendar and moonphase chronograph wristwatch by Onsa, the movement jewelled to the centre with seventeen jewels, 37mm. diameter. (Christie's S. Ken) £935

Eberhard, a gilt/steel limited edition chronograph and calendar with moon phase wristwatch with gilt bezel, the matt silvered dial with tachymetric scale, 40mm. diameter. (Christie's) £660

A stainless steel Mickey Mouse wristwatch, the dial signed *Disney Watch, Made in France*, the seconds in inset dial shown by a small red globe with Mickey Mouse ears. (Auction Team Köln) £56

A gold wrist chronograph with register, signed C. H. Meylan Watch Co., the silvered dial signed Marcus & Cie. £2,500

An 18 carat gold circular keyless lever wristwatch, by Chas. Frodsham & Co., London, with gold cuvette, 1912. (Phillips) £170

A Swiss gold wristwatch, gold cuvette inscribed in Russian, the dial signed in Cyrillic Pavel Buhre, 39mm. diam. £1,500

AUDEMARS PIGUET

Audemars Piguet, a yellow and white gold 'Philosophe' wristwatch, the silvered dial with raised baton numerals, 31mm. diameter.
(Christie's) £1,650

Audemars Piguet, a gold automatic wristwatch, the brushed gilt dial with raised dagger numerals, 35mm. diameter.
(Christie's) £1,035

Audemars Piguet, a stainless steel quartz wristwatch, model Royal Oak, with integral flexible steel bracelet and deployant clasp, 30mm. diameter.
(Christie's) £880

Audemars Piguet, an 18ct. gold automatic chronograph wristwatch in circular case with stepped bezel, the silvered dial with outer tachymetric scale, 40mm. diameter.
(Christie's) £4,180

Audemars Piguet, Genève, an 18ct. gold and diamond-set automatic calendar wristwatch, with integral woven and textured gold bracelet and clasp, 35 x 33mm.
(Christie's) £2,970

Audemars Piguet, an 18ct. gold and diamond-set calendar quartz wristwatch, model Royal Oak, in octagonal case with diamond-set bezel, 34mm. diameter.
(Christie's) £6,600

Audemars Piguet, an 18ct. pink gold calendar wristwatch, the matt silvered dial with Arabic numerals and subsidiary dial for the date, 32mm. diameter.
(Christie's) £1,430

Audemars Piguet, an 18ct. gold lady's moonphase wristwatch, signed, with circular nickel-finished jewelled lever movement, 25mm. diameter.
(Christie's) £1,113

Audemars Piguet, a gold chronograph wristwatch, the brushed silvered dial with outer tachymetric scale, 34mm. diameter.
(Christie's) £13,200

AUDEMARS PIGUET

Audemars Piguet, Geneve, a gold wristwatch, matt white dial with raised dagger numerals, 31mm. diameter.
(Christie's) **£1,035**

An 18ct. gold wristwatch, signed *Audemars Piguet, Geneve*, circa 1960, with nickel-finished lever movement, 31mm. diameter.
(Christie's) **£1,316**

Audemars Piguet, a gold wristwatch in octagonal shaped case with aventurine dial, 31 x 30mm.
(Christie's) **£1,320**

Audemars Piguet, a ladies tantalum and pink gold Royal Oak calendar quartz wristwatch with screwed pink gold bezel, with integral flexible tantalum and pink gold bracelet and deployant clasp, 24mm. diameter.
(Christie's) **£2,860**

Audemars Piguet, a gold automatic perpetual calendar wristwatch, snap-on back with maker's mark and further engraved *quantième perpetuel automatique No. 790*, 35mm. diameter.
(Christie's) **£6,600**

Audemars Piguet, a platinum perpetual calendar and moonphase automatic skeletonised wristwatch in circular case, the skeletonised dial with subsidiary rings for day, date and month, 35mm. diameter.
(Christie's) **£9,350**

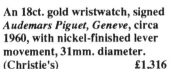

Audemars Piguet, Geneve, a gold wristwatch, blue dial with Roman numerals, 31mm. diameter.
(Christie's) **£920**

Audemars Piguet, a tantalum and pink gold calendar chronograph wristwatch in tantalum case with tantalum and pink gold signed bezel, 40mm. diameter.
(Christie's) **£3,220**

Audemars Piguet, an 18ct. gold automatic calendar wristwatch, the white dial with raised baton numerals, 32mm. diameter.
(Christie's) **£2,300**

AUDEMARS PIGUET

Audemars Piguet, a gold automatic wristwatch, the gilt dial with raised baton numerals, 32mm. diameter.
(Christie's) **£1,210**

Audemars Piguet, a ladies 18ct. gold wristwatch, the flecked grey dial with gold hands, 34 x 22mm.
(Christie's) **£1,150**

Audemars Piguet, a gold slim wristwatch in circular case, the white dial with baton numerals, 31mm. diameter.
(Christie's) **£1,610**

An 18ct. white gold wristwatch, signed *Audemars Piguet, Geneve*, circa 1965, with lever movement, mono-metallic compensation balance, 31mm. diameter.
(Christie's) **£1,771**

A gold wristwatch by Audemars Piguet, Geneve, the nickel adjusted 19-jewel movement with gold train, silvered dial, raised Arabic and abstract chapters and hands, dial and movement, 1940s.
(Christie's) **£893**

An 18ct. gold wristwatch with centre seconds, signed Audemars Piguet, with nickel 20-jewel movement with gold train. **£2,250**

Audemars Piguet, a gentleman's slim gold wristwatch in circular case, the white dial with raised baton numerals, 31mm. diameter.
(Christie's) **£1,320**

A thin gold wristwatch, signed Audemars Piguet, with nickel 20-jewel lever movement. **£1,250**

An 18ct. gold self-winding perpetual calendar wristwatch with moonphases, signed *Audemars Piguet, Automatic*, 36mm. diameter.
(Christie's) **£7,084**

AUDEMARS PIGUET

An 18ct. gold 'Royal Oak' wristwatch with bracelet, signed *Audemars Piguet, Royal Oak*, 30mm. wide.
(Christie's) £4,301

A platinum wristwatch, signed Audemars Piguet, on the movement and case, inscribed and dated 1926 in the interior. £6,000

Audemars Piguet, a gold automatic calendar wristwatch in circular case with stepped bezel, 32mm. diameter.
(Christie's) £3,740

Audemars Piguet, an 18ct. gold perpetual calendar and moonphase automatic wristwatch, the signed automatic movement with gold rim to the rotor, 35mm. diameter.
(Christie's) £6,600

A gold Audemars Piguet perpetual calendar automatic wristwatch, the signed movement with 36 jewels adjusted to heat, cold, isochronism and five positions, diam. 35mm.
(Christie's) £8,250

Audemars Piguet, a gold perpetual calendar and moonphase automatic wristwatch in circular case with stepped bezel, the white dial with raised baton numerals, with black leather strap, and green leather wallet, 35mm. diameter.
(Christie's) £6,050

Audemars Piguet, a gold wristwatch in circular case, signed movement jewelled to the centre with eighteen jewels, 31mm. diameter.
(Christie's) £1,210

A gold wristwatch within an 18ct. gold case, signed Audemars Piguet, with 14ct. mesh bracelet. £1,000

Audemars Piguet, Geneve, an unusual slim platinum and diamond-set wristwatch in circular case, the bezel set with diamonds, 34mm. diameter.
(Christie's) £3,565

BLANCPAIN

Blancpain, a ladies 18ct. gold automatic calendar and moonphase wristwatch in circular case, 26mm. diameter.
(Christie's) £1,430

Blancpain, an 18ct. gold automatic calendar wristwatch, the mother of pearl dial with raised Roman numerals, 33mm. diameter.
(Christie's) £1,980

Blancpain, a steel triple calendar and moonphase wristwatch, model J B 1735, in circular case, 33mm. diameter.
(Christie's) £990

Blancpain, an 18ct. gold perpetual calendar and moonphase automatic wristwatch in circular case, the signed movement with twenty-three jewels, 33mm. diameter.
(Christie's) £3,520

Blancpain, a gold automatic wristwatch in circular case with stepped bezel, matt white dial with raised Roman numerals, 33mm. diameter.
(Christie's) £1,760

Blancpain, a ladies 18ct. gold and diamond set calendar and moonphase automatic wristwatch, the white dial with diamond set numerals, 26mm. diameter.
(Christie's) £2,200

Blancpain, a gold steel automatic perpetual calendar wristwatch, in circular case with gold and steel stepped bezel, 33mm. diameter.
(Christie's) £3,850

Blancpain, a ladies 18ct. gold triple calendar automatic wristwatch, the white dial with raised Roman numerals, 26mm. diameter.
(Christie's) £1,725

Blancpain, a steel and gold triple calendar automatic moonphase wristwatch, the signed automatic movement engraved *CAL 6511*, 33mm. diameter.
(Christie's) £1,650

BREGUET

Breguet, No. 4286, a gold wristwatch, the gilt dial with Roman numerals, 31mm. diameter.
(Christie's) £3,080

An 18ct. gold wristwatch, signed *Breguet, No. 347*, with circular nickel-finished lever movement, 31mm. diameter.
(Christie's) £5,060

Breguet No. 4378, a gold wristwatch in drum shaped case with milled band and cabochon winder, 32mm. diameter.
(Christie's) £3,080

Breguet, an 18ct. gold skeletonised wristwatch in circular case, the textured gilt skeletonised movement, signed on a sector below the XII, 33mm. diameter.
(Christie's) £4,400

Breguet, No. 3730, a ladies fine 18ct. gold and diamond set moonphase wristwatch in drum shaped case, silver engine turned dial with Roman numerals, 25mm. diameter.
(Christie's) £9,350

Breguet, No. 567, a gentleman's fine 18ct. gold automatic calendar moonphase wristwatch, the silvered dial with Roman numerals, 36mm. diameter.
(Christie's) £7,700

Breguet, an 18ct. gold and diamond-set calendar and moonphase wristwatch in drum shaped case with ribbed band, 36mm. diameter.
(Christie's) £8,625

An 18ct. white gold wristwatch, signed *Breguet, No. 1065*, with nickel-finished lever movement, mono-metallic balance, 33mm. diameter.
(Christie's) £6,578

Breguet, No. 434, a fine 18ct. gold ladies power-reserve wristwatch, the silvered dial with secret signatures flanking the XII, 25mm. diameter.
(Christie's) £4,400

BREGUET

Breguet, No. 3727, a ladies fine 18ct. gold moonphase wristwatch in drum shaped case, with signed and numbered back 25mm. diameter.
(Christie's)   £3,080

A gold wristwatch, signed Breguet, no. 3150, with leather strap and 18ct. gold deployant buckle.   £2,250

An 18ct. gold self-winding perpetual calendar wristwatch with moonphases and up and down indicator, signed *Breguet, No. 5134 A*, 36mm. diameter.
(Christie's)   £30,360

Breguet, a modern 18ct. gold Tourbillon wristwatch no. 840, in drum shaped case, the silvered dial with eccentric chapter ring engraved *Brevet du 7 Messidor an IX* signed *Tourbillon Breguet No. .04*, 35mm. diameter.
(Christie's)   £22,000

Breguet, No. 2128, a gentleman's fine 18ct. gold automatic, calendar, moonphase and power reserve wristwatch in drum shaped case with milled band, with signed and numbered back, 36mm. diameter.
(Christie's)   £8,800

Breguet, a fine 18ct. gold calendar and moonphase and automatic wristwatch, the drum shaped case with ribbed band and cabochon winder, the silvered engine-turned dial with eccentric chapter ring, 35mm. diameter.
(Christie's)   £6,600

A platinum jump hour wristwatch, signed *Breguet, No. 51/400*, circular case with coin-edged band and sapphire-set crown, 36mm. diameter.
(Christie's)   £19,228

A steel wrist chronograph, signed Breguet, and another signed Henry K. Tournheim-Tourneau, without calendar.
                        £1,500

Breguet No. 3862, a gold calendar automatic Marine wristwatch, the silvered dial with Roman numerals, 36mm. diameter.
(Christie's)   £5,980

BREITLING

A chronograph wristwatch, signed *Breitling Cosmonaute*, the black matt dial with Arabic numerals, 41mm. diameter.
(Christie's) £800

Breitling, a 1950's water-resistant pink gold chronograph wristwatch, signed movement, 37mm. diameter.
(Christie's) £3,220

Breitling, a steel Chronomat automatic water-resistant calendar chronograph wristwatch, 38mm. diameter.
(Christie's) £825

Breitling, a pink gold waterproof and antimagnetic Première chronograph wristwatch, in circular case, the signed movement jewelled to the centre, 36mm. diameter.
(Christie's) £2,090

Navitimer, a stainless steel Breitling chronograph wristwatch with milled rotating bezel, the signed black dial with outer calculating scales, 40mm. diameter.
(Christie's) £495

A steel Breitling, Geneve, Navitimer chronograph wristwatch with rotating bezel, the black dial with outer tachymetric and telemetric scales, 40mm. diameter.
(Christie's S. Ken) £550

An 18ct. pink gold calendar wristwatch with chronograph, signed *Breitling, Geneve*, circa 1950, with nickel-finished lever movement, 36mm. diameter.
(Christie's) £2,783

A stainless steel chronograph wristwatch, signed *Breitling Cosmonaute, Navitime and Breitling Chronograph*, circa 1960, 36mm. diameter.
(Christie's) £750

A gentleman's stainless steel chronograph wristwatch, the silvered dial inscribed *Breitling Premier*, Arabic numerals, 35mm.
(Bonhams) £350

CARTIER

Cartier, a three colour gold quartz wristwatch, the white dial with secret signature at VII, 30mm. diameter.
(Christie's) £880

Cartier, a gold Ceinture automatic wristwatch, the white dial with Roman numerals, 32mm. diameter.
(Christie's) £2,860

Cartier, a 1920's gold Santos wristwatch, the white dial with Roman numerals and blued steel moon hands, 35 x 25mm.
(Christie's) £8,280

Cartier, a gold Baignoire wristwatch with cabochon winder, the matt white dial with Arabic numerals, the case secured by four screws in the band, 35 x 25mm.
(Christie's) £5,500

Cartier, a rare 18ct. gold minute repeating perpetual calendar wristwatch, model Pasha, the visible chased and engraved movement with skeletonised rotor, stamped *Cartier 179*, 37mm. diameter.
(Christie's) £35,200

Cartier, an 18ct. gold Panthere calendar quartz wristwatch in typical case, the white dial with Roman numerals, date aperture, sweep centre seconds, secret signature at VII, 38 x 27mm.
(Christie's) £4,290

Cartier, a 1920's platinum wristwatch in tortue case, the polished nickel plated bar movement signed *E. W. & C. Co. Inc*, 32 x 25mm.
(Christie's) £5,500

Cartier, a ladies gold Santos wristwatch, the white dial with Roman numerals and secret signature at X, the movement signed Cartier, 22mm. square.
(Christie's) £1,100

Cartier, a gold Santos quartz wristwatch, the white dial with Roman numerals, secret signature at VII, 32mm. diameter.
(Christie's) £2,645

CARTIER

Cartier, a gold steel Panthère quartz calendar wristwatch in square case, with protected cabochon winder, 40 x 20mm.
(Christie's)   £1,430

Cartier, a rare 1950's gold chronograph wristwatch in circular case, the movement signed *Jaeger*, 35mm. diameter.
(Christie's)   £13,200

Cartier, a ladies gold Baignoire backwind wristwatch, matt white dial with Roman and baton numerals, 29 x 20mm.
(Christie's)   £2,530

Cartier, a gold automatic calendar Santos wristwatch, the white dial with Roman numerals, date aperture and sweep centre seconds, 29mm. diameter.
(Christie's)   £2,990

Cartier, a ladies 1930's platinum and yellow gold diamond and onyx wristwatch in tortue case, the polished nickel bar movement signed *European Watch & Clock Co Inc*, 27 x 20mm.
(Christie's)   £3,520

A stainless steel and gold square sweep centre-seconds wristwatch with date and bracelet, signed *Cartier*, window for date at 5 o'clock, 27mm. wide.
(Christie's)   £1,063

Cartier, a fine early 1930's gold à Pattes wristwatch, the oval movement signed *European Watch and Clock Co. Inc.*, 19 x 33mm.
(Christie's)   £4,830

Cartier, a rare 1920's platinum Curvex Tonneau wristwatch, the polished bar movement signed *European Clock & Watch Co. Inc.*, 46 x 26mm.
(Christie's)   £11,000

Cartier, a ladies gold and diamond-set Tank wristwatch, the white dial with Roman numerals, secret signature at X, 20 x 20mm.
(Christie's)   £2,300

CARTIER

An 18ct. gold circular wrist-watch, the movement signed European Watch and Clock Co. Inc., the dial inscribed Cartier, 30mm. diam. £900

A gold and diamond wristwatch by Cartier, the case with diamond set shoulders, 20 x 27mm. £1,250

An 18ct. gold wristwatch by Cartier, hallmarked London 1963, 26mm. £3,000

A steel duoplan wristwatch, signed Jaeger, with oblong nickel lever movement, the white dial signed Cartier. £1,850

A square white gold diamond and baguette sapphire set wristwatch signed on the silvered dial Cartier, Paris, 23mm. square. (Christie's) £5,060

A rare tonneau-shaped single button chronograph wristwatch, signed *Cartier, European Watch & Co.*, circa 1935. (Christie's) £52,800

A Swiss gold curved rectangular wristwatch by Cartier, the signed dial with Roman numerals, the numbered case also marked *1326*, with cabochon winder. (Phillips) £3,600

An enamelled gold wristwatch, retailed by Cartier, the movement signed European Watch & Clock Co. £7,500

Cartier, a 1930s 18ct gold 'tank' wristwatch with ruby cabochon winder, white enamel dial with Roman numerals, the back secured by four screws in the band, 31 x 23mm. (Christie's) £3,300

CARTIER

A gold Cartier wristwatch, the movement signed E. W. & Co. Inc., length overall 30mm.   £3,750

An 18ct. gold wristwatch, retailed by Cartier, the movement signed Jaeger Le Coultre, with oblong duoplan nickel movement.   £5,000

A gold wristwatch by Cartier, with a double border enclosing the winder, 27mm. £1,500

Cartier, an 18ct gold chronograph wristwatch model Pasha, the rotating bezel with five-minute marks, the white dial with raised luminous dot five-minute marks, 38mm. diameter.
(Christie's)   £3,960

A Cartier gold wristwatch, rectangular face, hexagonal winder set with a sapphire.   £8,500

Cartier, a ladies gold and diamond-set quartz wristwatch in rectangular case, the shoulders set with diamonds, the white enamel dial with Roman numerals and secret signature at X, 28 x 21mm.
(Christie's)   £2,200

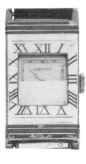

Cartier, an 18ct gold automatic calendar wristwatch model Pasha, with gold grill to the dial, the rotating bezel with ten-minute calibrations, 38mm. diameter.
(Christie's)   £4,950

An 18 carat gold 'Eclipse', wristwatch by Cartier, the rectangular case with circular movement, signed *European Watch and Clock Co. Inc.*, 35 x 19mm.
(Phillips)   £7,500

Cartier, a gentleman's gold wristwatch in 'turtle' case with cabochon winder, the white enamel dial with Roman numerals and secret signature at VII, 33 x 27mm.
(Christie's)   £4,180

CARTIER

Cartier, a ladies gold wristwatch in stepped square case, the signed movement with seventeen jewels, 18mm. square.
(Christie's) £935

Cartier, a ladies gold Eclipse wristwatch in stepped case, the signed movement with seventeen jewels, 26mm. diameter.
(Christie's) £1,100

Cartier, a ladies gold and diamond set octagonal wristwatch with diamond set sides, 25mm. square.
(Christie's) £1,980

Cartier, a slim gold Santos wristwatch, the white enamel dial with Roman numerals and secret signature at seven, 36 x 26mm.
(Christie's) £1,980

Cartier, a rare 18ct. gold and enamel rectangular wristwatch, model Eclipse, the later Cartier movement with twenty jewels, London import mark 1932, 38 x 20mm.
(Christie's) £23,100

Cartier, an 18ct. gold wristwatch in circular case, the white enamel dial with Roman numerals, the movement signed *Bueche-Girod*, 33mm. diameter.
(Christie's) £1,980

Cartier, a gold curvex wristwatch in tonneau case, silvered engine-turned dial, 39 x 26mm.
(Christie's) £2,310

Cartier, a ladies gold Ceinture wristwatch, the off-white dial with Roman numerals, 24mm. diameter.
(Christie's) £1,100

A stainless steel and gold sweep centre-seconds wristwatch with date and bracelet, signed *Cartier*, 30mm. diameter.
(Christie's) £1,417

CARTIER

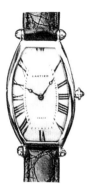

Cartier, a ladies gold and diamond-set tank wristwatch, the shoulders set with three rows of diamonds, 28 x 20mm. (Christie's) £2,530

Cartier, a ladies gold Gondola wristwatch in stepped case, with signed movement. (Christie's) £1,045

Cartier, a 1920's platinum tonneau curvex wristwatch, the movement stamped *E.W. & C. Co. Inc.*, 37 x 24mm. (Christie's) £13,200

Cartier, a ladies 18ct. gold and diamond set Baignoire wristwatch in oval case, the signed movement with seventeen jewels, 31 x 22mm. (Christie's) £2,420

Cartier, a ladies 1920's gold and enamel wristwatch in tortue case, the nickel plated movement signed *European Watch & Clock Co. Inc.*, 27 x 19mm. (Christie's) £3,300

Cartier, a ladies 18ct. gold and diamond set Panthère quartz wristwatch with diamond set bezel, the white dial with Roman numerals, 30 x 21mm. (Christie's) £5,500

Cartier, a ladies gold Tank wristwatch, the white dial with Roman numerals and inner minute ring, 26 x 21mm. (Christie's) £935

An 18ct. gold dual-time rectangular wristwatch, signed *Cartier, Paris*, with two nickel-finished lever movements, 45mm. long. (Christie's) £4,807

Cartier, a modern gold tonneau curvex wristwatch, the engine turned dial with Roman numerals, 39 x 26mm. (Christie's) £2,750

CHOPARD

An 18ct. white gold and hard-stone skeletonised wristwatch, signed Chopard, Geneve, with original leather strap and 18ct. white gold buckle.   £6,000

An 18ct. white gold and diamond wristwatch by Chopard, 34mm. circa 1970.   £1,850

A Swiss gold oval lady's wrist-watch, by Chopard, signed black dial with baton numerals, 26mm. wide, on a fancy link bracelet. (Phillips)   £360

GRUEN

A gold wristwatch with nickel 17-jewel movement, signed Gruen Watch Co., Curvex Precision.   £375

A 14ct. gold curvex wrist-watch, signed Gruen, with curved cushion shaped 17-jewel movement,   £1,000

A 14ct. gold curvex wrist-watch, signed Gruen Watch Co., with curved nickel 17-jewel movement.   £1,850

INTERNATIONAL WATCH CO.

A Swiss 18ct. gold wrist-watch with centre seconds, signed International Watch Co., with a 14ct. gold mesh bracelet.   £1,000

International Watch Co., a gold waterproof wristwatch in tonneau case, the brushed gilt dial with raised baton numerals and sweep centre seconds, 40 x 33mm.
(Christie's)   £605

A gold wristwatch, signed International Watch Co., Schaffhausen, with leather strap with 14ct. gold buckle and a spare crystal.   £1,500

JAEGER LE COULTRE

A gold plated calendar
wristwatch by Le Coultre,
circa 1940, 34x40mm.
£1,500

An 18ct. gold wristwatch
with fifteen jewel movement,
signed Le Coultre Co., dated
1934. £1,500

A Swiss gold circular wristwatch, by Jaeger le Coultre,
32mm. diam. (Phillips London)
£220

A gentleman's 14ct. gold
wristwatch, 'Le Coultre',
automatic, Master Mariner,
white dial and with a leather
band. £200

A Swiss gilt metal circular
gentleman's Futurematic
wristwatch by Le Coultre, the
signed silvered dial with
subsidiaries for seconds, 35mm.
diameter.
(Phillips) £150

A gold wristwatch by Jaeger
Le Coultre, the dial signed
Duoplan, 22mm. wide,
circa 1935. £2,400

A gentleman's 14ct. gold
wristwatch, LeCoultre, 17J,
complete with a leather strap.
£475

A Swiss gold 'Mystery' wristwatch by Jaeger-le-Coultre, with
backwind movement, the bezel
with enamelled baton numerals,
30mm. diam. (Phillips)
£2,700

A white gold mystery wristwatch by Le Coultre, 33mm.
diam., circa 1950. £1,000

403

JAEGER LE COULTRE

A gold Reverso wristwatch by Le Coultre, the matt dial with raised dagger numerals, 38 x 23mm.
(Christie's)   £3,300

Jaeger-LeCoultre, a gold rectangular wristwatch, the matt silvered dial with recessed centre, 27 x 20mm.
(Christie's)   £1,210

Jaeger-Le Coultre, a 9ct. gold and steel Reverso wristwatch, the signed movement with fifteen jewels, 38 x 22mm.
(Christie's)   £1,760

Jaeger-LeCoultre, an 18ct. gold calendar moonphase and chronograph wristwatch, model Odysseus No. 0136, the white dial with outer pulsations ring, 34mm. diameter.
(Christie's)   £1,760

An 18ct. pink gold Reverso wristwatch with date and up and down indicator, signed *Jaeger LeCoultre, No. 59/500*, circa 1991, with tonneau-shaped copper-finished lever movement, 42mm. long.
(Christie's)   £13,662

Jaeger le Coultre, an 18ct. gold triple calendar and moonphase automatic wristwatch, the white dial with raised baton numerals and Roman quarter hour divisions, 33mm. diameter.
(Christie's)   £1,870

Jaeger-LeCoultre, a 1950's gold Reverso wristwatch, the two-tone silvered dial with raised dagger numerals and subsidiary seconds, 39 x 22mm.
(Christie's)   £3,740

A 10ct. white and yellow trapezoidal wristwatch, signed *Le Coultre*, circa 1948, with tonneau-shaped nickel-finished lever movement, 39mm. long.
(Christie's)   £961

LeCoultre, a 1930's 18ct. gold and enamel wristwatch, the gilt dial with minute ring, hallmarked *London 1936*, 34 x 19mm.
(Christie's)   £1,540

JAEGER LE COULTRE

Jaeger-LeCoultre, a 1930's gold Reverso wristwatch, the silvered dial with raised dagger numerals, 38 x 22mm. (Christie's) £4,400

A gilt self-winding wristwatch with alarm and date, signed *Jaeger Le Coultre, Automatic*, 1960's, 39mm. diameter. (Christie's) £835

Jaeger-Le Coultre, a gold and steel Reverso wristwatch, the signed gilt movement with integral dust cover, 38 x 22mm. (Christie's) £2,420

An 18ct. gold calendar wristwatch, signed *Jaeger Le Coultre*, circa 1950, the silvered matt dial applied with triangular numerals, 35mm. diameter. (Christie's) £1,518

Jaeger-leCoultre, an 18ct. gold perpetual calendar and moonphase automatic wristwatch, the white enamel dial with raised gilt baton numerals, the signed movement with 47 jewels adjusted to four positions, 33mm. diameter. (Christie's) £3,520

Jaeger-LeCoultre, an 18ct. gold Odysseus triple calendar and moonphase chronograph wristwatch, the white dial with outer pulsations ring, 29mm. diameter. (Christie's) £1,650

Jaeger-Le Coultre, a 1950's gold triple calendar and moonphase wristwatch in circular case, the signed movement jewelled to the third, 35mm. diameter. (Christie's) £1,760

An 18ct. gold 'Reverso' wristwatch, signed *Jaeger LeCoultre, Reverso II*, retailed by Chaumet, with jewelled lever movement, 32mm. long. (Christie's) £2,125

Jaeger LeCoultre, a gold triple calendar with moonphase wristwatch, the silvered dial with outer date ring and central date hand, 33mm. diameter. (Christie's) £1,495

WRIST WATCHES

LONGINES

A stainless steel chronograph, signed Longines, with lever movement. **£225**

A large 1930s Longines aviator's hour angle watch, the enamel chapter ring signed *A. Cairelli, Roma*, 46mm. diameter. (Bonhams) **£2,400**

A large silver and stainless steel aviator's hour angle watch, to the designs of Charles A. Lindbergh, by Longines. **£5,500**

A gentleman's rectangular Swiss gold wristwatch by Longines, the signed movement numbered 3739388, 30 x 25mm. (Phillips) **£420**

Longines, a modern steel pilot's automatic hour-angle watch in circular case, the rotating bezel engraved with hours and quarters, the white enamel dial with Roman numerals, 36mm. diameter. (Christie's) **£418**

Longines, a steel military wristwatch, the rotating bezel calibrated in minutes with a locking screw in the band, the silvered dial with Arabic numerals and sweep centre seconds, 33mm. diameter. (Christie's) **£462**

MOVADO

A gent's Swiss gold wristwatch by Movado, 34mm. diam. **£1,850**

A Swiss gold circular gent's wristwatch, by Movado, the signed silvered dial with subsidiary seconds, 36mm. diam. (Phillips) **£280**

A gold wristwatch, signed Movado, with nickel 17 jewel movement, within a circular 14ct. gold case with unusual lugs. **£900**

MOVADO

A gold Movado calendar wristwatch made for Tiffany & Co., in circular case, the polished and matt silvered dial with outer date ring and central date hand, 31mm. diameter.
(Christie's S. Ken) £990

A gold wristwatch with calendar, signed Movado, within a reeded 14ct. gold case, and a self-winding 14ct. gold wristwatch, signed Bulova. £900

Movado, a pink gold and steel wristwatch with stepped pink gold bezel and faceted lugs, the two-tone silvered dial with Arabic numerals and outer seconds ring, 29mm. diameter. (Christie's) £440

OMEGA

A stainless steel Omega Flight-master wristwatch, the outer scale in five-minute divisions from 5 to 60, with screw back case, 53 x 42mm. (Christie's) £209

A gold wristwatch by Tissot, fitted with a gold Omega strap, circa 1970, 29mm. diam. £450

A rectangular Swiss gold gent's electronic wristwatch, by Omega, the gilt dial marked Constellation Chronometer, with centre seconds, 36mm. long. (Phillips) £600

A Swiss gold rectangular gentleman's wristwatch by Omega, the signed silvered dial with subsidiary seconds and Arabic numerals, 34 x 21mm. (Phillips) £380

Omega, a stainless steel automatic calendar diver's watch, model Seamaster 600 Professional, the rotating bezel calibrated in five-minute marks, 55 x 45mm. (Christie's) £550

A gold self-winding wrist-watch with centre seconds, signed Omega Seamaster, the leather strap with 14ct. gold buckle. £300

PATEK PHILIPPE

Patek Philippe, Geneve, an 18ct. pink gold Calatrava wristwatch, pink dial with raised dagger numerals, 30mm. diameter. (Christie's) £3,220

Patek Philippe, an 18ct. gold octagonal wristwatch with stepped bezel, the onyx dial with gold hands, 34mm. square. (Christie's) £1,980

Patek Philippe, an 18ct. gold square wristwatch, the brushed gilt dial with Roman numerals, 31mm. square. (Christie's) £1,380

Patek Philippe, an 18ct. gold quartz wristwatch in circular case with a textured bezel, the white dial with Roman numerals and date aperture, with signed quartz movement and battery, 33mm. diameter. (Christie's) £2,200

Patek Philippe, an 18ct. white gold Officer's Campaign wristwatch, the white enamel dial with Breguet numerals, subsidiary seconds and blued steel moon hands, 32mm. diameter. (Christie's) £9,680

Patek Philippe, a gentleman's 18ct. gold octagonal wristwatch with stepped bezel and black onyx dial, signed movement with 18 jewels, with maker's black leather strap and gold buckle, 34mm. square. (Christie's) £1,760

Patek Philippe, a ladies gold rectangular wristwatch, the white dial with Roman numerals, the case with snap on back and bar lugs, 25 x 22mm. (Christie's) £825

Patek Philippe, a 1950's gold Calatrava wristwatch, the brushed silvered dial with raised baton numerals, subsidiary seconds, 31mm. diameter. (Christie's) £2,750

Patek Philippe, Genève, a gold wristwatch in cushion case, the white dial with Roman numerals, with signed movement, 28mm. square. (Christie's) £1,650

PATEK PHILIPPE

Patek Philippe, a ladies 18ct. two-colour gold wristwatch, the brushed gilt dial with Roman numerals, 31mm. diameter.
(Christie's) £1,380

Patek Philippe, Geneve, a gold automatic wristwatch, brushed blue dial with raised baton numerals, 36 x 34mm.
(Christie's) £3,450

Patek Philippe, Genève, a gold automatic wristwatch, the matt silvered dial with raised Breguet numerals, 39 x 30mm.
(Christie's) £2,750

Patek Philippe, a gold automatic water resistant wristwatch with concealed winder, the brushed dial with raised baton numerals and sweep centre seconds, certificate of origin, and maker's plastic tag, 36mm. diameter.
(Christie's) £1,540

Patek Philippe, a ladies 18ct. gold oval watch with textured band and bezel, the pink coral dial with textured hands, the snap-on back with maker's mark no. 2769344 4267 1, 29 x 25mm.
(Christie's) £1,980

Patek Philippe, Genève, an 18ct. gold rectangular wristwatch, the textured gold dial with raised baton numerals, the signed movement jewelled to the centre with 18 jewels, with integral woven gold bracelet, 30 x 25mm.
(Christie's) £1,870

Patek Philippe, a rare 18ct. pink gold Calatrava wristwatch, the pink gold dial with raised pink gold baton numerals, 30mm. diameter.
(Christie's) £4,400

Patek Philippe, Genève, a ladies pink gold Calatrava wristwatch, the silvered dial with raised baton numerals, 20mm. diameter.
(Christie's) £770

Patek Philippe, a ladies 18ct. white gold oval wristwatch, the blue dial with raised baton numerals, the signed movement with 18 jewels, 29 x 25mm.
(Christie's) £1,650

PATEK PHILIPPE

An 18ct. rose gold world time wristwatch, signed Patek Philippe & Co., Geneva, with nickel movement jewelled through the centre. £25,000

A platinum tonneau-shaped jump hour wristwatch, signed *Patek Phillipe & Co., Geneve, No. 752957, 1989.* (Christie's) £52,800

A gold World Time wristwatch, signed Patek Philippe & Co., Geneva, no. 929572, the leather strap with 18ct. gold buckle. £15,000

An 18 carat gold gentleman's wristwatch by Patek Philippe, with chronograph, the signed movement with twenty-three jewels, London 1938, 33mm. diameter.
(Phillips) £16,000

A rare early 1950's Patek Philippe & Co, Geneve, Calatrava wristwatch made for Gubelin in typical case with white enamel dial and Breguet numerals, 31mm. diameter.
(Christie's S. Ken) £22,000

Patek Phillipe, a late 1940's gold wristwatch in circular case with fluted lugs, the silvered dial with raised dagger numerals and sweep centre seconds, 32mm. diameter.
(Christie's) £2,860

A gold wristwatch, signed P. Philippe & Co., Geneve, nickel eighteen-jewel cal. 23-300PM movement.
£1,500

A gold wristwatch, signed Patek Philippe & Co., Geneva, no. 1219325, with 18-jewel cal. 23-300 PM movement.
£1,600

An 18ct. gold wristwatch with nickel 18-jewel cal. 23-300 movement, signed Patek Philippe & Co., no. 781179.
£1,500

PATEK PHILIPPE

An 18ct. gold self-winding wristwatch with perpetual calendar, signed P. Philippe & Co., Geneve, no. 1119138. £8,000

An 18ct. gold wristwatch, signed Patek Philippe & Co., Geneva, no. 743586, with an 18ct. gold mesh bracelet. £1,250

A gold centre second wristwatch with perpetual calendar, signed Patek Philippe & Co., Geneva, no. 888001. £20,000

A gold wristwatch by Patek Philippe & Co., Geneve, the nickel adjusted 18-jewel movement with black dial, gold raised Arabic chapters and hands, subsidiary seconds. (Christie's) £3,828

Patek Philippe, a 1960's white gold automatic perpetual calendar wristwatch, the matt gilt dial with raised baton numerals, subsidiary date ring with sector for the moon, apertures for day and month, 37mm. diameter. (Christie's) £15,400

An 18 carat white gold perpetual calendar wristwatch with moonphases and chronograph, signed *Patek Phillipe & Co., Geneve, No. 875348, Ref. 3970.* (Christie's) £39,600

A gold wristwatch with centre seconds, signed P. Philippe & Co., Geneve, nickel eighteen-jewel cal. 27-SC movement. £1,850

A gold wrist chronograph, signed P. Philippe & Co., Geneve, no. 868978, nickel twenty-three jewel cal. 13-130 movement. £7,500

A white gold wristwatch, signed Patek Philippe, Geneva, with nickel 18-jewel cal. 23-300 movement. £2,500

PATEK PHILIPPE

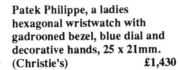

Patek Philippe, a ladies gold rectangular wristwatch, the blue dial with raised baton numerals, 23 x 19mm.
(Christie's) £990

Patek Philippe, a ladies hexagonal wristwatch with gadrooned bezel, blue dial and decorative hands, 25 x 21mm.
(Christie's) £1,430

Patek Philippe, a late 1940's gold rectangular wristwatch, with unusual block lugs and domed glass, 38 x 24mm.
(Christie's) £3,080

Patek Philippe, a yellow gold octagonal water resistant wristwatch, the blue dial with raised gold baton numerals and painted enamel crest of an Arabic State, 32 x 30mm.
(Christie's) £1,320

Patek Philippe, an 18ct. gold wristwatch, the case with snap on back, integral flexible gold bracelet and clasp, the movement numbered *791700*, 33mm. diameter.
(Christie's) £1,540

Patek Philippe, an 18ct. white gold wristwatch, the case with water resistant back and integral woven white gold flexible bracelet and clasp, 33mm. square.
(Christie's) £1,980

Patek Philippe & Co., Geneve, an early 1940's gold wristwatch, the dial signed *E. Gubelin*, 23mm. square.
(Christie's) £2,645

Patek Philippe, a gold ovaloid wristwatch, the brushed gilt dial with raised baton numerals, 32 x 27mm.
(Christie's) £1,210

Patek Philippe, a 1950's pink gold water resistant square wristwatch, the back with maker's mark, 36 x 26mm.
(Christie's) £4,600

PATEK PHILIPPE

Patek Philippe, an 18ct. gold wristwatch in circular case, the brushed silvered dial with baton numerals, 32mm. diameter.
(Christie's)   **£1,650**

Patek Philippe, a white gold square wristwatch, with integral textured flexible white gold bracelet, 25mm. square.
(Christie's)   **£1,980**

Patek Philippe, Geneve, a gold wristwatch, brushed silvered dial with alternating Arabic and dot numerals, 34mm. diameter.
(Christie's)   **£1,897**

Patek Philippe & Co., Geneve, a 1950's gold wristwatch in circular case with teardrop lugs, the silvered dial with alternating dot and Arabic numerals, 34mm. diameter.
(Christie's)   **£1,540**

Patek Philippe & Co., Genève, a 1940's stainless steel chronograph wristwatch, the matt silvered dial with outer tachymetric scale, jewelled to the centre with 23 jewels, 33mm.
(Christie's)   **£9,680**

Patek Philippe, a ladies 18ct. gold diamond, coral and onyx oval wristwatch, the bezel set with coral and diamonds, the oval dial set with onyx and pavé diamonds, 29 x 28mm.
(Christie's)   **£3,520**

Patek Philippe, Genève, a gold wristwatch in rectangular hexagonal shaped case, 36 x 28mm.
(Christie's)   **£2,090**

Patek Philippe, a gold oval wristwatch with blue textured dial and raised baton numerals, 32 x 27mm.
(Christie's)   **£1,320**

Patek Philippe, Geneve, a ladies white gold wristwatch, the brushed blue dial with raised baton numerals, 22 x 19mm.
(Christie's)   **£1,430**

PATEK PHILIPPE

An 18ct. gold self-winding wristwatch, signed Patek Philippe & Co., no. 116018, with signed 18ct. gold buckle to leather strap. £1,500

Patek Philippe, Genève, an 18ct. gold and diamond-set ladies wristwatch in circular shaped case, the bezel and dial set with diamonds, 30mm. diameter. (Christie's) £3,630

An 18ct. gold perpetual calendar wristwatch, 1950/52, by Patek Philippe, no. 967642, 34mm. diam. £12,500

An 18ct. thin white gold wristwatch, signed Patek Philippe & Co., the nickel 18-jewel movement with Geneva Observatory seal. £1,850

A very rare gold and diamond-set skeletonised automatic wristwatch by Patek Philippe, Geneve, the bezel with 12 diamonds, the case with sapphire crystal to the front and back, 34mm. diameter. (Christie's) £19,800

A Swiss gold circular gentleman's wristwatch by Patek Philippe, the signed silvered dial with subsidiary seconds, 34mm. diam. (Phillips) £2,800

An 18ct. white gold timezone wristwatch, signed Patek Philippe & Co., Geneva, with nickel 18-jewel cal. 27-HS 400 movement. £7,500

A circular Swiss gold gent's wristwatch, by Patek Philippe, the signed movement jewelled to the centre, 32mm. diam. (Phillips) £1,000

A Swiss gold circular gentleman's wristwatch by Patek Philippe, the case with rounded splayed lugs, 35mm. diam. (Phillips) £1,500

PATEK PHILIPPE

An 18ct. gold wristwatch with nickel 18-jewel cal. 27-AM400 movement, signed Patek Philippe & Co., no. 731479.   £1,000

Patek Philippe, a fine and rare gold wristwatch in turtle case with wire lugs, the matt white dial with black enamel Arabic numerals, 26 x 26mm. (Christie's)   £6,600

A platinum wristwatch, signed Patek Philippe & Co., with nickel 18-jewel movement, signed on movement and case.   £4,250

An 18 carat pink gold perpetual calendar chronograph wristwatch with moon phases, signed *Patek Philippe & Co., Geneve, No. 868248*, circa 1950. (Christie's)   £108,240

Patek Philippe, a fine 18ct gold officer's campaign watch made as a limited series of 2,000 pieces for the company's 150th anniversary in 1989, maker's attestation and commemorative medal, 33mm. diameter. (Christie's)   £7,700

A circular Swiss gold gent's wristwatch, by Patek Philippe, Geneve, the signed dial with subsidiary seconds and raised gilt numerals, 34mm. diam. (Phillips)   £1,725

An 18ct. gold wristwatch, signed P. Philippe & Co., Geneve, nickel eighteen-jewel cal. 9'''-90 movement.   £3,000

A Swiss gold gent's wristwatch, by Patek Philippe, the signed circular steel bar movement jewelled to the centre, 25mm. square. (Phillips)   £1,200

An 18ct. gold wristwatch, signed Patek Philippe & Co., Geneva, with circular nickel movement jewelled to the centre.   £2,500

PATEK PHILIPPE

Patek Philippe, an 18ct. gold oval wristwatch, the matt gilt dial with Roman numerals, 35 x 27mm.
(Christie's)   £1,540

Patek Philippe, a slim gold wristwatch in circular case, the matt silvered dial with Roman numerals, 30mm. diameter.
(Christie's)   £1,760

Patek Philippe, an early 1950's gold rectangular wristwatch, with signed movement jewelled to the centre, 35 x 26mm.
(Christie's)   £2,420

Patek Philippe, a gold waterproof wristwatch made for Favre-Leuba & Co., the matt silvered dial with raised gold baton numerals and subsidiary seconds, the bimetallic balance with micrometer regulation, 34mm. diameter.
(Christie's)   £2,200

Patek Philippe, a modern 18ct. gold perpetual calendar chronograph wristwatch, model 3970/E, calibre CH27-70Q, the case with maker's adhesive sticker, 35mm. diameter.
(Christie's)   £33,000

Patek Philippe, a ladies gold and diamond set rectangular wristwatch, the bezel set with diamonds to the sides, the two tone gilt dial with diamond set quarter hour marks, certificate of origin dated November 1985, 24 x 22mm.
(Christie's)   £1,155

Patek Philippe, an 18ct, gold oval automatic wristwatch, the blue dial with white enamel Roman numerals and white hands, 38 x 33mm.
(Christie's)   £2,200

Patek Philippe, a ladies gold oval wristwatch, the simulated lapis lazuli dial with decorative hands, with integral flexible gold bracelet and clasp, 31 x 27mm.
(Christie's)   £2,310

Patek Philippe, 18ct. white oval wristwatch, the blue dial with raised baton numerals and painted crest of an Arab State, 34 x 30mm.
(Christie's)   £1,540

PATEK PHILIPPE

Patek Philippe, an 18ct. gold calendar quartz wristwatch with milled bezel, the white dial with Roman numerals.
(Christie's) £2,310

Patek Philippe, Geneve, a gold wristwatch, the gilt textured dial with Roman numerals, 23 x 26mm.
(Christie's) £2,300

Patek Philippe, a modern 18ct. yellow gold perpetual calendar automatic wristwatch with glazed back, 35mm. diameter.
(Christie's) £16,500

Patek Philippe, an 18ct. gold rectangular wristwatch with ribbed bezel and black onyx dial, the signed movement with cabochon winder, 18 jewels, adjusted to heat, cold, isochronism and to five positions, 33 x 29mm.
(Christie's) £1,320

Patek Philippe, a fine 1940's pink gold wristwatch with down turned faceted lugs, the monometallic balance with micrometer regulation, 34mm. diameter.
(Christie's) £3,740

Patek Philippe, an 18ct. white gold oval wristwatch, the blue dial with diamond-set quarter hour marks, the signed movement with 18 jewels, adjusted to heat, cold, isochronism and to five positions, 32 x 27mm.
(Christie's) £2,200

Patek Philippe, a ladies gold diamond and coral set wristwatch, with integral woven gold bracelet and clasp, 29 x 26mm.
(Christie's) £2,860

Patek Philippe, an 18ct. white gold tonneau wristwatch, the brushed brown dial with raised silvered baton numerals, 32 x 27mm.
(Christie's) £1,150

Patek Philippe, a ladies gold cushion cased wristwatch, the signed movement jewelled to the centre with eighteen jewels, 20mm. square.
(Christie's) £1,100

PATEK PHILIPPE

A lady's platinum wrist-watch, signed P. Philippe & Co., Geneve. £650

An 18ct. gold self-winding wristwatch with perpetual calendar, signed Patek Philippe & Co. £10,000

An 18ct. gold gentleman's wristwatch, Patek Philippe, Geneve, 15J. £1,500

A platinum wristwatch, signed Patek Philippe & Co., Geneva, signed on movement and case. £6,000

An 18ct. gold wristwatch, signed P. Philippe & Co., Geneve, nickel eighteen-jewel cal. 23-300 movement. £2,500

An 18ct. gold shaped oblong wristwatch, signed Patek Philippe, signed on movement and case. £4,250

Gold automatic calendar watch by Patek Philippe, with leather strap, 35mm. diam. £2,250

18ct. gold chronograph wristwatch by Patek Philippe, London, 1958, with leather strap. £3,500

A gentleman's 18ct. gold wristwatch, Patek Philippe, Geneva, with white dial. £1,000

PATEK PHILIPPE

A wristwatch by Patek Philippe, 29mm., circa 1900. £1,250

A lady's 18ct. yellow gold wristwatch, Patek Philippe, jewelled Swiss movement. £1,250

A slim gold wristwatch by Patek Philippe, 33mm. diam., circa 1965. £1,250

A stainless steel wristwatch, signed Patek Philippe & Co., with shaped oblong 18-jewel nickel lever movement. £1,250

A gold and stainless steel wristwatch with calendar, signed Patek Philippe & Co., Geneva, Nautilus model with reeded black dial. £3,250

A Swiss 18ct. gold wrist-watch, signed Patek Philippe and Co., Geneva, signed on movement. £2,250

A lady's platinum and dia-mond wristwatch, signed P. Philippe & Co., Geneve, no. 199809. £1,200

A gold wristwatch and brace-let, signed P. Philippe & Co., Geneve, no. 851446, 18ct. £1,000

An 18ct. gold wristwatch by Patek Philippe, import mark London 1965, 35mm. £1,000

PATEK PHILIPPE

Patek Philippe, a ladies gold wristwatch in circular case, matt gilt dial with baton numerals, 25mm. diameter.
(Christie's)   £715

Patek Philippe, Geneve, a gold quartz wristwatch, two-tone grey and black dial, 32 x 29mm.
(Christie's)   £1,150

Patek Philippe, an 18ct. gold oval automatic wristwatch, the matt gilt dial with enamelled Roman numerals, 39 x 32mm.
(Christie's)   £2,200

Patek Philippe, Genève, a large 1950's gold Calatrava wristwatch, the signed movement with eighteen jewels, the monometallic balance with micrometer regulation, 35mm. diameter.
(Christie's)   £2,860

Patek Philippe, a ladies 18ct. gold octagonal wristwatch with black onyx dial and cabochon winder, the signed movement with 18 jewels, adjusted to heat, cold, isochronism and to five positions, 24mm. square.
(Christie's)   £1,100

Patek Philippe, Geneve, an early 1940's small stainless steel waterproof Calatrava wristwatch, the silvered dial with raised baton numerals and Arabic quarter hour marks, 28mm. diameter.
(Christie's)   £2,760

Patek Philippe, Geneve, a late 1940's gold wristwatch, the brushed silvered dial with raised baton numerals, subsidiary seconds, 33mm. diameter.
(Christie's)   £2,185

Patek Philippe, Geneve, a gold early 1970's backwind automatic wristwatch, the textured blue dial with raised baton numerals, 34mm. diameter.
(Christie's)   £2,530

Patek Philippe, a pink gold Calatrava wristwatch, the white enamel dial signed by the makers and also by Gubelin, 32mm. diameter.
(Christie's)   £13,200

PATEK PHILIPPE

Patek Philippe, Geneve, a gold water-resistant automatic calendar wristwatch, the signed automatic movement with gold rotor, 35mm. diameter.
(Christie's) £2,530

Patek Philippe, a white gold wristwatch in cushion case, the signed movement jewelled to the centre with eighteen jewels, 31mm. square.
(Christie's) £1,430

Patek Philippe, an 18ct. gold wristwatch in circular case, the signed movement jewelled to the centre with eighteen jewels, 33mm. diameter.
(Christie's) £935

Patek Philippe, an 18ct. gold Officer's Campaign wristwatch, the white enamel dial with Breguet numerals, subsidiary seconds and blued steel moon hands, the case with hinged back, 32mm. diameter.
(Christie's) £7,700

Patek Philippe, a ladies 18ct. white gold bracelet watch with oval bezel and blue dial, snap-on back with maker's mark no. 2746566 4151/1, the signed movement with 18 jewels, width of bracelet 28mm.
(Christie's) £1,320

Patek Philippe, Genève, a gold oval wristwatch made for Cartier, brushed gold dial with Roman numerals, the signed movement jewelled to the centre with 18 jewels, adjusted to heat, 32 x 27mm.
(Christie's) £1,650

An 18ct. pink gold perpetual calendar chronograph wristwatch with moonphases, signed *Patek Philippe & Co., Geneve, No. 867241*, circa 1948, 35mm. diameter.
(Christie's) £54,340

Patek Philippe, a ladies 18ct. white gold and diamond-set wristwatch in circular case, the oval bezel set with diamonds, the silvered dial with raised baton numerals, 28 x 24mm.
(Christie's) £2,530

Patek Philippe, a platinum waterproof perpetual calendar and chronograph wristwatch, the matt silvered dial with raised baton numerals, 35mm. diameter.
(Christie's) £62,000

PATEK PHILIPPE

A gold self-winding wrist-watch, signed Patek Philippe & Co., within a signed 18ct. gold waterproof case. £2,250

A rectangular Swiss gold lady's wristwatch, by Patek Philippe, the signed gilt dial marked Gubelin, 23mm. long. (Phillips) £950

A Swiss 18ct. gold case wristwatch, signed Patek Philippe and Co., Geneva. £1,250

A Swiss gold circular gentleman's self-winding wristwatch by Patek Philippe, the movement with signed gold rotor, 34mm. diameter. (Phillips) £2,400

An 18 carat gold perpetual calendar wristwatch with moonphases and chronograph, signed *Patek Phillipe & Co., Geneve, No. 863178*, circa 1944. (Christie's) £55,000

A gold wristwatch with nickel 18-jewel cal. 23-300 move-ment, signed Patek Philippe & Co., no. 782328, and a 14ct. gold watch signed Omega. £1,850

An 18ct. gold wristwatch, signed Patek Philippe & Co., with nickel 18-jewel lever movement. £1,500

An 18ct. gold wristwatch, signed P. Philippe & Co., Geneve, nickel eighteen-jewel movement. £1,500

An 18ct. gold wristwatch, signed Patek Philippe & Co., retailed by Cartier. £3,250

PATEK PHILIPPE

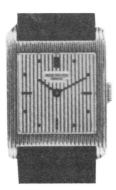

An 18ct. thin gold wrist-watch, signed Patek Philippe, with nickel 18-jewel cal. 10-200 movement.   £1,200

A gold wristwatch, signed Patek Philippe & Co., Geneva, no. 794766, with 18-jewel cal. 23-300 movement.
£1,850

A lady's stainless steel wrist-watch with calendar, signed Patek Philippe & Co., Geneva, Nautilus model.   £1,000

A gold wristwatch chrono-graph with perpetual calendar and moon phases, signed Patek Philippe & Co., Geneve, circa 1946-50.
£30,000

A fine gold calendar wrist chronograph with perpetual calendar, signed Patek Philippe, Geneve, No. 869392, the nickel 23-jewel movement with mono-metallic balance. (Christie's)
£23,428

A Swiss gold circular wristwatch by Patek Philippe, Geneve, with signed silvered dial, applied batons and subsidiary seconds, 29mm. diameter.
(Phillips)   £1,600

An 18ct. gold wristwatch, signed Patek Philippe & Co., retailed by Cartier, with fitted box.   £1,500

An 18ct. gold wristwatch, by Patek Philippe, no. 834704, length overall 36mm.   £2,500

A stainless steel wristwatch, signed Patek Philippe & Co., Geneve, with nickel 18-jewel movement.   £1,250

PIAGET

Piaget, a gold, ruby and diamond-set wristwatch, the bezel set with calibré cut rubies and diamonds, 34mm. diameter.
(Christie's) £4,370

Piaget, a ladies 18ct. yellow and white gold and diamond-set quartz wristwatch in tonneau case, 25 x 27mm.
(Christie's) £5,720

Piaget, an 18ct. two colour gold oval wristwatch with polished dial and bezel, the back with maker's mark, 35 x 24mm.
(Christie's) £1,540

Piaget, a ladies 18ct. gold automatic wristwatch, model Polo, in circular case with brushed and polished design to the case and dial, 27mm. diameter.
(Christie's) £1,320

Piaget, a ladies white gold and diamond-set dress watch, the silvered dial under hinged diamond-set cover with baton numerals, total length of bracelet 180mm.
(Christie's) £1,870

Piaget, a ladies 18ct. gold, diamond and coral hexagonal wristwatch with bulbous lugs, the bezel set with pink coral, the dial set with diamonds, 29 x 23mm.
(Christie's) £1,210

Piaget, a white gold automatic wristwatch in cushion case, signed automatic movement with gold microrotor, 33 x 31mm.
(Christie's) £2,200

Piaget, an 18ct. gold two-time zone wristwatch retailed by Asprey, the two movements signed by Piaget, 31 x 23mm.
(Christie's) £1,210

Piaget, an impressive 18ct. gold and diamond-set quartz wristwatch, the bezel set with diamonds, pavé diamond dial, 30mm. diameter.
(Christie's) £12,650

ROLEX

Rolex, a 1950's gold Oyster perpetual chronometer wristwatch, the brushed gilt dial with raised dagger numerals and sweep centre seconds, 32mm. diameter.
(Christie's) £2,530

Rolex, a ladies 1950's gold, sapphire and diamond-set dress watch, the matt silvered dial with dagger quarter hour marks and dot five minute divisions, total length of bracelet 185mm.
(Christie's) £3,300

Rolex, a 1920's 9ct. two-colour gold tonneau wristwatch, the signed Prima movement timed to six positions and for all climates, import mark for Glasgow 1928, 40 x 27mm.
(Christie's) £1,320

Rolex, a gold Oyster chronometer observatory wristwatch, the two-tone silvered dial with outer seconds ring, sweep centre seconds, Arabic numerals, 28mm. diameter.
(Christie's) £1,980

Rolex, a rare 1930's 9ct. two colour gold jump-hour rectangular wristwatch in flared case, the signed Extra Prima observatory quality movement timed to six positions, 42 x 25mm.
(Christie's) £7,700

A stainless steel and pink gold self-winding waterproof hooded wristwatch with sweep centre-seconds, signed *Rolex*, circa 1945, the bordeaux dial with triangular and Arabic numerals, 32mm. diameter.
(Christie's) £2,000

Rolex, a pink gold Oyster perpetual chronometer bubble-back wristwatch, silvered dial with baton numerals and Roman quarter hour marks, 32mm. diameter.
(Christie's) £4,370

Rolex, a gold/steel Oyster perpetual chronometer bubble back wristwatch in tonneau case with gold hooded lugs and chamfered bezel, 31mm. diameter.
(Christie's) £2,310

Rolex, an 18ct. gold cushion case Oyster wristwatch, the signed Prima movement timed to six positions, with fifteen jewels and Elinvar hairspring, 27mm. square.
(Christie's) £3,080

ROLEX

A wristwatch, signed Rolex Prince, the 9ct. gold case bearing Glasgow import mark for 1930. £3,250

A 'Rolex Oyster Perpetual Submariner' wristwatch in stainless steel case.
(Bearne's) £540

An 18ct. two-colour gold Rolex Prince, 1930, no. 70864, length overall 41mm. £4,250

A Swiss steel Oyster Perpetual GMT Master by Rolex, the signed black dial with centre seconds and additional twenty-four hour hand, 39mm. diameter.
(Phillips) £500

An 18ct. gold Rolex chrono-graph wristwatch with black bezel, calibrated in units per hour, the silvered dial with applied gold luminous baton numerals, 37mm. diameter.
(Christie's) £4,180

A Swiss steel Oyster Perpetual cosmograph Daytona wristwatch, by Rolex, the signed white dial with subsidiaries for seconds, minutes and for hours elapsed, 38mm. diameter.
(Phillips) £3,200

A Swiss gold Oyster perpetual date wristwatch by Rolex, the signed grey dial with date aperture, 35mm. diam.
(Phillips) £2,000

An 18ct. gold self-winding calendar wristwatch with centre seconds, signed Rolex Oyster Perpetual, and a gold filled bracelet. £2,250

A lady's 18ct. gold self-winding wristwatch, signed Rolex Perpetual Super Precision, signed on movement and case. £1,250

ROLEX

A gold Oyster wristwatch
by Rolex, with self sealing
winder, 30mm., circa 1950.
£1,250

An 18ct. pink gold Rolex Oyster-
perpetual 'day-date' wristwatch
in tonneau shaped case.
(Bearne's) £1,450

A two-colour calendar
Oyster wristwatch by
Rolex, 36mm., circa
1965. £900

A steel Rolex Oyster Perpetual
date submariner wristwatch
with black revolving bezel, the
matt black dial with dot and
baton numerals, 40mm.
diameter.
(Christie's S. Ken) £990

A gold steel Rolex Oyster
Perpetual chronometer bubble-
back wristwatch with gold bezel,
the pink dial with Arabic
quarter-hour marks, 30mm.
diameter.
(Christie's S. Ken) £825

Rolex, gentleman's 18ct. rose
gold round cased wristwatch,
nickel seventeen jewel
chronometer, hand wound
movement with centre seconds,
circa 1960, 35mm.
(Bonhams) £440

An 18ct. gold self-winding
wristwatch with centre
seconds, signed Rolex Oyster
Perpetual, with gold bracelet.
£1,250

A stainless steel self-winding
wristwatch with centre seconds,
signed Rolex Oyster Perpetual,
Explorer, with Oyster crown
and steel bracelet. £425

A 14ct. gold self-winding
wristwatch with centre
seconds, signed Rolex Oyster
Perpetual, with a 14ct. gold
bracelet. £1,850

ROLEX

Rolex, an 18ct. gold octagonal Oyster wristwatch, the signed Extra Prima movement timed to eight positions for all climates, Glasgow import mark 1927, 34 x 31mm.
(Christie's)   £2,420

Rolex, a 1920's 9ct. gold octagonal Oyster wristwatch, the signed Ultra Prima movement timed to six positions and with fifteen jewels, 27 x 30mm.
(Christie's)   £1,650

Rolex, a gold steel Oyster perpetual Cosmograph Daytona chronometer chronograph wristwatch, the gold bezel calibrated in units per hour, 38mm. diameter.
(Christie's)   £4,400

Rolex, a pink gold and steel Oyster perpetual wristwatch with pink gold bezel and winder, the silvered dial with alternating dagger and Arabic numerals, 31mm. diameter.
(Christie's)   £1,265

Rolex, a 9ct. gold Oyster perpetual chronometer wristwatch, the brushed silvered dial with raised Arabic ¼-hour marks and dagger five minute divisions, 33mm. diameter.
(Christie's)   £880

Rolex, a gold steel bubble-back Oyster perpetual chronometer wristwatch, the gold bezel with five minute marks, Mercedes hands, sweep centre seconds, 31mm. diameter.
(Christie's)   £1,870

Rolex, a gold steel Oyster perpetual chronometer Daytona chronograph wristwatch, with gold steel bracelet, 38mm. diameter.
(Christie's)   £4,620

Rolex, a rare gold Oyster perpetual chronometer wristwatch, the blue and white chequered dial with raised baton numerals, 33mm. diameter.
(Christie's)   £2,640

Rolex, a stainless steel Cosmograph Daytona chronograph wristwatch, the so called Paul Newman model, 36mm. diameter.
(Christie's)   £5,280

ROLEX

Rolex, a stainless steel
Cosmograph chronograph
wristwatch, the bezel calibrated
with units per hour, the brushed
steel dial with raised bezel
numerals, 36mm. diameter.
(Christie's) £2,750

Rolex, a 1930's 9ct. gold Prince
wristwatch in rectangular case
with raised bezel, the signed
Ultra Prima Chonometer
movement timed to six positions,
37 x 20mm.
(Christie's) £2,310

Rolex, a rare pink gold triple
calendar and moonphase
perpetual chronometer
automatic wristwatch, the
brushed silvered dial with outer
date ring, 37mm. diameter.
(Christie's) £7,150

Rolex, a rare pink gold and steel
Oyster perpetual chronometer
wristwatch with inset hooded
lugs, the silvered dial with
Arabic numerals and sweep
centre seconds, 40 x 31mm.
(Christie's) £2,750

Rolex, a 14ct. gold Oyster
perpetual date chronometer
wristwatch, the brushed gilt dial
with raised baton numerals,
date aperture under magnifying
glass, 33mm. diameter.
(Christie's) £1,430

Rolex, a gold Oyster perpetual
chronometer wristwatch, the
milled bezel with five minute
marks, the black dial with raised
baton numerals and sweep
centre seconds, 31mm. diameter.
(Christie's) £2,640

Rolex, a rare pink gold and steel
bubble-back Oyster perpetual
chronometer wristwatch with
hooded pink gold lugs and bezel,
38 x 30mm.
(Christie's) £2,860

Rolex, an 18ct. gold Oyster
perpetual datejust chronometer
wristwatch, with outer
packaging and guarantee dated
October 1987, 30mm. diameter.
(Christie's) £2,420

Rolex, an early 9ct. gold Oyster
tonneau wristwatch, the signed
Ultra Prima movement timed to
six positions and for climates, 29
x 29mm.
(Christie's) £1,430

ROLEX

A stainless steel and gold self-winding wristwatch with centre seconds, signed Rolex Oyster Perpetual. £1,250

An 18 carat gold Oyster day-date wristwatch by Rolex, import mark London 1974, 36mm. diam. £4,750

A stainless steel and gold self-winding wristwatch with centre seconds, signed Rolex Oyster Perpetual. £475

A gold and diamond set Oyster day-date wristwatch by Rolex, 36mm. diam. £4,250

Rolex, a gold quarter Century Club wristwatch in flared case, the two-tone silvered dial signed *Eaton*, the signed *Ultra Prima* chronometer movement with eighteen jewels and timed to six positions, 42 x 23mm. (Christie's) £2,860

A stainless steel self-winding wristwatch with centre seconds, signed Rolex Oyster Perpetual. £750

A Swiss gold square gent's wristwatch, by Rolex, the movement stamped Rolex Prima, 25mm. square. (Phillips) £220

A gentleman's 1960's period Rolex Oyster Perpetual wristwatch, the circular silvered dial inscribed *Rolex Oyster Perpetual – Officially Certified Chronometer*. (Spencer's) £400

A gold Prince wristwatch by Rolex, with an Extra Prima movement, circa 1930, 24 x 45mm. £2,250

ROLEX

A stainless steel and gold self-winding centre seconds wrist-watch with calendar, signed Rolex Oyster Perpetual. £700

A gold automatic calendar Oyster wristwatch by Rolex, 35mm. diam., circa 1955. £1,500

A 9 carat gold Oyster wrist-watch by Rolex, 35mm. diam., Birmingham 1939. £1,000

A white gold Prince wrist-watch by Rolex with Ultra Prima movement, circa 1930. £2,750

A 9ct. gold Rolex Oyster Speedking wristwatch, the silvered dial with raised dagger numerals and subsidiary seconds, the case with screw-down winder, 28mm. diameter. (Christie's S. Ken) £770

An 18 carat white and yellow gold Prince wristwatch by Rolex, 25 x 43mm., Glasgow 1929. £4,500

A Swiss gold cushion shaped gent's wristwatch, by Rolex, with Arabic numerals and subsidiary seconds, 36mm. long. (Phillips) £250

An 18ct. gold Rolex Cosmograph Daytona chronograph wristwatch, so-called Paul Newman model, the gold bezel with tachymetric scale, 36mm. diameter. (Christie's S. Ken) £19,250

A gold self-winding wrist-watch with centre seconds, signed Rolex Oyster Perpetual, the leather strap with 14ct. gold buckle. £1,850

431

ROLEX

Rolex, a rare 1930's white gold Prince wristwatch in rectangular flared case with domed glass, the black dial with baton numerals, 42 x 27mm.
(Christie's) **£3,960**

Rolex, a steel chronograph wristwatch, the black dial with Arabic numerals, outer tachymetric scale, 35mm. diameter.
(Christie's) **£2,990**

Rolex, a ladies pink gold Oyster perpetual datejust chronometer wristwatch, the brushed silvered dial with raised baton numerals, 24mm. diameter.
(Christie's) **£1,980**

Rolex, a gold Oyster perpetual GMT-Master chronometer wristwatch the rotating bezel with 24 hour notation, brown dial with raised dot and baton numerals, central 24 hour hand, 38mm. diameter.
(Christie's) **£2,970**

Rolex, a pink gold Oyster perpetual datejust chronometer wristwatch, with milled bezel, the black dial with raised gilt baton numerals, signed movement with 25 jewels, 35mm. diameter.
(Christie's) **£2,640**

Rolex, a 1930's 9ct. two colour gold Prince wristwatch in flared case with white shoulders to the yellow case, the matt silvered dial with eccentric chapter ring and Arabic numerals, 43 x 25mm.
(Christie's) **£2,860**

Rolex, a gold asymmetric King Midas water-resistant wristwatch, the case with integral flexible gold bracelet with maker's mark, 27 x 27mm.
(Christie's) **£3,080**

Rolex, a gold steel Oyster perpetual Cosmograph Daytona chronometer wristwatch, the white dial with raised gilt baton numerals, 38mm. diameter.
(Christie's) **£5,720**

Rolex, a rare pink gold rectangular Prince wristwatch, silvered dial with Roman numerals and large subsidiary seconds, 45 x 25mm.
(Christie's) **£4,600**

ROLEX

Rolex, a gold Oyster perpetual chronometer bubble-back wristwatch, the matt white dial with raised dagger numerals, 32mm. diameter.
(Christie's) £1,955

Rolex, a 1930's steel Prince rectangular wristwatch, the signed Extra Prima observatory quality movement timed to six positions, 35 x 20mm.
(Christie's) £1,870

Rolex, a 1940's stainless steel chronograph wristwatch, the matt silvered dial with outer tachymetric and telemetric scales, 35mm. diameter.
(Christie's) £2,875

A pink gold rectangular wristwatch by Rolex with scalloped corners and hooded lugs, the signed lozenge movement jewelled to the centre with seventeen jewels, 37 x 21mm.
(Christie's) £1,045

Rolex, a gold Oyster perpetual day-date chronometer wristwatch with milled bezel, the brushed gilt dial with raised baton numerals, the signed movement with 26 jewels, 35mm. diameter.
(Christie's) £2,200

Rolex, a ladies pink gold Oyster perpetual wristwatch, the silvered dial with alternating dagger and Arabic numerals, the enclosed chronometer movement signed on the rotor, 22mm. diameter.
(Christie's) £1,320

Rolex, a ladies 18ct. gold Oyster perpetual datejust chronometer wristwatch, the brushed silvered dial with raised baton numerals, 25mm. diameter.
(Christie's) £3,080

Rolex, a fine and rare 9ct. gold Scientific Chronometer wristwatch, with signed Ultra Prima chronometer movement, 30mm. diameter.
(Christie's) £3,520

Rolex, an 18ct. pink gold Oyster perpetual day-date chronometer wristwatch, the pink gilt dial with raised baton numerals, 35mm. diameter.
(Christie's) £3,960

ROLEX

An early waterproof wrist-watch, signed Rolex, within a silver case hinged to outer protective silver case. £1,500

A two-colour gold wrist-watch with box and certifi-cate, signed Rolex, Prince, no. 77625.   £6,000

A 14ct. gold self-winding wristwatch with centre seconds, signed Rolex Oyster Perpetual.   £700

A stainless steel and gold self-winding wristwatch with centre seconds, signed Rolex Oyster Perpetual, with 14ct. gold and stainless steel brace-let.   £1,850

A gentleman's 9ct. gold Oyster wristwatch, the two-tone silvered dial inscribed *Rolex Oyster*, subsidiary seconds, Glasgow 1934. (Bonhams)   £1,000

A Swiss gold oyster perpetual day-date wristwatch, by Rolex, the signed gilt dial with centre seconds and with diamond numerals, (Phillips)   £3,200

A gent's Swiss gold Oyster perpetual day-date wrist-watch, by Rolex, the signed chocolate coloured dial with centre seconds, (Phillips)   £2,600

An 18 carat yellow and white gold Prince wristwatch by Rolex, with an Extra Prima movement, 25 x 40mm., import mark Glasgow 1930.   £4,500

A gentleman's stainless steel cased Rolex wristwatch, the champagne dial with luminous Arabic numerals, in a case of plain circular form. (Spencer's)   £260

ROLEX

A gold wristwatch by Rolex,
the copper dial signed,
36mm. diam., circa 1960.
£375

A 14ct. gold gentleman's
wristlet watch by Rolex
with perpetual chronometer
movement.   £1,250

A gold self-winding wristwatch with centre seconds,
signed Rolex Oyster Perpetual.
£1,850

A Swiss gold circular Rolex
wristwatch, the signed white dial
marked in 1/sth seconds, with
Arabic numerals and red sweep
seconds, 29mm. diameter.
(Phillips)   £600

A 9ct. gold Rolex Prince
wristwatch in rectangular case,
the matt silvered dial with
Arabic numerals and large
subsidiary seconds, 39 x 21mm.
(Christie's S. Ken)   £3,080

Rolex, a gold steel Oyster
perpetual chronometer
wristwatch in tonneau case with
pink gold bezel and winder,
31mm. diameter.
(Christie's)   £990

A Swiss steel and gilt metal
circular gentleman's wristwatch
by Rolex, the signed circular
movement marked *'patented
super balance'*, 35mm. diameter.
(Phillips)   £280

A Swiss gold circular lady's
wristwatch, by Rolex, the
stamped movement with
painted dial with Arabic
numerals, 27mm. diam.
(Phillips)   £280

Rolex Oyster, chrome plated
wristwatch, white enamel dial,
black Roman figures, nickel
lever movement, in a cushion
shaped case, 32mm.
(Bonhams)   £210

ROLEX

Rolex, a gold steel Oyster perpetual chronometer bubble-back wristwatch, 30mm. diameter.
(Christie's)   £1,100

Rolex, a gold Prince wristwatch in waisted case, with signed observatory quality movement, 41 x 24mm.
(Christie's)   £3,080

Rolex, a white gold Oyster perpetual day-date wristwatch with milled bezel, 35mm. diameter.
(Christie's)   £2,860

Rolex, a steel Cosmograph Daytona chronograph wristwatch, the so-called Paul Newman model, the bezel calibrated in units per hour, the black dial with outer seconds ring, 36mm. diameter.
(Christie's)   £4,840

Rolex, a steel and gold bubble-back Oyster perpetual chronometer wristwatch with gold bezel and winder, the black dial with Arabic numerals and unusual inner 24 hour ring, 31mm. diameter.
(Christie's)   £1,320

Rolex, an 18ct. gold Oyster perpetual chronometer Daytona chronograph wristwatch, the gold bezel calibrated in units per hour, the black dial with raised gilt baton numerals, 38mm. diameter.
(Christie's)   £9,350

Rolex, a rare 1940's pink gold and steel Oyster perpetual chronometer bubble-back wristwatch in tonneau case, 31mm. diameter.
(Christie's)   £3,910

Rolex, a 1940's 9ct. gold rectangular Chronometer wristwatch, with signed Ultra Prima Chronometer movement, 32 x 21mm.
(Christie's)   £1,870

Rolex, a stainless steel Oyster perpetual Cosmograph Daytona wristwatch, the black dial with raised baton numerals, 38mm. diameter.
(Christie's)   £3,740

ROLEX

Rolex, a 9ct. two-colour gold
Prince wristwatch in flared case,
Extra Prima movement of
observatory quality, 43 x 26mm.
(Christie's) £3,220

Rolex, a rare 1930's gold and
steel Oyster wristwatch, the
signed movement with fifteen
jewels, 30mm. diameter.
(Christie's) £3,300

Rolex, a 1930's 9ct. gold
rectangular wristwatch, with
9ct. gold flexible bracelet and
clasp, hallmarked *Glasgow 1937*.
(Christie's) £1,100

Rolex, a gold and steel Oyster
perpetual chronometer bubble-
back wristwatch, the black dial
with Roman numerals in the
upper half and Arabic numerals
in the lower half, 31mm.
diameter.
(Christie's) £1,100

Rolex, a gold Oyster perpetual
day-date chronometer
wristwatch with milled bezel,
the brushed gilt dial with raised
baton numerals, with original
leather presentation box, 35mm.
diameter.
(Christie's) £3,740

Rolex, a steel Oyster Daytona
Cosmograph wristwatch, the
bezel calibrated in units per
hour, brushed silvered dial with
raised baton numerals, with
presentation box, 37mm.
diameter.
(Christie's) £5,060

Rolex, a 1920's 18ct. gold Oyster
Extra Precision wristwatch in
cushion case, the two-tone gilt
dial with Arabic numerals,
28mm. square.
(Christie's) £1,955

Rolex, a late 1940's steel Oyster
chronograph anti-magnetique
triple calendar wristwatch with
outer-date ring and central date
hand, 35mm. diameter.
(Christie's) £8,050

Rolex, a 9ct. gold Oyster
chronometer observatory
wristwatch in tonneau case, the
signed chronometer movement
with eighteen jewels, 36 x 30mm.
(Christie's) £3,190

ROLEX

A gentleman's gold wrist-watch, the movement with 17 rubies, signed Rolex Precision. £625

A steel Oyster perpetual bubble back gent's wristwatch, by Rolex, Arabic numerals, 39mm. long. (Phillips) £340

A 9ct. white and yellow striped gold Rolex Prince, 1931, length overall 41mm. £4,000

A Swiss 9 carat gold wristwatch by Rolex, the signed quartered silvered dial with subsidiary seconds, 1935, 27mm. diameter. (Phillips) £782

A gold self-winding wristwatch with centre seconds, signed Rolex Oyster Perpetual. £1,000

A gold and stainless steel self-winding wristwatch with centre seconds, signed Rolex Oyster Perpetual, with original guarantee certificate. £1,250

An 18ct. automatic calendar gold oyster wristwatch by Rolex, circa 1980. £3,000

A stainless steel self-winding wristwatch with centre seconds, signed Rolex Oyster Perpetual, Submariner. £700

A lady's rose gold wristwatch, signed Rolex, gold hands 17-jewel movement with an 18ct. gold bracelet. £950

TIFFANY

Platinum and diamond wrist watch by Tiffany & Co., circa 1925.
£1,500

A steel triple calendar and moonphase wristwatch made for Tiffany by Record Watch Co., the brushed steel dial with Arabic numerals, 34mm. diameter.
(Christie's) £330

A gold wristwatch, signed Audemars Piguet, with 18ct. gold bracelet, signed Tiffany & Co. £1,500

A gold wristwatch by C. H. Meylan Watch Co., the dial signed Tiffany & Co., 19 x 35mm., circa 1935. £700

A 1920's gold curvex tonneau wristwatch, the matt white dial with gilt Arabic numerals, signed *Tiffany & Co.*, 35 x 26mm.
(Christie's) £1,265

A gold wristwatch, signed Agassiz Watch Co., dial signed Tiffany & Co., in an 18ct. gold case. £1,500

UNIVERSAL

A stainless steel calendar and moon phase wristwatch, inscribed 'Universal, Geneve', the signed movement jewelled to the third, diam. 34mm.
(Christie's) £275

Universal, a pink gold triple calendar and moonphase chronograph wristwatch, the silvered dial with outer tachymetric scale, alternating raised pink dagger and Arabic numerals, 36mm. diameter.
(Christie's) £1,540

A 19ct. gold chronograph wristwatch in circular case, the matt silvered dial signed Universal, Geneve, 33mm. diam. (Christie's) £605

VACHERON & CONSTANTIN

Vacheron Constantin, Geneve, a gold slim wristwatch in circular case with unusual shaped arrow-head lugs, 32mm. diameter.
(Christie's) £1,150

Vacheron Constantin, a late 1940's gold rectangular wristwatch with waisted case and faceted crystal, 39 x 23mm.
(Christie's) £4,140

Vacheron & Constantin, a white gold wristwatch in circular case with brushed white gold dial, dated *1976*, 33mm. diameter.
(Christie's) £1,380

Vacheron & Constantin, a 1950's pink gold triple calendar wristwatch, the two-tone gilt dial with raised Roman $1/4$-hour marks and dagger five minute divisions, 34mm. diameter.
(Christie's) £3,520

Vacheron & Constantin, Geneve, a rare 1950's gold triple calendar and moonphase wristwatch, bi-metallic balance with lever escapement and micrometer regulation, 35 x 42mm.
(Christie's) £13,800

An early silver wristwatch in cushion shaped case with wire lugs, the white enamel dial signed *Vacheron & Constantin* with Breguet numerals, 29mm. square.
(Christie's) £825

Vacheron & Constantin, Geneve, a gold automatic wristwatch in cushion shaped case, the brushed silvered dial with raised baton numerals, 31mm. square.
(Christie's) £2,530

Vacheron Constantin, a slim gold wristwatch in circular case, the signed movement with seventeen jewels, 33mm. diameter.
(Christie's) £1,320

Vacheron Constantin, an 18ct. gold perpetual calendar and moonphase automatic wristwatch, the signed movement with gold rim to the rotor, 35mm. diameter.
(Christie's) £6,600

VACHERON & CONSTANTIN

Vacheron & Constantin, Geneve, a pink gold wristwatch, the black dial with raised dagger numerals, 31mm. diameter. (Christie's) £1,955

Vacheron Constantin, an 18ct. gold automatic chronograph wristwatch, the textured white dial with raised baton numerals, 37mm. diameter. (Christie's) £4,400

Vacheron Constantin, a gold automatic calendar wristwatch, the gilt dial with raised baton numerals, 34mm. diameter. (Christie's) £1,980

Vacheron & Constantin, Genève, a rare and early gold wristwatch in cushion shape with offset winder, the white enamel dial with Arabic numerals and offset seconds, 1919, 30mm. square. (Christie's) £3,740

Vacheron & Constantin, an unusual 1950's 18ct. slim wristwatch, the signed movement adjusted to temperatures, with monometallic balance and micrometer regulation, 35mm. diameter. (Christie's) £1,320

Vacheron & Constantin, Genève, a 1950's gold wristwatch, the black dial with alternating baton and dot five minute marks, the monometallic balance with micrometer regulation, 35mm. diameter. (Christie's) £1,320

Vacheron & Constantin, Geneve, a rare gold wristwatch, the off-white dial with raised dagger five-minute marks and Arabic quarter hour numerals, 33 x 24mm. (Christie's) £3,335

Vacheron Constantin, a slim 18ct. gold wristwatch with unusual straight lugs, the off-white dial with baton numerals, 32mm. diameter. (Christie's) £1,760

Vacheron & Constantin, a rare 1920's two colour gold Semaphore wristwatch in square case, the back with designer's mark V F, 26mm. square. (Christie's) £4,400

18ct. gold calendar wristwatch by Vacheron & Constantin, London, 1954, 35mm. diam.
£1,850

An 18ct. gold skeletonised wristwatch, signed Vacheron & Constantin, with signed 18ct. gold buckle to leather strap.
£4,250

A white gold mysterieuse wristwatch by Vacheron & Constantin & Le Coultre, 33mm., circa 1965. £1,500

An 18ct. gold wristwatch, signed Vacheron & Constantin, with nickel 17-jewel P 453/3B movement, signed on movement and case
£2,000

Vacheron & Constantin, Genève, an 18ct. gold perpetual calendar and moonphase automatic wristwatch, cream dial with raised baton numerals, 35mm. diameter.
(Christie's)
£7,480

An 18ct. gold wristwatch with nickel 17-jewel movement, signed Vacheron & Constantin, no. 421150.
£2,250

An 18ct. gold bracelet watch, signed Vacheron & Constantin, on movement, case and bracelet.
£2,000

A Swiss gold circular automatic gentleman's wristwatch by Vacheron & Constantin, Genève, with signed gilt dial with centre seconds and Roman numerals, 36mm. diameter.
(Phillips)
£1,437

An 18ct. white gold minute repeating wristwatch, signed Vacheron & Constantin, Geneva.
£40,000

INDEX

Lund & Blockley 113, 132, 343
Lux Clock Mfg. Co. 210
Lynford 51
Lyre Clocks 256
Lytle, James 343

Maclennan, Kenth 43
Macors 220
Magson, David 288
Magson, Jon. 344
Mahogany 58-70, 166-175, 257, 258
Mahr, W. 264
Makin, George & Sons 126
Mallett, Peter 178
Manhart, Sebastian 212
Manlove, Willm. 198
Manners & Sons 60
Manneville 245
Mannheim 239
Mansion, Gabriel 345
Mantel Clocks 208-213
Maple & Co. 168
Mappin & Webb Ltd. 87
Marble 259, 260
Marc, Hy 113, 114, 117, 119, 139, 141, 232,
   243, 264, 274, 275, 283
Marchak & Linzeler 218
Margaine 87, 89, 95, 95, 97, 106, 111, 112,
   115, 117, 118, 120
Margetts 205
Marham, J. 345
Markwick Markham Perigal 78
Marquetry 71, 176-179
Marr, J., 195
Marriott 73, 345
Marsh, Gilbert & Co. 289, 298
Marsh, Humphrey 149
Marshall, John 176
Marti, J. & Cie 143
Marti, L. et Cie 224
Marti, S. & Cie 132, 234
Martie, F. 266
Martin 344
Martin Bros. 275
Martin, Robert 166
Martin, S. 231
Martin, T. 112, 170
Martineau 367
Martinot, Jerome 40
Masonic 370
Massey 48, 72, 150, 199, 345
Masson 285
Massy, Jacob 79
Masurier 245
Mathey, E. 313
Matthey-Doret, Paul 344
Maurer, Iohan 57
Maurice et Cie 90, 99
Mauris 359
Mawley, Robt. 124, 325
May, T. 345
McCabe, James 71, 106, 110, 212, 229, 232
McGregor, D & Co. 125
McInnes, Dobbie Ltd 126
McInnes, Jas. 55
McKay & Chisholm 91
McMillan, A. 194
McNair, J.H. 222
Melling, Jno. 207
Mendys 386
Menil, Vincent 183
Mercer, Thomas 125, 126
Mercier & Fils 98
Merttins, George 203
Metal 71, 261-268
Meyer 277
Meylan, C.H. 344, 397
Middleton 325
Miles, Septimus 344
Miller & Co. 270
Miller & Sons 272
Miller, John 62
Miller, M. 60
Milleret & Tissot 344
Minas, Michaele 92
Miroy 236
Mirror Clocks 289
Mobilis 345
Mohslinger, Franz 327
Molteni, J. et Cie 322
Monkhouse, Thos. 202

Montre Royale 383
Moore 319
Moreau, Aug. 233
Morgan, Joseph 198
Morgan, Joshua 198
Morgan, Will 42
Morisset, R. & Lukins,, 364 C. 357
Morris, Benjamin 174
Morse, Jno. 166
Mortimer, John 109
Mortlock, Thos. 152
Motley, John 178
Mottram, John 69
Mottu 344
Moulinie Bautte & Moynier 345
Movado 344, 345, 380, 406
Movements 290
Muddle, Tho. 155, 157
Muirhead, James 101, 125, 238
Munger & Benedict 289
Munger, Asa 289
Munoz Degrain 369
Munro, Thos. 345
Murray, James 100, 277, 344
Murray, Jas & Co. 120
Museum, Weeks 258
Musical 180, 181
Muston & Garth 276
Mynuel 40
Mystery Clocks 291

Nardin, Ulysse 346, 361, 381
Nawe, Francis 376
Neal, John 303
Neill, Robt 346
Nepveu 234
Ness, P.R.J. 346
Nestle's Milk 33
Nethercott, John 160
New Haven Clock Co. 32, 321, 329
Newman, Edward 55
Newman, John 315
Newton, John 346
Nicholas, W. 186
Nichols, Peter 50
Nicole & Capt. 346
Nielsen, Nicole & Co. 118, 346
Noir, Etienne 122
Norris, George 61
Notron, Yeldrae 74

Oak & Mahogany 185, 186
Oak 71-74, 182-184
Oak Cased 269
Obelisks 136
Ogden, Thomas 175
Olbrich, Josef M. 230
Oldmeadon, Thos. 60
Ollivant & Botsford 113
Omega 385, 407
Orme, Del 346
Ormolu & Porcelain 270-273
Oudin, Ch. 86, 249, 346
Oval Case 97, 98
Owen, Henry 346

Pace, Thomas 63
Painted 187
Palethorpes Sausages 31
Paliand a Besancon 41
Pan American Exposition 33
Papavoine, Isaac 44
Parker, Tho. 203
Parkinson & Frodsham 127, 357
Parks, Jno. 150
Pashier, Edwd. 315
Passchier, Reijnier 365
Patek Phillippe 353, 356-57, 360, 371, 376, 408
Patron, J.S. 347
Payne & Co. 85, 90
Payne & Son 113
Payne 48, 61, 83, 247
Pearce, Henry 190
Peatt, John 171
Pendleton, Richd 166
Pendules D'Officier 291
Penn 198
Pennock, John 154
Pere, Blanc & Fils 333
Perigal & Duterrau 55
Perigal 62, 66

Perigal, Francis 29, 72
Perigal, Marwick Markham 78
Petit, Jacob 140, 273
Peyton, Richd. 204
Philippe, Louis 243
Philippe, Patek & Co. 309
Phillip & Phillip 347
Piaget 384, 386, 424
Picard, Lucien 386
Pickman, Wm. 347
Picture Clocks 292
Pierce 382
Piguet & Co. 372
Piguet & Meylan 369
Pillar & Scroll Clocks 293, 294
Pine 188
Pingo, R. 53
Piolaine 284
Pister, Edward 49, 57
Pitts, Saml. 48
Plante, H.H. 258
Pleasance, C.R. 347
Plumly, Wm. 347
PM 100
Pomroy, Joseph 59
Poole 126, 127
Porcelain 274, 275
Porcelain Mounted 99, 100
Porthouse 347
Post, William 44
Potter, Albert H. & Co. 347
Potter, Harry 347
Potts, W. & Sons 317
Prentice, Daniel 63
Prescott, Wm. 162
Price, J. 77
Pridgin 174
Prior 375
Prior, Edward 364
Prior, Geo 72, 311, 317, 347
Pryor, Josephus 43
Puller, Jonathan 52
Purvis, A. 72
Pyne, Natha. 179

Quare & Horseman 65
Quare, Dan 45, 160, 197

R & C 136, 273
R & Co. 94, 103
Rabby 281
Radford 348
Raingo 129, 232, 234, 275
Ramsey, Robt. 50
Raw Bros. 79
Read, Thos. 81
Record Watch Co. 348
Red Walnut 74
Redi, Willem 206
Redier, A. 225
Reed, Isaac 171
Regulators 189, 190
Reid & Auld 258
Reid, J.D. 195
Reid, Thomas 376
Reimirol & Cie 348
Religieuse 74
Rentzsch 348
Requier 136
Rhodes, Mamoah & Sons 84
Richard & Co. 90, 94
Riddels Ltd 302
Riddle, Henry 30
Rigaud, Pre. 211
Rimbault, Stepn. 51, 58
River, David 175
Rivers & Son 65, 66
Robert & Courvoisier 348
Robert 186, 357
Robin 213, 260
Robinson, D. 156, 192
Robinson, Fra. 51, 68, 164
Robinson, Jm. 370
Robinson, Robert 155
Rodanet, A.H. 86
Rogers, Isaac 71, 150
Rolex 147, 425
Rollin 133, 280
Rolling Ball 295
Rollison 315
Romilly 372